APPROXIMATION OF FUNCTIONS

PROCEEDINGS OF THE SYMPOSIUM ON APPROXIMATION OF FUNCTIONS, GENERAL MOTORS RESEARCH LABORATORIES, WARREN, MICHIGAN, 1964

Edited by

HENRY L. GARABEDIAN

General Motors Research Laboratories,
Warren, Michigan (U.S.A.)

ELSEVIER PUBLISHING COMPANY

AMSTERDAM · LONDON · NEW YORK

1965

ELSEVIER PUBLISHING COMPANY
335 JAN VAN GALENSTRAAT, P.O. BOX 211, AMSTERDAM

AMERICAN ELSEVIER PUBLISHING COMPANY, INC.
52 VANDERBILT AVENUE, NEW YORK, N.Y. 10017

ELSEVIER PUBLISHING COMPANY LIMITED
RIPPLESIDE COMMERCIAL ESTATE, BARKING, ESSEX

LIBRARY OF CONGRESS CATALOG CARD NUMBER 65-20137

WITH 20 ILLUSTRATIONS

PRINTED IN NORTHERN IRELAND

LIST OF CONTRIBUTORS

F. L. Bauer, *Technische Hochschule, Munich, Germany*

Garrett Birkhoff, *Harvard University, Cambridge, Massachusetts*

R. C. Buck, *University of Wisconsin, Madison*

E. W. Cheney, *University of California, Los Angeles*

Lothar Collatz, *Universität Hamburg, Germany*

Philip J. Davis, *Brown University, Providence, Rhode Island*

Carl R. De Boor, *General Motors Research Laboratories, Warren, Michigan*

A. A. Goldstein, *University of Washington, Seattle*

Michael Golomb, *Purdue University, Lafayette, Indiana*

G. G. Lorentz, *University of Syracuse, New York*

John R. Rice, *General Motors Research Laboratories, Warren, Michigan*

Arthur Sard, *Queens College, Flushing, New York*

E. L. Stiefel, *Eidgenössische Technische Hochschule, Zürich, Switzerland*

J. L. Walsh, *Harvard University, Cambridge, Massachusetts*

PREFACE

On August 31 through September 2, 1964, a Symposium on the Approximation of Functions was held at the General Motors Research Laboratories in Warren, Michigan. The 1964 Symposium was the eighth in an annual series starting in 1957. The principal motivating influence for the selection of a symposium topic has been a subject of general interest to the scientific community as well as one in which personnel of the Research Laboratories have exhibited special competence. The 1964 Symposium was unique in that it was the first ever held within the General Motors Corporation in a field of pure mathematics. These Proceedings contain, with one exception, the papers presented orally at the Symposium.

The notion of APPROXIMATION has existed since the beginning of mathematics, and has a meaning in every discipline of science using mathematics as a tool. Even among professional mathematicians, approximation theory has several different connotations, and is thus too broad a subject to be the theme of a single conference. The Symposium has therefore been restricted to the Approximation of Functions, the theory and applications of which have proven to be of immense interest within the Research Laboratories.

The theory of approximation of functions, in the sense of present day specialists, has occupied the attention of many mathematicians over a period of many decades, without creating more of a stir than many other branches of mathematics. Why then within the past decade has this branch of mathematics suddenly burst into spectacular prominence? The large scale electronic digital computer seems to be the answer to this question. To quote from the paper by P. J. Davis in these Proceedings, "The principal impact of computers on approximation theory is that they have simultaneously created the need for approximations and provided the means for fulfilling this need. A second impact of computers is that their tremendous power has raised our horizons. We are no longer afraid of doing things where the theory is known and the practice difficult, but we are also spurred on to tackle problems where the theory is unknown, but the practice may be possible".

The support and sympathetic guidance of the executive officers of the Research Laboratories: L. R. Hafstad, Vice-President, A. F. Underwood, Manager, and J. M. Campbell, Scientific Director, in the planning and execution of the Symposium is herewith gratefully acknowledged. Moreover, the help of the host of people, from within and without the Research Laboratories, who contributed their services so generously in many diverse facets of the Symposium is deeply appreciated.

After the excitement and exhilaration of a symposium subsides there remains of course the long and arduous task of editing the Proceedings. This writer pays tribute to John R. Rice, James A. Ayers, Leona Junko, and Norma Porter, of the Mathematics Department, for their dedicated and unselfish help in the editorial work.

H. L. GARABEDIAN

CONTENTS

Preface vii

The Convergence of Sequences of Rational Functions of Best Approximation with Some Free Poles
by J. L. WALSH 1
Uses of Hilbert Space in Approximation
by ARTHUR SARD 17
Applications of Duality in Approximation Theory
by R. C. BUCK 27
Inclusion Theorems for the Minimal Distance in Rational Tschebyscheff Approximation with Several Variables
by LOTHAR COLLATZ 43
Rational Approximation on Finite Point Sets
by P. FOX, A. A. GOLDSTEIN, and G. LASTMAN 57
Phase Methods for Polynomial Approximation
by E. L. STIEFEL 68
Optimal and Nearly-Optimal Linear Approximation
by MICHAEL GOLOMB 83
Approximation by Generalized Rational Functions
by E. W. CHENEY 101
Nonlinear Approximation
by J. R. RICE 111
Nonlinear Sequence Transformations
by F. L. BAUER 134
Approximation Theory in the First Two Decades of Electronic Computers
by P. J. DAVIS 152
Piecewise Polynomial Interpolation and Approximation
by GARRETT BIRKHOFF and C. R. DE BOOR 164
Russian Literature on Approximation in 1958–1964
by G. G. LORENTZ. 191

Index 217

THE CONVERGENCE OF SEQUENCES OF RATIONAL FUNCTIONS OF BEST APPROXIMATION WITH SOME FREE POLES[1]

J. L. WALSH

Harvard University, Cambridge, Massachusetts

There have recently been published a number of papers [**6**, **7**, **8**, **9**] concerning the convergence of sequences of rational functions of best approximation with some poles prescribed and others free, with reference both to degree of approximation and regions of convergence. In the present paper various previous results are brought together and unified, new ones are added, and open problems are particularly emphasized.

In §1 we discuss degree of convergence, in §2 regions of convergence, and in §3 exact degree of convergence. In §4 we treat degree of convergence of poles, in §5 norms involving pth powers, and in §6 properties of the Padé functions. Sharper results on degree of convergence are treated in §7, further sequences of rational functions in §8, and the Γ-function in §9.

1. **Degree of convergence.** Let the function $f(z)$ be continuous on a closed bounded set E of the z-plane, and let j and k be non-negative integers. Let $R_{jk}(z)$ denote the (or a) rational function of type (j, k), namely of form

$$R_{jk}(z) \equiv \frac{a_0 z^j + a_1 z^{j-1} + \cdots + a_j}{b_0 z^k + b_1 z^{k-1} + \cdots + b_k}, \qquad \sum |b_i| \neq 0, \tag{1}$$

of best approximation to $f(z)$ on E; such a rational function exists (if E is dense in itself) but need not be unique [**5**, Chapter 12]. Best approximation here means minimizing the Tchebycheff norm

$$\|f(z) - r_{jk}(z)\| = [\max |f(z) - r_{jk}(z)|, z \text{ on } E] \tag{2}$$

of $f(z) - r_{jk}(z)$ for all functions of type (j, k). The $R_{jk}(z)$ thus form a table of double entry [**4**], analogous to that of Padé [**1**], who bases his table of rational functions $P_{jk}(z)$ on a given function $\phi(z) = c_0 + c_1 z + c_2 z^2 + \cdots$ analytic at the origin, and requires that for each pair (j, k) the function $P_{jk}(z)$ of form (1) shall be chosen so that $\phi(z) - P_{jk}(z)$ has a zero of the highest possible order at $z = 0$.

For each (j, k) we set (with $R_{jk}(z)$ extremal)

$$\delta_{jk} = \|f(z) - R_{jk}(z)\|, \tag{3}$$

and there follows the inequality

$$\delta_{mn} \leqq \delta_{jk}, \qquad m \geqq j, \qquad n \geqq k. \tag{4}$$

---

[1] Research sponsored (in part) by Air Force Office of Scientific Research.

We shall proceed to establish **[6]**:

THEOREM 1. *Let E be a closed bounded point set whose complement is connected, and is regular in the sense that it possesses a Green's function G(z) with pole at infinity. Let Γ_σ denote generically the locus $G(z) = \log \sigma\ (>0)$ and E_σ the interior of Γ_σ. Let f(z) be analytic on E, meromorphic with precisely ν poles (that is, poles of total multiplicity ν) in E_ρ, $1 < \rho \leqq \infty$. Then we have*

$$\limsup_{n\to\infty} \delta_{n\nu}^{1/n} \leqq 1/\rho. \tag{5}$$

Theorem 1 is analogous to, and is to be proved by means of, the first part of a theorem on approximation by polynomials [5, §4.6]:

THEOREM 2. *With the notation of Theorem 1, let the function φ(z) be analytic throughout E_ρ, $1 < \rho \leqq \infty$; then there exist polynomials $p_n(z)$ of respective degrees n, namely of form $a_{nn}z^n + a_{n,n-1}z^{n-1} + \cdots + a_{n0}$, such that for the Tchebycheff norm on E we have*

$$\limsup_{n\to\infty} \|\phi(z) - p_n(z)\|^{1/n} \leqq 1/\rho. \tag{6}$$

Conversely, if φ(z) is defined on E and if (6) *is valid for suitably chosen polynomials $p_n(z)$ of respective degrees n, defined for every n, then the sequence $p_n(z)$ converges uniformly on any closed bounded set in E_ρ, so φ(z) can be analytically extended from E to be analytic throughout E_ρ.*

The first part of Theorem 2 is precisely the case of Theorem 1 for $\nu = 0$.

To prove Theorem 1 we denote by $r_0(z)$ the sum of the principal parts of the poles of $f(z)$ interior to E_ρ, so that $f(z) - r_0(z)$ is analytic interior to E_ρ. By the first part of Theorem 2 we have for suitably chosen polynomials $p_n(z)$ of respective degrees n

$$\limsup_{n\to\infty} \|f(z) - [p_n(z) + r_0(z)]\|^{1/n} \leqq 1/\rho\,.$$

The function $p_n(z) + r_0(z)$ is a rational function $r_{n+\nu,\nu}(z)$ of type $(n + \nu, \nu)$, so we may write

$$\limsup_{n\to\infty} \|f(z) - r_{n+\nu,\nu}(z)\|^{1/(n+\nu)} \leqq 1/\rho\,,$$

and there follows by the extremal properties of the $R_{n+\nu,\nu}(z)$

$$\limsup_{n\to\infty} \|f(z) - R_{n+\nu,\nu}(z)\|^{1/(n+\nu)} \leqq 1/\rho,$$

which is (5).

We mention explicitly that E may consist of several—indeed of an infinite number of—components, and $f(z)$ need not be a monogenic function on E if the locus Γ_ρ separates the plane into more than two regions. In the latter case we consider E_ρ to be the union of the interiors of the Jordan curves composing Γ_ρ.

2. **Regions of convergence.** Regions of convergence of the sequence $R_{n\nu}(z)$ under the hypothesis of Theorem 1 depend more on the degree of convergence than on extremal properties [**6, 7**]:

THEOREM 3. *Let E and $f(z)$ satisfy the conditions of Theorem* 1, *and let the $R_{n\nu}(z)$ of respective types (n, ν) but not necessarily extremal satisfy*

$$\limsup_{n\to\infty} \|f(z) - R_{n\nu}(z)\|^{1/n} \leqq 1/\rho. \tag{7}$$

Let D denote E_ρ with the ν poles of $f(z)$ deleted. Then for n sufficiently large the function $R_{n\nu}(z)$ has precisely ν finite poles, which approach respectively the ν poles of $f(z)$ in E_ρ. The functions $R_{n\nu}(z)$ approach $f(z)$ throughout D. For any closed bounded set S in D and in the closed interior of E_σ, $1 < \sigma < \rho$, we have

$$\limsup_{n\to\infty} [\max |f(z) - R_{n\nu}(z)|, z \text{ on } S]^{1/n} \leqq \sigma/\rho. \tag{8}$$

Proof of the second part of Theorem 2 is based primarily on the generalized Bernstein lemma [**5**, §4.6], that if $P_n(z)$ is a polynomial in z of degree n, then we have

$$|P_n(z)| \leqq \sigma^n \|P_n(z)\|, \qquad z \text{ on } E_\sigma + \Gamma_\sigma. \tag{9}$$

The proof of Theorem 3 is correspondingly based (compare [**6**] and [**7**]) on

LEMMA 1. *With the notation and conditions on E of Theorem* 1, *let rational functions $r_{n\nu}(z)$ of respective types (n, ν) satisfy the inequality*

$$\limsup_{n\to\infty} \|r_{n\nu}(z)\|^{1/n} \leqq 1/\rho_1, \qquad 1 < \rho_1 \leqq \infty, \tag{10}$$

where ν is constant. Suppose the finite poles of the $r_{n\nu}(z)$ are uniformly bounded. Let S be a closed set in the closed interior of E_σ, $1 < \sigma < \rho_1$, and containing no limit point of the poles of the $r_{n\nu}(z)$. Then the sequence $r_{n\nu}(z)$ converges uniformly to zero on S, and we have

$$\limsup_{n\to\infty} [\max |r_{n\nu}(z)|, z \text{ on } S]^{1/n} \leqq \sigma/\rho_1. \tag{11}$$

The $r_{n\nu}(z)$ need not be defined for every n.

The function $r_{n\nu}(z)$ can be written as the quotient of a polynomial $P_n(z)$ of degree n by a polynomial of degree ν having unity as the coefficient of its highest power of z. For n sufficiently large and for z on S, the latter polynomial has a positive lower bound m_1 independent of n, whence

$$|r_{n\nu}(z)| \leqq |P_n(z)|/m_1, \qquad z \text{ on } S. \tag{12}$$

For z on E the denominator polynomial of $r_{n\nu}(z)$ has a bound M_1 independent of n, whence

$$|P_n(z)|/M_1 \leqq |r_{n\nu}(z)|, \qquad z \text{ on } E, \tag{13}$$

$$\|P_n(z)\|/M_1 \leqq \|r_{n\nu}(z)\|. \tag{14}$$

Inequality (9) is useful here in the form

$$[\max |P_n(z)|, \ z \text{ on } S] \leqq \sigma^n \|P_n(z)\|. \tag{15}$$

Inequality (11) now follows by successive application of (12), (15), (14), and (10).

We proceed to establish Theorem 3. Let $f_0(z)$ denote $f(z)$ minus the sum $r_0(z)$ of the principal parts of the ν poles of $f(z)$ in E_ρ, and let $r_n(z)$ denote the sum of the principal parts of the finite poles of $R_{n\nu}(z)$. By Theorem 2 there exist polynomials $p_n(z)$, taken now of respective degrees $n - \nu$, satisfying

$$\limsup_{n\to\infty} \|f_0(z) - p_n(z)\|^{1/n} \leqq 1/\rho. \tag{16}$$

We denote the polynomial $R_{n\nu}(z) - r_n(z)$ by $p_n(z) + q_n(z)$, whence by (7) and (16)

$$\limsup_{n\to\infty} \|r_0(z) - r_n(z) - q_n(z)\|^{1/n} \leqq 1/\rho, \tag{17}$$

an inequality of form (10), where n and ν in (10) are to be replaced by $n + \nu$ and 2ν of Theorem 3. If $R_{n\nu}(z)$ has effectively ν finite poles, it may be written as a rational function $r_n(z)$ of type $(\nu - 1, \nu)$ plus a polynomial $p_n(z) + q_n(z)$ of degree $n - \nu$; if $R_{n\nu}(z)$ has fewer than ν finite poles, the degree of the remaining polynomial is correspondingly increased, but not beyond n. We assume temporarily that the finite poles of the $R_{n\nu}(z)$ are uniformly bounded; this restriction will be removed later.

The function $r_0(z)$ in (17) is independent of n, and we now discuss the finite poles of $r_n(z)$, namely of the function $r_n(z) + q_n(z)$ which approaches $r_0(z)$. If α is a typical pole of $r_0(z)$ interior to E_ρ, we construct $\nu + 1$ mutually disjoint open annuli A_j interior to E_ρ, each with center α, so that each A_j separates α from all zeros of $r_0(z)$ and from all poles of $r_0(z)$ other than α. *If any subsequence of the $r_n(z)$ is chosen, there exists a new subsequence having no limit point of poles in at least one annulus A_j.* If the original subsequence has no limit point of poles in A_1, this conclusion is established; if it has a limit point of poles in A_1, a new subsequence has for each term at least one pole in A_1 and that same limit point of poles. If the new subsequence has no limit point of poles in A_2, the conclusion is established, and if it has a limit point of poles in A_2 we continue the former procedure. We must eventually reach an annulus $A_{\nu+1}$ which for n sufficiently large contains no pole of some subsequence of the original subsequence. If C is a circle which lies in $A_{\nu+1}$ and whose center is α, the subsequence of the $r_n(z) + q_n(z)$ converges uniformly to $r_0(z)$ on C, by Lemma 1. Under such conditions it is readily shown [**6**, Lemma 1] that for n sufficiently large the subsequence of the $r_n(z)$ must have at least as many poles interior to C as does $r_0(z)$. This discussion applies to each of the ν poles α of $r_0(z)$ in E_ρ, so every subsequence of the $r_n(z)$ (which has at most ν finite poles) admits a new subsequence having for n sufficiently large in a suitable neighborhood of each α at least as many poles as does $r_0(z)$, so the new subsequence has in such a neighborhood precisely as many poles as does $r_0(z)$, namely a totality of ν. It follows that the original sequence $r_n(z)$ has this same property, of having for n sufficiently large in the neighborhood of each α precisely as many poles as does $r_0(z)$, and has no other poles. That is to say, for n sufficiently large, $R_{n\nu}(z)$ has precisely ν finite poles which approach respectively the ν poles of $f(z)$ interior to E_ρ. Inequality (8) follows from (17) by Lemma 1 and from (16) = (6) and the corollary to Theorem 2 proved in [**5**, §4.7]:

$$\limsup_{n\to\infty} [\max |\phi(z) - p_n(z)|, z \text{ on } S]^{1/n} \leqq \sigma/\rho; \tag{18}$$

inequality (18) is indeed a consequence of the generalized Bernstein lemma, and of (6).

To complete the proof of Theorem 3 it remains to be proved that the finite poles of the $R_{n\nu}(z)$ are uniformly bounded. If these poles are not uniformly bounded, as we now suppose, Lemma 1 cannot be applied to the study of the sequence $r_0(z) - r_n(z) - q_n(z)$. There exists a subsequence of the latter functions denoted by $\psi_n(z)$, such that a certain number μ of the finite poles α_j of each $\psi_n(z)$ become infinite as n becomes infinite, while the remaining poles ($2\nu - \mu$ or fewer in number) are uniformly in modulus less than some A, where E_ρ lies in the circle whose center is the origin and radius A. If, say, μ' poles β_j of $\psi_n(z)$ are in modulus greater than A, we replace $\psi_n(z)$ in the sequence by

$$\phi_n(z) \equiv \psi_n(z) \cdot \prod_{j=1}^{\mu'} \frac{z - \beta_j}{-\beta_j}, \qquad 1 \leqq \mu' \leqq \mu, \tag{19}$$

where the β_j depend on n, and where $\phi_n(z)$ has no more than $2\nu - \mu$ finite poles. This replacement alters neither the limit of $\psi_n(z)$ interior to the circle nor such a relation as (17). Our discussion of the $\psi_n(z)$ as already given, commencing with (17), applies now to the modified sequence, and shows that the modified functions $r_n(z)$ have for n sufficiently large at least ν finite poles approaching the respective poles of $r_0(z)$, which is impossible because the modified $r_n(z)$ have fewer than ν finite poles. This contradiction shows that the finite poles of the $r_n(z)$ are bounded, and completes the proof of Theorem 3.

3. **Exact degree of convergence.** Theorem 3 thus far has dealt merely with an upper bound to the degree of convergence of the $R_{n\nu}(z)$, but more specific results exist:

THEOREM 4. *With the hypothesis of Theorem* 3, *let the $R_{n\nu}(z)$ be defined for every n and let ρ be the largest number such that $f(z)$ is meromorphic with precisely ν poles in E_ρ; then the equality sign holds in* (7) *and* (8), *provided S is a locus Γ_σ not passing through a pole of $f(z)$.*

Let us suppose the first member of (7) to be $1/\rho_1$ ($<1/\rho$); then for the norm on E we have

$$\limsup_{n\to\infty} \|R_{n+1,\nu}(z) - R_{n\nu}(z)\|^{1/n} \leqq 1/\rho_1,$$

so by Lemma 1 the sequence $R_{n\nu}(z)$ converges uniformly, necessarily to $f(z)$ or its analytic extension, throughout some annular region (or set of annular regions) containing E_ρ in its interior, which contradicts the definition of ρ. We have used here the new hypothesis that the $R_{n\nu}(z)$ are defined for every n.

If $S = \Gamma_\sigma$ contains precisely μ poles of $f(z)$ in its interior, we have $(\Gamma_\sigma)_{\rho/\sigma} = \Gamma_\rho$, so by (8) the hypothesis of Theorem 4 is satisfied where now ρ/σ, $\nu - \mu$, and E_σ take the roles of ρ, ν, and E in Theorem 4; to be sure there is the distinction that both $f(z)$ and $R_{n\nu}(z)$ have μ poles in E_σ, but that is unessential. By the part of Theorem 4 already proved, it now follows that the equality sign holds in (8), so Theorem 4 is established.

In Theorems 2–4 we have not assumed the $R_{n\nu}(z)$ to be rational functions of type (n, ν) of best approximation to $f(z)$ on E, but it is clear from Theorem 1 that they may be so chosen:

THEOREM 5. *If the $R_{n\nu}(z)$ are the rational functions of respective types (n, ν) of best (Tchebycheff) approximation to $f(z)$ on E, the hypotheses of Theorems 2–4 are satisfied; in particular,* (7) *and* (8) *follow if the $R_{n\nu}(z)$ are defined for every n and if ρ is the largest number such that E_ρ contains precisely ν poles of $f(z)$.*

We add a further result [7; **10**, **11**] without proof here, based in part on results due to Ostrowski:

THEOREM 6. *With the hypothesis of Theorem* 4, *let S in D be a continuum not a single point, and let S lie in the closed interior of E_σ but not in the closed interior of any $E_{\sigma'}$, $\sigma' < \sigma$. Then we have*

$$\limsup_{n\to\infty} [\max |f(z) - R_{n\nu}(z)|, \ z \text{ on } S]^{1/n} = \sigma/\rho. \tag{20}$$

The sequence $R_{n\nu}(z)$ converges uniformly in no region containing a point of Γ_ρ.

Theorem 5 deals with the convergence of various rows of the table of the $R_{n\nu}(z)$ mentioned in connection with (2), namely the convergence of those rows $R_{n\nu}(z)$ where some E_ρ contains precisely ν poles of $f(z)$. If $f(z)$ is meromorphic in each finite point of the plane; if no more than one pole lies on each E_σ, Theorem 5 applies in turn to each row of the array; but if more than one pole lies on some E_σ, the convergence properties of certain rows of the array are not included in Theorem 5.

It is of some interest to note that if $f(z)$ is given merely continuous on E (not known to satisfy the conditions of Theorem 1), and if the $R_{n\nu}(z)$ (extremal or not) are given for every n satisfying (7) with or without the equality sign, then little is known about the further properties of $f(z)$. To be sure, we can deduce

$$\limsup_{n\to\infty} [\max |R_{n+1,\nu}(z) - R_{n\nu}(z)|, \ z \text{ on } E]^{1/n} \leqq 1/\rho,$$

where the function whose modulus occurs is rational of type $(n + \nu + 1, 2\nu)$, but its poles may conceivably be everywhere dense in the plane. We can deduce that

$f(z)$ is not meromorphic with precisely μ poles in E_ρ, $\nu < \mu < \infty$, for then (7) could be used as in the proof of Theorem 3 to show that each $R_{n\nu}$ for n sufficiently large has at least μ finite poles, approaching the μ poles of $f(z)$ in E_ρ. We cannot disprove the possibility that $f(z)$ may be meromorphic with fewer than ν poles in E_ρ; compare [7, Theorem 5].

4. **Degree of convergence of poles.** Since we have considered (§§1–3) degree of convergence of functions $R_{n\nu}(z)$, it is of some interest to study the degree of convergence of the ν finite poles of the $R_{n\nu}(z)$ to the poles of $f(z)$ interior to Γ_ρ, a subject not treated in any of the references yet highly important in numerical analysis. Indeed, the results to be proved apply in far more general circumstances than §§1–3.

THEOREM 7. *Let the function $f(z)$ have a simple pole in the point $z = \alpha$, but otherwise be analytic and different from zero in the closed disk δ: $|z - \alpha| \leqq 3b/2$, $b > 0$, let the function $f_n(z)$ have a simple pole α_n interior to δ but otherwise be analytic and different from zero in δ, and suppose*

$$(21) \qquad |f(z) - f_n(z)| \leqq \varepsilon_n \quad \text{in} \quad \delta_1\colon b/2 \leqq |z - \alpha| \leqq 3b/2,$$

where $\varepsilon_n \to 0$. Then we have

$$(22) \qquad \alpha - \alpha_n = O(\varepsilon_n).$$

We write for z on γ: $|z - \alpha| = b$

$$f'(z) - f_n'(z) \equiv \frac{1}{2\pi i}\int \frac{f(t) - f_n(t)}{(t - z)^2}\,dt,$$

where the integral is taken over the boundary of δ_1; there follows

$$(23) \qquad [\max |f'(z) - f_n'(z)|,\ z \text{ on } \gamma] = O(\varepsilon_n).$$

We have further

$$(24) \qquad \alpha_n - \alpha = \frac{1}{2\pi i}\int_\gamma \frac{zf'(z)f_n(z) - zf(z)f_n'(z)}{f(z)f_n(z)}\,dz,$$

where the numerator in the integrand can be written $zf'(f_n - f) + zf(f' - f_n')$. The relation (22) now follows by (21) and (23).

We continue by studying the slightly more general situation where $f(z)$ has a pole of order k in $\alpha = 0$ but is otherwise analytic and different from zero in δ, and where $f_n(z)$ has a totality of k poles $\alpha_1, \alpha_2, \cdots, \alpha_k$ (depending on n) interior to δ but is otherwise analytic and different from zero in δ, and where (21) is valid. The relation (23) follows as before, and we add to (24) the equations

$$(25) \qquad -k\alpha^m + \sum_{j=1}^{k}\alpha_j^m = \frac{1}{2\pi i}\int_\gamma \frac{z^m f'(z)f_n(z) - z^m f(z)f_n'(z)}{f(z)f_n(z)}\,dz, \qquad m \leqq k,$$

where for convenience we take $\alpha = 0$. For fixed n the α_j are the zeros of a polynomial $Q(z) \equiv z^k + p_1 z^{k-1} + \cdots + p_k$, where we have $s_m = \sum_{j=1}^k \alpha_j^m$,

$$
\begin{aligned}
&s_1 + p_1 = 0,\\
&s_2 + p_1 s_1 + 2p_2 = 0,\\
&\cdots\cdots\cdots,\\
&s_k + p_1 s_{k-1} + \cdots + p_{k-1}s_1 + kp_k = 0.
\end{aligned}
\tag{26}
$$

By (25) we have $s_m = O(\varepsilon_n)$, and by (26) we then have

$$p_m = O(\varepsilon_n), \qquad m \leqq k. \tag{27}$$

By a theorem due to R. D. Carmichael **[14]** an upper bound to the moduli of the zeros of $Q(z)$ is $\sum_{j=1}^k |p_j|^{1/j} = O(\varepsilon_n^{1/k})$, so we have established

$$\alpha - \alpha_j = O(\varepsilon_n^{1/k}), \tag{28}$$

of which (22) is a special case.

Inequality (28) is sharp, when considered to be a consequence of (21), as is shown by the example $f(z) \equiv z^{-k}$, $f_n(z) \equiv (z^k - \varepsilon_n)^{-1}$, and on the unit circumference γ we have

$$f(z) - f_n(z) \equiv \frac{-\varepsilon_n}{z^k(z^k - \varepsilon_n)} \sim \varepsilon_n.$$

The poles of $f_n(z)$ have the common modulus $\varepsilon_n^{1/k}$, whence for each j

$$|\alpha - \alpha_j| \sim \varepsilon_n^{1/k}.$$

Our conclusions (22) and (28) clearly apply with the hypothesis of Theorem 6, for we may choose the set S of Theorem 6 as the annulus δ_1 of Theorem 7, with σ appropriately chosen. It is to be noticed, however, that Theorem 6 gives an exact degree of convergence of the $R_{n\nu}(z)$, while (22) and (28) give merely upper bounds on $\alpha - \alpha_j$. With the hypothesis (7) and using the equality sign or not, we may have $\alpha_j = \alpha$ for all j and n, as in the proof of Theorem 1, so a reverse inequality to (22) and (28) does not exist.

These general results on degree of convergence of poles might well be compared with a result on degree of convergence of the principal parts of the poles in Theorem 3:

THEOREM 8. *With the hypothesis of Theorem 3, let $R_0(z)$ and $R_n(z)$ denote respectively the principal parts of a pole α of $f(z)$ in E_ρ and of the totality of poles of $R_{n\nu}(z)$ which approach α. Then we have*

$$\limsup_{n\to\infty} [\max |R_0(z) - R_n(z)|,\ z \text{ on } T]^{1/n} \leqq \sigma/\rho,$$

where T is any closed bounded set not containing α and α lies on Γ_σ.

Let γ be a circle exterior to T with center α and lying in E_λ, $\sigma < \lambda < \rho$, containing on or within it no pole of $f(z)$ other than α. For z in T we have for n sufficiently large

$$R_0(z) - R_n(z) \equiv \frac{1}{2\pi i}\int_\gamma \frac{R_0(t) - R_n(t)}{t - z}dt \equiv \frac{1}{2\pi i}\int_\gamma \frac{r_0(t) - r_n(t) - q_n(t)}{t - z}dt.$$

By (17) and Lemma 1 we have

$$\limsup_{n\to\infty} [\max |r_0(z) - r_n(z) - q_n(z)|, z \text{ on } \gamma]^{1/n} \leqq \lambda/\rho,$$

so the conclusion of Theorem 8 follows with the second member replaced by λ/ρ, and we can allow λ to approach σ.

It may be noted that here as in Theorem 7 we have merely an upper bound on degree of convergence; this is the most that one can expect from the hypothesis of degree of convergence of the $R_{n\nu}(z)$, for in the auxiliary functions used to prove Theorem 1 and to obtain the degree of convergence of the $R_{n\nu}(z)$ we have $R_n(z) \equiv R_0(z)$.

Still with the hypothesis of Theorem 3, it seems worth while to consider the degree of convergence of $q_n(z)$ to zero. Let $\alpha_1, \alpha_2, \cdots, \alpha_\nu$ be the poles of $f(z)$ in E_ρ, where $\Phi(\alpha_1) \leqq \Phi(\alpha_2) \leqq \cdots \leqq \Phi(\alpha_\nu)$, $\Phi(z) \equiv \exp G(z)$ in the notation of Theorem 1. Suppose S is a closed bounded set in D; if S is contained in E we set $\sigma_0 = 1$, otherwise $\sigma_0 = [\max \Phi(\alpha_\nu), z \text{ on } S]$. Choose circles $\gamma_1, \gamma_2, \cdots, \gamma_\nu$ (mutually exterior when distinct) whose centers are the respective α_k, which lie exterior to S but in E_σ where $\sigma > \sigma_0$, $\rho > \sigma > \Phi(\alpha_\nu)$; for n sufficiently large and z on S we integrate over $\Gamma_\sigma + \gamma_1 + \gamma_2 + \cdots + \gamma_\nu$:

$$r_0(z) - r_n(z) - q_n(z) \equiv \frac{1}{2\pi i}\int \frac{r_0(t) - r_n(t) - q_n(t)}{t - z}dt.$$

By Lemma 1 and (17) we have

$$\limsup_{n\to\infty} [\max |r_0(z) - r_n(z) - q_n(z)|, z \text{ on } S]^{1/n} \leqq \sigma/\rho,$$

and by allowing σ to approach $\sigma_1 = \max [\sigma_0, \Phi(\alpha_\nu)]$,

$$\limsup_{n\to\infty} [\max |r_0(z) - r_n(z) - q_n(z)|, z \text{ on } S]^{1/n} \leqq \sigma_1/\rho.$$

Combination of this inequality with Theorem 8 applied to each pole α_k yields the desired result:

$$\limsup_{n\to\infty} [\max |q_n(z)|, z \text{ on } S]^{1/n} \leqq \sigma_1/\rho.$$

If S here lies in the closed interior of the locus $\Phi(z) = \Phi(\alpha_\nu)$, and in particular if $S = E$, we have $\sigma_1 = \Phi(\alpha_\nu)$.

5. **Norms involving pth powers.** Hitherto we have considered only the Tchebycheff norm as a measure of approximation of $R_{n\nu}(z)$ to $f(z)$ on E, but it is clear that

other norms may be used in defining the table of functions $R_{n\nu}(z)$ and the norms $\delta_{n\nu}$. For instance, suppose E is a closed rectifiable Jordan arc C or a closed Jordan region bounded by a rectifiable curve C and $f(z)$ is continuous on E; then

$$\delta_{n\nu}^{(p)} = \left[\int_C |f(z) - R_{n\nu}(z)|^p \, |dz| \right]^{1/p}, \qquad p > 0, \tag{29}$$

is a suitable norm to measure the deviation of $R_{n\nu}(z)$ from $f(z)$ on C. Use of $\delta_{n\nu}^{(p)}$ as norm leads to a new double-entry table of extremal functions $R_{n\nu}(z)$ of respective types (n, ν) and a new table of deviations. With the notation (2) and (3) it is clear from (29) that we have for all n and ν

$$\delta_{n\nu}^{(p)} \leqq l^{1/p} \cdot \delta_{n\nu}$$

where l is the length of C, so with E as just described and with the hypothesis of Theorem 1 on $f(z)$ there follows the analogue of (5):

$$\limsup_{n \to \infty} \delta_{n\nu}^{(p)1/n} \leqq 1/\rho. \tag{30}$$

Under these same conditions on E and $f(z)$, the analogue of Theorem 3 is valid with the hypothesis (30) instead of (7). The analogue of Lemma 1 is true if the norm in (29) is used in (10), thanks to a previously known lemma concerning the norm of (29) as used in approximation by polynomials, and (7) in its present form follows [7, Corollary to Theorem 1] for the $R_{n\nu}(z)$ minimizing the pth power norm, as do the consequences of (7) already set forth.

If E consists of a finite number of mutually exterior closed rectifiable Jordan arcs or closed Jordan regions each bounded by a rectifiable Jordan curve, or of the union of a finite number of mutually disjoint such arcs and curves, we may use as norm on E the sum of the norms on the respective components. It is still true [7, Theorem 8] that (7) for the Tchebycheff norm on E follows for the $R_{n\nu}(z)$ minimizing the pth power norm, with numerous consequences.

If E consists of one or several mutually exterior Jordan regions, a suitable norm is (29) where the integral over C is now replaced by the double integral over E. If $f(z)$ satisfies the conditions of Theorem 1, again by a suitable modification of Lemma 1, inequality (7) for the new norm and for the Tchebycheff norm on E follows [7]; there are again numerous consequences.

6. **Properties of Padé functions.** The Padé functions $P_{jk}(z)$ defined in §1 have been widely studied as approximating functions, especially in their relation to continued fractions. An important result, proved by Montessus de Ballore [2] by use of Hadamard's theory of the polar singularities of a function represented by Taylor's series, is closely related to that part of Theorem 3 which describes the convergence of $R_{n\nu}(z)$ (but not degree of convergence) and its poles, and indeed gave the impetus for the proof of Theorem 3:

THEOREM 9. (Montessus de Ballore) *Let the function* $f(z) \equiv c_0 + c_1 z + c_2 z^2 + \cdots$ *be analytic in* $z = 0$, *and meromorphic with precisely* ν *poles in* $|z| < \rho$. *Let the*

Padé table be normal, in the sense that certain determinants formed from the c_k are different from zero so that the P_{jk} are uniquely determined. Then the sequence $P_{n\nu}(z)$ which forms the $(\nu + 1)$st row of the Padé table converges to $f(z)$ throughout the region D formed by $|z| < \rho$ with the poles of $f(z)$ deleted, uniformly on any closed bounded set in D. The ν finite poles of $P_{n\nu}(z)$ approach respectively the ν poles of $f(z)$ in $|z| < \rho$.

Of course the methods used by Montessus de Ballore are so closely identified with the use of the Taylor series that they are not useful in the proof of Theorem 3, even when D is a circular disk. Nevertheless there is far more than an analogy between Theorem 9 and Theorem 3, for the $P_{jk}(z)$ are the limits of $R_{jk}(z)$, extremal on E, as the suitably chosen point set E tends to 0:

THEOREM 10. *Let $f(z)$ satisfy the conditions of Theorem 9, and let $R_{jk}(\varepsilon, z)$ be the function of type (j, k) of best Tchebycheff approximation to $f(z)$ on the set E: $|z| \leqq \varepsilon\ (>0)$. Then we have uniformly on any closed bounded set containing no pole of $P_{jk}(z)$*

$$\lim_{\varepsilon\to 0} R_{jk}(\varepsilon, z) = P_{jk}(z).$$

Theorem 10 can be proved [9] by studying explicitly the formulas for the determination of $P_{jk}(z)$ and $R_{jk}(\varepsilon, z)$ in terms of the Taylor coefficients of $f(z)$.

Montessus de Ballore did not consider degree of convergence of the $P_{jk}(z)$ to $f(z)$, but on this topic the analogy with Theorems 3 and 4 is still striking [9]:

THEOREM 11. *Under the conditions of Theorem 9 let ρ be the largest number such that $f(z)$ is meromorphic with precisely ν poles interior to $|z| < \rho$. If S is any closed bounded continuum (not a single point) in D, and if $\sigma = [\max |z|, z$ on $S]$, then we have*

$$\limsup_{n\to\infty} [\max |f(z) - P_{n\nu}(z)|,\ z \text{ on } S]^{1/n} = \sigma/\rho. \tag{31}$$

Of course (31) is well known in the case that $f(z)$ has no poles in $|z| < \rho$, namely the case that $\nu = 0$ and $P_{n0}(z)$ is a section of the Taylor development of $f(z)$.

7. **Sharper results on degree of convergence.** There exist various refinements of such degrees of convergence as are indicated by (5), (7), and (8), which have not hitherto received attention in the literature, and which we shall consider very briefly.

Let E be the closed interior of an analytic Jordan curve, and let $f(z)$ be analytic on E, meromorphic with precisely ν poles on E_ρ, and [13] on Γ_ρ of class $L(k, \alpha)$ with $0 < \alpha < 1$ or of class $Z(k)$ with $\alpha = 1$, where k may be negative. We set $f(z) \equiv f_0(z) + r_0(z)$, z in E_ρ, where $r_0(z)$ is the sum of the principal parts of the ν poles of $f(z)$ in E_ρ, and $f_0(z)$ is analytic in E_ρ and on Γ_ρ of class $L(k, \alpha)$ with $0 < \alpha < 1$ or of class $Z(k)$ with $\alpha = 1$. There exist [13] polynomials $p_n(z)$ of respective degrees n such that we have

$$|f_0(z) - p_n(z)| \leqq \frac{A}{\rho^n n^{k+\alpha}}, \qquad z \text{ on } E; \tag{32}$$

here and below the letter A with or without a subscript denotes a constant independent of n and z, not necessarily the same constant with repeated occurrences. We can write (32) as

$$|f(z) - r_{n+\nu,\nu}(z)| \leqq \frac{A}{\rho^n n^{k+\alpha}}, \qquad z \text{ on } E,$$

with $r_{n+\nu,\nu}(z) \equiv r_0(z) + p_n(z)$, a function of type $(n + \nu, \nu)$, or we can write

$$(33) \qquad |f(z) - r_{n\nu}(z)| \leqq \frac{A_1}{\rho^n n^{k+\alpha}}, \qquad z \text{ on } E.$$

That is to say, we have established the existence of the $r_{n\nu}(z)$ of type (n, ν) satisfying (33). The functions $R_{n\nu}(z)$ of best Tchebycheff approximation to $f(z)$ on E satisfy (33) a fortiori. Henceforth we suppose the $r_{n\nu}(z)$ of type (n, ν) to satisfy (33), whether extremal or not. It follows by Theorem 3 that as $n \to \infty$ the poles of $r_{n\nu}(z)$ approach those of $f(z)$ in E_ρ.

Let the $r_{n\nu}(z)$ satisfying (33) be given, and let $r_n(z)$ denote the sum of the principal parts of the finite poles of $r_{n\nu}(z)$, where $f(z)$ is as before. With (33) we combine (32), where $p_n(z)$ is now a polynomial of degree $n - \nu$, and obtain

$$(34) \qquad |r_0(z) - r_n(z) - q_n(z)| \leqq \frac{A_1}{\rho^n n^{k+\alpha}}, \qquad z \text{ on } E,$$

where $q_n(z)$ is a polynomial of degree $n - \nu$. The function whose modulus appears in (34) is of type $(n + \nu, 2\nu)$, whose finite poles lie in the poles of $r_0(z)$ and in the poles of $r_n(z)$, which approach the poles of $r_0(z)$. By the method of proof of Lemma 1, we have for an arbitrary closed set S containing no pole of $r_0(z)$ and lying in the closed interior of E_σ, $1 < \sigma < \rho$,

$$(35) \qquad |r_0(z) - r_n(z) - q_n(z)| \leqq \frac{A_2\sigma^n}{\rho^n n^{k+\alpha}}, \qquad z \text{ on } S.$$

It follows **[13]** from (32) that we have

$$(36) \qquad |f_0(z) - p_n(z)| \leqq \frac{A_3\sigma^n}{\rho^n n^{k+\alpha}}, \qquad z \text{ on } S,$$

so by (35) there follows

$$(37) \qquad |f(z) - r_{n\nu}(z)| \leqq \frac{A_4\sigma^n}{\rho^n n^{k+\alpha}}, \qquad z \text{ on } S;$$

it is to be noted that (37) is a consequence merely of (33) and of the hypothesis on $f(z)$; inequality (37) is considerably sharper than (8).

For this same $f(z)$, inequality (37) holds for the same functions $r_{n\nu}(z)$ on Γ_ρ, provided we have $k + \alpha > 0$, for in this case (35) holds with $\sigma = \rho$ on Γ_ρ and (36) holds with $\sigma = \rho$ if the $p_n(z)$ are suitably chosen, so we have

$$(38) \qquad |f(z) - r_{n\nu}(z)| \leqq \frac{A_5}{n^{k+\alpha}}, \qquad z \text{ on } \Gamma_\rho.$$

This result is valid and seems to be new even for the case $\nu = 0$.

However, if (33) is given for functions $r_{n\nu}(z)$ defined for every n without knowledge of the properties of $f(z)$ except its continuity on E, we deduce

$$|r_{n+1,\nu}(z) - r_{n\nu}(z)| \leqq \frac{A}{\rho^n n^{k+\alpha}}, \qquad z \text{ on } E,$$

so by the method of proof of Lemma 1 we have merely

$$|r_{n+1,\nu}(z) - r_{n\nu}(z)| \leqq \frac{A_1 \sigma^n}{\rho^n n^{k+\alpha}}, \qquad z \text{ on } S;$$

where S lies in the closed interior of E_σ, $1 < \sigma < \rho$, and contains no limit point of the poles of the $r_{n\nu}(z)$; if the $r_{n\nu}(z)$ have finite poles that are not bounded, we proceed as in the proof of Theorem 3. Conceivably these poles are everywhere dense interior to E_ρ, so our knowledge of the properties of $f(z)$ remains slight. But if now we assume also that $f(z)$ is meromorphic with precisely ν poles in E_ρ, our previous discussion shows that the poles of $r_{n\nu}(z)$ approach those of $f(z)$. We then have

$$|r_{n+1,\nu}(z) - r_{n\nu}(z)| \leqq \frac{A_1}{n^{k+\alpha}}, \qquad z \text{ on } \Gamma_\rho,$$

whence it follows **[12]** that $f(z)$ is of class $L(k-1, \alpha)$ on Γ_ρ provided $k + \alpha > 1$ and provided Γ_ρ has no multiple points.

Further results analogous to (33), (37), and (38) can be established, as the writer plans to show on another occasion.

8. **Further sequences of rational functions.** The reader will have noticed that under certain conditions the degree of approximation to a given function $f(z)$ on a set E by rational functions may be readily obtainable, whereas the location of free poles and regions of convergence may be far less accessible; indeed, the free poles may lie everywhere dense in the entire plane or a portion of it. This observation may be carried further, as we shall now indicate.

In the preceding theorems we have considered convergence of rows of the table of functions $R_{n\nu}(z)$ of best approximation; ν is fixed while n becomes infinite. Both degree of approximation and regions of convergence depend heavily on the location of the poles of $f(z)$, where we suppose $f(z)$ to be analytic on E, meromorphic in a region containing E. We proceed now to consider convergence of columns of the table $R_{\nu n}(z)$ of functions of best approximation; ν is fixed while n becomes infinite. Here both degree of approximation and regions of convergence depend essentially on the location of the zeros of $f(z)$, where we suppose $f(z)$ to be analytic on E, meromorphic in a region containing E. The following theorem has been established **[8]**:

THEOREM 12. *Let E and E_σ be as in Theorem* 1. *Let the function $F(z)$ be analytic and different from zero on E, meromorphic with precisely ν zeros interior to E_ρ,*

$1 < \rho \leqq \infty$. Let the rational functions $R_{\nu n}(z)$ of respective types (ν, n) satisfy for the Tchebycheff norm on E

$$\limsup_{n\to\infty} \|F(z) - R_{\nu n}(z)\|^{1/n} \leqq 1/\rho. \tag{39}$$

Then the poles of the $R_{\nu n}(z)$ interior to E_ρ approach either E_ρ or the respective poles of $F(z)$ interior to E_ρ, and every pole of $F(z)$ interior to E_ρ is approached by precisely an equal multiplicity of poles of $R_{\nu n}(z)$. If D denotes the interior of E_ρ with the poles of $F(z)$ deleted, the functions $R_{\nu n}(z)$ approach $F(z)$ throughout D, and for any closed bounded set S in D and in the closed interior of E_σ we have

$$\limsup_{n\to\infty} [\max |F(z) - R_{\nu n}(z)|,\ z \text{ on } S]^{1/n} \leqq \sigma/\rho. \tag{40}$$

If the $R_{\nu n}(z)$ are the rational functions of type (ν, n) of best Tchebycheff approximation to $F(z)$ on E, then (39) *is satisfied.*

Thus far the $R_{\nu n}(z)$ need not be defined for every n, but below they shall be so defined.

Whether the $R_{\nu n}(z)$ are extremal or not, let ρ be the largest number such that $F(z)$ is meromorphic with precisely ν zeros interior to E_ρ, $1 < \rho \leqq \infty$. If (39) *holds, then* (39) *holds with the equality sign, as does* (40) *with $S = E_\sigma$, provided $1 < \sigma < \rho$, and provided no pole of $F(z)$ lies on E_σ.*

Theorem 12 may be regarded as the dual of previous theorems, where the roles of zeros and poles of both $f(z)$ and the approximating functions are interchanged, that is, where $f(z)$ is replaced by its reciprocal; this not to imply that the extremals $R_{n\nu}(z)$ and $R_{\nu n}(z)$ are reciprocals of each other, but nevertheless in suitable comparison sequences ($n \to \infty$) rational functions of types (n, ν) and (ν, n) approximating $f(z)$ and $1/f(z)$ respectively may be chosen as mutually reciprocal.

The treatment given in **[8]**, like Theorem 12, is restricted to use of the Tchebycheff norm. Other norms may be treated at once provided E consists of a finite number of mutually disjoint closed Jordan regions, by the method used in **[6]**.

Theorem 12 is clearly complementary to Theorems 1, 3, 4, and 5. Together these theorems give considerable information concerning the convergence of rows and columns of the array $R_{jk}(z)$ of rational functions of best approximation. These theorems apply also to the degree of convergence of diagonal (i.e., not horizontal or vertical) sequences formed from that array. As an illustration, suppose $f(z)$ to be meromorphic for all finite values of z, and suppose the hypothesis of Theorem 1 fulfilled for the pairs of parameters of the sequence $\nu = \nu_1, \nu_2, \nu_3, \cdots \to \infty$; $\rho = \rho_1, \rho_2, \rho_3, \cdots \to \infty$. With the notation (3) we have by (4) for n sufficiently large and for fixed ν_j

$$\lim_{n\to\infty} \delta_{nn}^{1/n} = 0, \qquad \delta_{nn} \leqq \delta_{n\nu_j}, \qquad \limsup_{n\to\infty} \delta_{nn}^{1/n} \leqq \limsup_{n\to\infty} \delta_{n\nu_j}^{1/n} \leqq 1/\rho_j. \tag{41}$$

Inequality (41) follows also by a similar consideration of the functions $R_{\nu n}(z)$ if $f(z)$ has no zeros on E.

If $f(z)$ is no longer meromorphic for all finite values of z, but is meromorphic at every point interior to E_{ρ_0}, and if $f(z)$ has infinitely many poles interior to E_{ρ_0}, we can consider appropriate pairs of parameters of the sequences $\nu = \nu_1, \nu_2, \cdots \to \infty$; $\rho = \rho_1, \rho_2, \cdots \to \rho_0$, so chosen that for each pair the hypothesis of Theorem 1 is fulfilled. There follows by the method just used

$$\limsup_{n \to \infty} \delta_{nn}^{1/n} \leqq 1/\rho_0.$$

Further results on the degree of convergence of the $R_{nn}(z)$ are established in [3], namely (41) remains valid if $f(z)$ is analytic on E and if the singularities of $f(z)$ in the extended plane form a reducible set, that is to say, a set one of whose derivatives is a null set. However, the general investigation of the sequence δ_{nn} for an arbitrary $f(z)$ (studied also in [**15**]), and more particularly the determination of the regions of convergence of the sequence $R_{nn}(z)$, must be regarded as an open problem.

9. **The Γ-function.** The theory outlined in §§1–8 above and some computational work on rational approximations to the Γ-function [**16**] by Dr. John R. Rice were commenced and well developed quite independently of each other. Rice chooses E as the segment $2 \leqq z \leqq 3$; the function $w = w(z)$ which maps the plane slit along E onto $|w| > 1$ with $w(\infty) = \infty$ is given by

$$z = \frac{1}{4}\left(w + \frac{1}{w}\right) + \frac{5}{2}, \qquad w = 2z - 5 \pm 2(z^2 - 5z + 6)^{1/2}.$$

Thus the locus E_ρ passes through the point $z(\leqq 0)$ if and only if

$$\rho = 5 - 2z + 2(z^2 - 5z + 6)^{1/2}.$$

The poles of $\Gamma(z)$ lie in the points $0, -1, -2, -3, \cdots$, and the corresponding values of ρ are $5 + 2 \cdot 6^{1/2}$, $7 + 4 \cdot 3^{1/2}$, $9 + 4 \cdot 5^{1/2}$, $11 + 2 \cdot 30^{1/2}, \cdots$. Since the Γ-function is meromorphic at every point of the plane, this is precisely the case considered in §8 with the (greatest) values of ρ just enumerated, and respectively $\nu_1 = 0$, $\nu_2 = 1$, $\nu_3 = 2, \cdots$. Rice has computed $R_{n\nu}(z)$ for suitable values of n and ν, and strangely enough, even for small values of those indices the law (7) with the equality sign can be verified quite exactly; compare [**16**].

References

1. H. Padé, *Sur la représentation approchée d'une fonction par des fractions rationelles*, Thèse, Paris, 1892.

2. R. de Montessus de Ballore, *Sur les fractions continues algébriques*, Bull. Soc. Math. de France **30** (1902), 28–36.

3. J. L. Walsh, *On the overconvergence of certain sequences of rational functions of best approximation*, Acta Math. **57** (1931), 411–435.

4. ———, *On approximation to an analytic function by rational functions of best approximation*, Math. Zeit. **38** (1934), 163–176.

5. ———, *Interpolation and approximation by rational functions in the complex domain*, Amer. Math. Soc. Coll. Pubs. **20** (1935).

6. ———, *The convergence of sequences of rational functions of best approximation*, Math. Annalen **155** (1964), 252–264.

7. ———, *The convergence of sequences of rational functions of best approximation. II.*[1]

8. ———, *Note on the convergence of approximating rational functions of prescribed type*, Proc. Nat. Acad. Sci. **50** (1963), 791–794.

9. ———, *Padé approximants as limits of rational functions of best approximation*, J. Math. and Mech. **13** (1964), 305–312.

10. ———, *The analogue for maximally convergent polynomials of Jentzsch's theorem*, Duke Math. J. **26** (1959), 605–616.

11. ———, *Overconvergence, degree of convergence, and zeros of sequences of analytic functions*, Duke Math. J. **13** (1946), 195–234.

12. ———, *Note on approximation by bounded analytic functions*, Proc. Nat. Acad. of Sciences **37** (1951), 821–826.

13. J. L. Walsh and H. M. Elliott, *Polynomial approximation to harmonic and analytic functions: generalized continuity conditions*, Trans. Amer. Math. Soc. **68** (1950), 183–203.

14. R. D. Carmichael, *Elementary inequalities for the roots of an algebraic equation*, Bull. Amer. Math. Soc. **24** (1917–18), 286–296.

15. V. Erohin, *On the best approximation of analytic functions by rational functions with free poles*, Doklady Akad. Nauk **128** (1959), 29–32.

16. J. R. Rice, *On the* L_∞ *Walsh Arrays for* $\Gamma(x)$ *and* Erf c(x), Math. Comp. **18** (1964).

---

[1] To be published in Trans. Amer. Math. Soc.

USES OF HILBERT SPACE IN APPROXIMATION

ARTHUR SARD
Queens College, Flushing, New York

1. **Introduction.** In a Hilbert space minimizations are related to perpendicularity. Bases may be constructed and projections calculated. Linear continuous functionals are inner products. Linear continuous operators may be studied closely. It is, therefore, advantageous to use Hilbert spaces in the formulation of problems, wherever the preproblem allows such use.

Many Hilbert spaces, as will be seen, are defined in terms of a measure μ. The usual choices of μ seem to me to constitute a small fraction of available choices. Preproblems which have been converted into problems in non-Hilbert spaces often could alternatively have become problems in Hilbert spaces.

The present paper is expository. In §§2, 3, I describe a few Hilbert spaces that are pertinent to approximation. In §§4–6, I discuss the problem of efficient approximation. In §7, I refer to the use of variance, an operator on a Hilbert space. The reader may find definitions, proofs, references to other proofs, and illustrative examples in Chapters 9, 10 of my book *Linear Approximation* [**14**].

2. L^2**-spaces.** Suppose that S is an arbitrary nonempty set and that μ is a measure on S. Here and elsewhere my statements may be informal. Thus μ is really a measure on a sigmafield $\mathscr{S}$ of subsets of S, called the measurable sets, rather than on S. The L^2-space $H(S, \mu)$ is defined as the space of functions x, on almost all (μ) of S to the complex numbers, which are measurable (μ) and such that

$$\int_S |x(s)|^2 \, d\mu(s) < \infty;$$

any two such functions are considered equivalent if equal almost everywhere (μ). The inner product in $H(S, \mu)$ is

$$(x, y) = \int_S x(s)\bar{y}(s) \, d\mu(s), \qquad x, y \in H(S, \mu).$$

Then $H(S, \mu)$ is a Hilbert space. If $H(S, \mu)$ is separable, it is either finite dimensional and Euclidean or of dimension $\aleph_0$. Modest conditions on S, μ insure separability. For example, it is sufficient that S be a Borel set in Euclidean space and that μ be a Stieltjes measure [**14,** p. 335].

If the preproblem involves functions on S, one may seek a measure μ which would make $H(S, \mu)$ appropriate to the preproblem. The role of μ may be described in part as follows. Suppose that the error e committed in the approximation is an element of $H(S, \mu)$. Then its square norm is

$$\|e\|^2 = \int_S |e(s)|^2 \, d\mu(s).$$

Thus values $e(s)$ near $s = s_0$ are given more or less weight according as $d\mu(s_0)$ is large or small.

To fix our ideas, consider a first problem. Suppose that M is a closed linear subspace of a Banach space X and that we wish to approximate an arbitrary $x \in X$ by $y \in M$. It is natural to choose y so as to minimize $\|y - x\|$ among all $y \in M$. If X is a Hilbert space, y is given by the orthogonal projection

$$y = \text{Proj}_M \, x, \qquad x \in X.$$

The operator Proj_M is single valued, linear, continuous, and self-adjoint. Furthermore, there is an explicit process, almost an algorithm, for calculating the projection. One form of the calculation is as follows. Let $\mathscr{F}$ be a countable set of elements of M, not necessarily independent, whose span is dense in M. Apply the Gram-Schmidt process to $\mathscr{F}$ to construct an othonormal basis $\mathscr{B}$ for M. Then

$$\text{(1)} \qquad \text{Proj}_M \, x = \sum_{u \in \mathscr{B}} (x, u)u, \qquad x \in X.$$

Alternatively, if M is finite dimensional and generated by independent elements $a_1, a_2, \cdots, a_k$ of X, then

$$\text{Proj}_M = \mathscr{M}(\mathscr{M}^*\mathscr{M})^{-1}\mathscr{M}^*,$$

where $\mathscr{M}$ is the matrix with k columns $a_1, \cdots, a_k$ and elements of X are considered as column matrices with $(b, c) = c^*b$; $b, c \in X$. If X were not a Hilbert space, analogous calculations would be more difficult.

If X is the L^2-space $H(S, \mu)$, the convergence in the series (1), being relative to the norm in X, is convergence in the mean square (μ). This has perhaps deterred some utilization of $H(S, \mu)$. It seems to me, however, that if μ is appropriate to the preproblem, the convergence here will also be appropriate. The many different types of convergence of infinite series of functions are all mathematically interesting; pointwise convergence or pointwise convergence almost everywhere (μ) should not have a preferred status. A counterpart of this theoretical comment is very practical: depth for depth, approximation in the mean square by a partial sum of a Fourier series requires fewer terms than pointwise approximation. Furthermore, the material handling of a series in an L^2-space is not difficult. Its truncations may be evaluated as partial sums almost everywhere (μ), if desired; and if the terms of the series are grouped properly, the infinite sum may be evaluated pointwise almost everywhere (μ).

The fact that two functions on S which are equal almost everywhere (μ) are considered to be the same in $H(S, \mu)$ has extensive consequences—well known if μ is Lebesgue measure and perhaps not fully appreciated in other cases.

It may be objected that the introduction of the measure μ in a problem of approximation is a subjective act. Subjective judgments in the formulation of mathematical problems, however, must be present, whether emphasized or not.

A subjective element is present in minimax approximation in that we there elect to minimize

$$\sup_{s \in S} w(s)\, |e(s)|,$$

where e is the error and w is a non-negative function indicating the relative importance to us of different parts of the domain S. The choice

$$w(s) = 1, \qquad \text{all } s \in S,$$

is no less a choice than any other.

If $x \in H(S, \mu)$ and s_0 is a fixed element of S, then the functional value $x(s_0)$ may not be well defined, because values of x are determined only to within null (μ) sets. Thus $x(s_0)$ is a linear continuous functional on $H(S, \mu)$ if and only if s_0 is a point of positive measure (μ). This is an aspect of the fact that sheer functional values are sometimes inadequate, as indicated also by the Runge phenomenon [**13**], by results of Tietze which imply that the effect of bounded errors in a central Lagrangian interpolation at equally spaced points of a line can be unbounded [**15**], and by results of Banach on divergence [**2**]. Of course there are cases in which $x(s_0)$ is firm information. One is that cited above in which $\mu\{s_0\} > 0$. Another case is this: $x(s_0)$ may stand for an average of values $x(s)$, s near s_0. For suitable averages, the average is a linear continuous functional on $H(S, \mu)$.

One of the strong points of L^2-theory is that it does not restrict the dimensionality of S. Indeed, the theory extends to maps into Euclidean spaces, as follows. Suppose that S is arbitrary, that μ is a measure on S, and that E^k is a Euclidean space. Let $H(S, \mu, E^k)$ be the space of maps x, of almost all (μ) of S into E^k, which are measurable (μ) and such that

$$\int_S \|x(s)\|_{E^k}^2 \, d\mu(s) < \infty;$$

any two such maps are considered equivalent if equal almost everywhere (μ). The inner product in $H(S, \mu, E^k)$ is defined as

$$(x, y)_{H(S,\mu,E^k)} = \int_S (x(s), y(s))_{E^k} \, d\mu(s), \qquad x, y \in H(S, \mu, E^k).$$

Then $H(S, \mu, E^k)$ is a Hilbert space [**12**, pp. 57–59]. The image space E^k may in fact be replaced by an arbitrary Hilbert space but the proofs are then complicated [**8**, p. 146; **5**, p. 133].

3. **Other Hilbert spaces.** I will cite a few other instances of Hilbert spaces which are pertinent to approximation and analysis.

Let I be an interval in E^1 and n a positive integer. Suppose that μ is a measure on I such that the Lebesgue measure of A is zero whenever $\mu A = 0$, $A \subset I$. Suppose that $w^0, w^1, \cdots, w^{n-1}$ are positive constants, and that $a \in I$. Let X

be the space of numerical functions x on I which are such that the $(n-1)$st derivative x_{n-1} is absolutely continuous on I and the nth derivative x_n is an element of the L^2-space $H(I, \mu)$, with inner product

$$(x, y) = \sum_{i=0,\cdots,n-1} x_i(a)\bar{y}_i(a)w^i + \int_I x_n(s)\bar{y}_n(s)\,d\mu(s), \qquad x, y \in X.$$

Then X is a Hilbert space. Each element x of X is an unambiguous function and $x(s_0)$ for any fixed $s_0 \in I$ is a linear continuous functional on I. In the present case, where I is a linear interval, the topology of X is in fact independent of a and $w^0, \cdots, w^{n-1}$. The choice of $a, w^0, \cdots, w^{n-1}$ may however affect our numerical judgments.

If $n = 1$ and μ is Lebesgue measure, for example, the inner product in X is

$$(x, y)_X = x(a)\bar{y}(a)w^0 + \int_I x_1(s)\bar{y}_1(s)\,ds, \qquad x, y \in X.$$

Some authors consider a space Y like X, except that the inner product is

$$(x, y)_Y = \int_I x(s)\bar{y}(s)\,ds + \int_I x_1(s)\bar{y}_1(s)\,ds, \qquad x, y \in X.$$

Now X and Y have the same topology and so for many purposes are equivalent. The space X, however, has the advantage that $x(a)$ and x_1 are independent of one another for each $x \in X$, whereas x and x_1 are not. Sharp appraisals in terms of $\|x\|_X$ will be more accessible than those in terms of $\|x\|_Y$.

The next example of a Hilbert space uses the space **B** [**14**, p. 199] of functions defined on an m-dimensional interval I. I shall take $m = 2$ and use the notation of the reference. Suppose that $\mu^{p,q}$ is a measure on I such that the two-dimensional Lebesgue measure of $A \subset I$ is zero whenever $\mu^{p,q} A = 0$; also that $\mu^{i,j}$, $(i, j) \in \bar{\omega}_{s,b}$, are measures on I_s with the analogous one-dimensional property; also that $\mu^{i,j}$, $(i, j) \in \bar{\omega}_{a,t}$, are similar measures on I_t. Suppose that $w^{i,j}$, $(i, j) \in \bar{\omega}_{a,b}$, are positive constants. Define X as the space of functions x which are elements of **B** such that

$$x_{p,q}(s, t) \in H(I, \mu^{p,q}); \qquad x_{i,j}(s, b) \in H(I_s, \mu^{i,j}), \qquad (i, j) \in \bar{\omega}_{s,b};$$
$$x_{i,j}(a, t) \in H(I_t, \mu^{i,j}), \qquad (i, j) \in \bar{\omega}_{a,t};$$

with inner product

$$(x, y) = \sum_{\omega_{a,b}} x_{i,j}(a, b)\bar{y}_{i,j}(a, b)w^{i,j} + \sum_{\omega_{s,b}} \int_{I_s} x_{i,j}(s, b)\bar{y}_{i,j}(s, b)\,d\mu^{i,j}(s)$$
$$+ \text{dual sum} + \iint_I x_{p,q}(s, t)\bar{y}_{p,q}(s, t)\,d\mu^{p,q}(s, t), \qquad x, y \in X.$$

Then X is a Hilbert space, a generalization of the previous example. The many individual terms in (x, y) are independent of one another.

Further examples of Hilbert spaces are given in [**1**; **3**; **4**; **6**; **8**, Chapters 13, 14; **10**; **11**] and elsewhere.

There are a number of engineering questions relevant to the use of Hilbert space. Which inner product, among those that seem appropriate, will make the calculation simplest and the results deepest? In considering a countable set $\mathscr{F}$ from which a basis is to be calculated, in what order should the elements of $\mathscr{F}$ be introduced to the process of orthogonalization? The process, or at least its beginning, may be programmed [**14**, pp. 345 ff.]. If $\mathscr{F}$ is finite, one might instruct a machine to try different orders of $\mathscr{F}$, which may be variously susceptible to effects of rounding errors.

4. **Efficient approximation; the preproblem.** I shall now discuss a problem which seems to me to lie at the center of the theory of approximation. Although the problem is classical, the results obtained in my writings are new.

Suppose than an input $x + \delta x \in X$ will be operated on by a process of approximation A to produce the output $A(x + \delta x) \in Y$ and that $A(x + \delta x)$ will be used as an approximation of $Gx \in Y$, where X, Y are given spaces and A, G are operators on X to Y. The error in the approximation will be

$$e = A(x + \delta x) - Gx \in Y.$$

We may say that x is the ideal input, $x + \delta x$ the actual input, δx the error therein, Gx the desired output, and $A(x + \delta x)$ the actual output. Also, that A is to filter out the effect of δx and to approximate G. The operator G may be the identity or a differentiation or an integration or something else.

Suppose that $\mathscr{A}$ is a set of acceptable operators. We seek to choose $A \in \mathscr{A}$ and to study e.

It is reasonable to envisage a multiplicity of inputs x and δx, perhaps of unequal importance. A powerful way to describe such multiplicities is to use the theory of probability: take x and δx to be stochastic processes. Some stochastic mechanism produces elements x and $\delta x \in X$. In each trial (i.e., action of the stochastic mechanism), we are given $x + \delta x$ but not x.

Our criterion of choice of $A \in \mathscr{A}$ will be to make the expected value of the error as small as possible, in some sense.

5. **The precise problem.** Adding a few hypotheses, I shall convert the preproblem into a mathematical problem for which a strong theory will be possible.

Suppose that

T, Ω are nonempty spaces;

m is a measure on T and p is a probability on Ω;

$Y = H(T, m)$ is the L^2-space of functions on T absolute square integrable (m);

$\Psi = H(\Omega, p)$; Y and Ψ are separable;

X is an arbitrary separable Hilbert space;

X, Y, Ψ contain elements other than 0;

$\mathscr{A}$ is a linear set of linear continuous operators on X to Y;

$x + \delta x$ is an element of the direct product $X\Psi$;

y is an element of the direct product $Y\Psi$.

This completes the statement of the data of the problem.

The direct product of two Hilbert spaces is sometimes called the tensor product; it is different from the direct sum [**14**, pp. 353 ff.]. The direct product $Y\Psi$ is an L^2-space because each factor is; indeed

$$Y\Psi = H(T \times \Omega, mp).$$

Thus y is a complex function on almost all (mp) of $T \times \Omega$, measurable (mp), such that

$$\|y\|^2_{Y\Psi} = \int_T E\,|y(t, \omega)|^2\, dm(t) < \infty,$$

where the expected value sign E indicates integration over Ω relative to p:

$$Eu = \int_\Omega u(\omega)\, dp(\omega).$$

For each fixed $\omega \in \Omega$ with null (p) exceptions,

$$(x + \delta x)_\omega \in X \quad \text{and} \quad y_\omega \in Y.$$

Thus $x + \delta x$ and y are stochastic processes; y will play the role of Gx in our preproblem. If Ω' is any measurable (p) subset of Ω then $p\Omega'$ is the probability that a trial will produce an ω which is an element of Ω', with corresponding input $(x + \delta x)_\omega$ and desired output y_ω.

For any linear continuous operator A on X to Y there exists a unique linear continuous operator A' on $X\Psi$ to $Y\Psi$ such that [**14**, p. 372]

$$A'(\phi u) = \phi\, Au \quad \text{whenever} \quad \phi \in \Psi, \qquad u \in X.$$

Since A' is the natural extension of A and since

$$A'(1u) = A'u = 1Au = Au, \qquad u \in X,$$

I shall henceforth drop the prime. The context will indicate whether A is an operator on X to Y or its extension on $X\Psi$ to $Y\Psi$.

Put

$$e = A(x + \delta x) - y \in Y\Psi = H(T \times \Omega, mp), \qquad A \in \mathscr{A};$$

e is a stochastic process. For each fixed $\omega \in \Omega$ with null (p) exceptions, $e(t, \omega)$, $t \in T$, is an element of Y and is the error in the approximation of $y(t, \omega)$, $t \in T$, by $A(x + \delta x)_\omega$. For each fixed $t \in T$ with null (m) exceptions,

$$E\,|e(t, \omega)|^2$$

measures the expected error at t. And

$$E\,\|e(t, \omega)\|^2_Y = \int_T E|e(t, \omega)|^2\, dm(t) \tag{2}$$

measures the expected overall error. In these expressions, ω is a bound variable absorbed by E; in the last line, t also is absorbed.

In considering A^0, $A \in \mathscr{A}$, put

$$e^0 = A^0(x + \delta x) - y, \qquad e = A(x + \delta x) - y.$$

We say that $A^0 \in \mathscr{A}$ is efficient if, for all $A \in \mathscr{A}$,

$$E \, \|e^0\|_Y^2 \leqq E \, \|e\|_Y^2.$$

And that $A^0 \in \mathscr{A}$ is strongly efficient if, for all $A \in \mathscr{A}$,

$$E \, |e^0(t, \omega)|^2 \leqq E \, |e(t, \omega)|^2, \qquad \text{almost all } (m) \; t \in T.$$

The last inequality holds except on a null (m) subset of T, which exceptional set may depend on A. If A^0 is strongly efficient, a fortiori A^0 is efficient, by (2).

To attain the minima may be impossible or, if possible, may require too much computation. We therefore introduce the concepts of near efficiency and near strong efficiency.

Let ρ be a positive number. We say that $A^0 \in \mathscr{A}$ is within ρ of efficiency if

$$E \, \|e^0\|_Y^2 < E \, \|e\|_Y^2 + \rho^2$$

for all $A \in \mathscr{A}$. And that $A^0 \in \mathscr{A}$ is within ρ of strong efficiency if a function $\zeta \in Y = H(T, m)$ exists such that

$$\|\zeta\|_Y^2 < \rho^2$$

and

$$E \, |e^0(t, \omega)|^2 \leqq E \, |e(t, \omega)|^2 + |\zeta(t)|^2, \qquad \text{almost all } (m) \; t \in T,$$

for all $A \in \mathscr{A}$. If A^0 is within ρ of strong efficiency, a fortiori A^0 is within ρ of efficiency.

We say that efficiency is strong if, for all $\rho > 0$, any operator within ρ of efficiency is within ρ of strong efficiency and any efficient operator is strongly efficient.

One may now establish the following facts [**14**, pp. 386 ff.]. There is a unique element $\sigma \in Y\Psi$, which may be calculated by a projection, such that

$A^0 \in \mathscr{A}$ is efficient if and only if $A^0(x + \delta x) = \sigma$;

$A^0 \in \mathscr{A}$ is within ρ of efficiency if and only if

$$E \, \|A^0(x + \delta x) - \sigma\|_Y^2 < \rho^2, \qquad \rho > 0.$$

If σ is known to within $\rho > 0$, one may construct an operator A within ρ of efficiency. Although the efficient operator A^0, if existent, need not be unique, the error that it induces is unique, being

$$e^0 = \sigma - y.$$

These results are elementary.

For each $t \in T$ with null (m) exceptions, there is an element $\tau(t) \in \Psi$, which may be calculated by a projection, such that efficiency is strong if and only if

$$\tau(t) = \sigma(t), \qquad \text{almost all } (m) \; t \in T,$$

where $\sigma(t)$ is the element of Ψ obtained by fixing t in $\sigma(t, \omega)$ and $\sigma \in Y\Psi$ is the element of the preceding paragraph. This result is quite natural but hard to prove.

I know of no proof except in my writings. The difficulty occurs in establishing the necessity in the case in which no efficient operator exists.

A linear continuous operator A on X to Y is said to be of finite rank if the image AX is finite dimensional.

If $\mathscr{A}$ includes all operators of finite rank, then efficiency is strong.

The above theorems are established by the use of Hilbert space.

It may be of interest to consider how restrictive our assumptions have been. The hypothesis that each $A \in \mathscr{A}$ is linear has been essential; it would obtain only if the preproblem involved linear operators as approximators. The other hypotheses seem to me not unduly restrictive. Because of the wide choice of Hilbert spaces and L^2-spaces, we may often find spaces X, Y relative to which the operators in $\mathscr{A}$ become continuous. If the initial set $\mathscr{A}$ of acceptable operators were not linear, we could replace $\mathscr{A}$ by its span. There has been no assumption that $\mathscr{A}$ is topologically closed.

Our analysis has depended on the stochastic processes $x + \delta x$ and y. How we would acquire knowledge of these processes is a pertinent question, although of the sort which arises in any use of probability. In some situations, one might be given the stochastic processes from outside. In some situations, one might observe the working of earlier trials and deduce therefrom estimates of the stochastic processes. Statistical theories of estimation of stochastic processes will, one may hope, be developed. Finally, in some situations, one might assume tentatively that $x + \delta x$ and y were thus and so, and then observe the extent to which deductions therefrom seem to fit observation. Our tentative processes can be quite simple. One would not expect anything as jittery as a Brownian motion to be pertinent to problems of approximation.

In the theory of Wiener-Kolmogorov, T is the time axis, $x + \delta x$ and y are stationary, and $\mathscr{A}$ consists of operators on the past [**7**, Chapter 12]. These special assumptions permit the use of the spectral representation or alternatively the correlations. If the correlations are known, they are sufficient for our Pythagorean calculations [**14**, pp. 432 ff.]. Thus the Wiener-Kolmogorov theory uses no less information than the theory in Hilbert space.

6. **Applications.** A number of illustrations are given in [**14**, pp. 404 ff.]. A number of applications are suggested in [**9**, Chapters 5–8].

The following example involves the smoothing and approximation of a function given a table of contaminated values [**14**, pp. 415 ff.].

Suppose that $X = H(T, \mu)$ and $Y = H(T, m)$ are L^2-spaces of functions on the same space T relative to different measures μ and m. Suppose that μ is atomic, with atoms at $t^1, t^2, \cdots, t^k \in T$. This means that there are positive numbers $w^1, \cdots, w^k$ such that for any subset R of T,

$$\mu R = \sum_{t^i \in R} w^i.$$

Then the k points $t^1, \cdots, t^k$ constitute almost all (μ) of T. An element u of X is characterized by its values $u(t^i)$, $i = 1, \cdots, k$; these values describe u almost everywhere (μ) and therefore are a complete description of u as an element of X. Note that

$$\|u\|_X^2 = \sum_{i=1,\cdots,k} |u(t^i)|^2 w^i.$$

This relation shows in what sense w^i measures the importance of $u(t^i)$ and how the values of $u(t)$ except at $t = t^i$, $i = 1, \cdots, k$, are immaterial.

Suppose that m is a measure on T such that the norm in $H(T, m)$ is appropriate to the purpose of our approximation. Suppose that Ω, p are the probability underlying the stochastic mechanism that produces the inputs. As before, put $\Psi = H(\Omega, p)$. Then

$$X\Psi = H(T \times \Omega, \mu p), \qquad Y\Psi = H(T \times \Omega, mp).$$

Finally, suppose that

$$x + \delta x \in X\Psi, \qquad y = x \in Y\Psi.$$

Then for each $\omega \in \Omega$ with null (p) exceptions, $x + \delta x$ is a table of values of a function on T contaminated by δx; and $y = x$ is the set of true values of the function, with null (m) exceptions. We may think of a set of cards, each corresponding to an $\omega \in \Omega$ and each carrying a table of $x + \delta x$. A stochastic mechanism produces a card. We operate on it by an element $A \in \mathscr{A}$, producing $A(x + \delta x)$ as an approximation of x, where $\mathscr{A}$ is a given linear set of acceptable linear operators on X to Y.

Since X is finite dimensional, any linear operator on X is continuous. The set $\mathscr{A}$, for example, may be the set of all linear operators on X to Y. Then efficiency will be strong. For any $\rho > 0$, we may find a linear operator A^0 on X to Y within ρ of strong efficiency (details in [**14**, pp. 417–418]). In each trial $A^0(x + \delta x)$ is a description almost everywhere (m) on T of an approximation of x. If ρ is sufficiently small, $A^0(x + \delta x)$ is adequately close to the best approximation that can be produced by a linear operator. The operator A^0 gives a single machine program, applicable whatever the outcome of the trial.

7. **Variance.** Among other applications of the theory of Hilbert space, I will mention only the use of variance. Consider a stochastic process $\delta x \in X\Psi$, where X, Ψ are as in §5 above. Usually δx is an error. The variance V of δx is a linear continuous operator, nonnegative, self-adjoint, of finite trace, on X to X [**14**, pp. 460 ff.]. The advantage of V derives from the following fact. If Y is a separable Hilbert space and A, B are linear continuous operators on X to Y (and, therefore, by extension on $X\Psi$ to $Y\Psi$), then

$$E(A\delta x, B\delta x)_Y = \text{trace } AVB^*.$$

References

1. N. Aronszajn, *Theory of reproducing kernels*, Trans. Amer. Math. Soc. **68** (1950), 337–404.

2. S. Banach, *Sur la divergence des interpolations*, Studia Math. **9** (1940), 156–163.

3. S. Bergman, *The kernel function and conformal mapping*, Amer. Math. Soc., New York, 1950.

4. S. Bergman and M. Schiffer, *Kernel functions and elliptic differential equations in mathematical physics*, Academic Press, New York, 1953.

5. N. Bourbaki, *Intégration, Éléments de Mathématique*, Livre VI, Chapitres I–IV, Hermann, Paris, 1952.

6. P. J. Davis, *Interpolation and approximation*, Ginn, New York, 1963.

7. J. L. Doob, *Stochastic processes*, John Wiley, New York, 1953.

8. N. Dunford and J. T. Schwartz with the assistance of W. G. Bade and R. G. Bartle, *Linear operators*. Interscience, New York, I, 1958, II, 1963.

9. J. H. Laning, Jr. and R. H. Battin, *Random processes in automatic control*, McGraw-Hill, New York, 1956.

10. P. D. Lax, *On Cauchy's problem for hyperbolic equations and the differentiability of solutions of elliptic equations*, Comm. Pure Appl. Math. **8** (1955), 615–633.

11. F. J. Murray, *Linear transformations between Hilbert spaces and the application of this theory to linear partial differential equations*, Trans. Amer. Math. Soc. **37** (1935), 301–338.

12. F. Riesz and B. Sz.-Nagy, *Functional analysis*, translated by L. F. Boron, Ungar, New York, 1955.

13. C. Runge, *Über empirische Funktionen und die Interpolation zwischen äquidistanten Ordinaten*, Z. Math. Phys. **46** (1901), 224–243.

14. A. Sard, *Linear approximation*, Amer. Math. Soc., Providence, R. I., 1963.

15. H. Tietze, *Eine Bemerkung zur Interpolation*, Z. Math. Phys. **64** (1914), 74–90.

APPLICATIONS OF DUALITY IN APPROXIMATION THEORY

R. C. BUCK
University of Wisconsin, Madison

1. **Introduction.** The duality relations in linear spaces pair up an extremal problem in a space with a corresponding extremal problem in the dual space. We will discuss the applications of these to problems in approximation of functions, and show that it is theoretically possible to use these techniques to determine both the *best* approximations and the *good* approximations; moreover, we shall point out the central role that is played by the extreme linear functionals in certain convex sets. In special cases, this leads to a general class of alternation type theorems.

While the main applications we have in mind are to spaces of functions, it is easier to work in a more general context. Let E be a (real) linear space with a norm $\| \ \|$. The dual space of continuous linear functionals L is denoted by E^*, which is a Banach space with norm

$$\|L\| = \sup_{\|x\| \leq 1} |L(x)|.$$

Let M be a subspace of E. Many of the problems which are central to approximation theory are most naturally stated in terms of norms. (See Buck [**4**].) For example, a problem in error analysis in numerical integration leads to the problem of evaluating $\|I - L\|_M$, the norm on the subspace M of the functional $I - L$ where

$$I(x) = \int_0^1 x(t)\,dt \quad \text{and} \quad L(x) = \sum_1^N c_j x(t_j).$$

Likewise, the problem of approximating a function $z \in E$ by a best function $x \in M$ leads to the problem of evaluating

$$\rho_M(z) = \inf_{x \in M} \|z - x\|.$$

Credit for observing that such extremal problems arise in pairs, and that functional analysis can assist in their solution, probably goes back to Kreĭn [1938] and indeed to Banach. However, many others have made this discovery independently, and used it in a variety of ways; an incomplete list would mention Nikol'skiĭ [1946], Havinson [1950], Rogosinski [1950], H. S. Shapiro [1952], Bonsall [1956]. (See [**10**], [**14**], [**8**], [**18**], [**19**], [**20**], [**2**], [**24**], [**12**].)

The basic duality relations stem from the polar mapping between convex sets in E and convex sets in E^*. If C is convex and $C \subset E$, let C^0 be the set of all $L \in E^*$ such that $L(x) \leq 1$ for all $x \in C$. For example, if $C = S$, the unit sphere in E, then $C^0 = S^*$, the unit sphere in E^*. If we choose C to be the subspace M, then C^0 will be the subspace $M^\perp \subset E^*$ consisting of all functionals L which vanish on M. We wish to exploit the relationship between M and $M^\perp$. The two main results are as follows:

THEOREM 1. *If $M \subset E$ and $M^\perp$ is its annihilator in E^*, then for any $L_0 \in E^*$*

$$\min_{L_0 \in M^\perp} \|L_0 - L\| = \sup_{\substack{x \in M \\ \|x\| \leq 1}} |L_0(x)|. \tag{1}$$

THEOREM 2. *For any $x_0 \in M$,*

$$\inf_{x \in M} \|x_0 - x\| = \max_{\substack{L \in M^\perp \\ \|L\| \leq 1}} |L(x_0)|. \tag{2}$$

The similarity of these relations is obvious. Each can be stated in other ways. For example, that which appears in (1) can also be given as

$$\rho_{M^\perp}(L_0) = \|L_0\|_M$$

where the number on the left is the distance in E^* from L_0 to the subspace $M^\perp$, and the quantity on the right is the norm (on M) of the functional that is obtained by restricting L_0 to the subspace M. A similar restatement can be given for (2), with the right hand side replaced by $\|\hat{x}_0\|_{M^\perp}$, where we have used $\hat{x}$ to denote the image of x in the canonical embedding of E in E^{**}. (See Day **[6]**.)

An understanding of these duality relations can best be obtained by an examination of certain quotient spaces. (See **[21]** or **[2]**.) If E is a normed space, and F a closed subspace of E, then there is a natural definition of norm in the linear space E/F under which the canonical mapping of E onto E/F is continuous. If X is a point in E/F (an equivalence class), and $y \in X$, then $|||X|||$ is defined to be $\inf_{x \in F} \|y - x\|$. Consider the mapping ϕ from E^* into M^* defined by $\phi(L) = L|_M$, the restriction of L to M. The kernel (null space) of ϕ is clearly $M^\perp$; by the Hahn-Banach theorem, the mapping ϕ is *onto*. Thus, $E^*/M^\perp$ is isomorphic to M^*. Theorem 1 asserts that, in addition, this isomorphism is norm preserving. Theorem 2 asserts the existence of a similar norm preserving isomorphism between $M^\perp$ and $(E/M)^*$.

For completeness, we include brief proofs of both theorems.

PROOF OF THEOREM 1. Let $x \in M$ and $L \in M^\perp$ with $\|x\| < 1$. Then

$$|L_0(x)| = |(L_0 - L)(x)| \leqq \|L_0 - L\| \, \|x\|$$

and

$$\sup_{\substack{x \in M \\ \|x\| \leq 1}} |L_0(x)| = \|L_0\|_M \leqq \inf_{L \in M^\perp} \|L_0 - L\|.$$

To show that equality holds, and that "inf" can be replaced by "min", restrict L_0 to M, and then extend it to E as a functional L_1 for which $\|L_1\| = \|L_0\|_M$. Then, $L = L_0 - L_1$ is in $M^\perp$, and $\|L_0 - L\| = \|L_1\|$ establishing (1).

PROOF OF THEOREM 2. If $x \in M$ and $L \in M^{\perp}$ with $\|L\| \leqq 1$, then

$$|L(x_0)| = |L(x_0 - x)| \leqq \|x_0 - x\|$$

and

$$\sup_{L} |L(x_0)| \leqq \inf_{x \in M} \|x_0 - x\| = \rho.$$

Define a linear functional L_1 on $N = M + (x_0)$ by setting $L_1 = 0$ on M, and $L_1(x_0) = \rho$. The norm of L_1 on N is

$$\sup_{y \in N} \frac{|L_1(y)|}{\|y\|} = \frac{\rho}{\inf_{x \in M} \|x - x_0\|} = 1.$$

Appealing to the Hahn-Banach theorem, extend L_1 to E to obtain a functional L in $M^{\perp}$ with $\|L\| = 1$ and $L(x_0) = \rho$, thus proving (2).

2. **Applications of the duality theorems.** Many of the classical problems in approximation theory deal with questions of the degree of approximation, rather than that of finding optimal approximations. For example, one may have a sequence of subspaces $M_1 \subset M_2 \subset M_3 \subset \cdots$, and be concerned about the rate of decrease of the sequence

$$\delta_k(z) = \rho_{M_k}(z) = \inf_{x \in M_k} \|z - x\|$$

for a specific function z, or for all functions z in some class C. In such cases, it is clear that Theorem 2 may enable one to determine estimates for $\delta_k(z)$. For example, any choice of $L \in M^{\perp}$, with $\|L\| \leqq 1$, and any choice of $x \in M$ gives a pair of bounds on $\rho_M(z)$, namely

$$|L(z)| \leqq \rho_M(z) \leqq \|z - x\|.$$

An especially elegant example of this is to be found in the solution of the so-called interpolation problem for H^∞, as given in a recent paper by Shields and Shapiro [**21**]. Let H^∞ be the space of functions f that are holomorphic in the unit disc D and are bounded there. The interpolation problem asked for necessary and sufficient conditions on a sequence $z_n \in D$ such that for any bounded sequence $\{w_n\}$ of complex numbers, there shall exist a function $f \in H^\infty$ with $f(z_n) = w_n$, $n = 1, 2, 3, \cdots$. In raising this question in 1956, I had conjectured that it was sufficient if $|z_n| \to 1$ rapidly, in the sense that $d(z_n, z_{n+1}) \geqq \delta > 0$. Here, $d(a, b)$ is the non-euclidean distance between a and b in D. This was confirmed, and the original question answered completely by L. Carleson [**5**] in 1958, with partial solutions obtained by Hayman [**9**] and Newman [**13**].

Let $B_n(z)$ be a Blaschke product whose zeros are at the points $z_1, z_2, \cdots, z_n$. Then, a partial solution to the interpolation problem can be found by writing

$$h_n(z) = B_n(z)R_n(z) - B_n(z)g(z),$$

where R_n is the rational function

$$R_n(z) = \sum_{k=1}^{n} \frac{w_k(1 - \bar{z}_k z)}{b_{nk}(z - z_k)}$$

and g is any function in H^∞. This is essentially Lagrange interpolation, and the function h_n obeys $h_n(z_k) = w_k$ for $k = 1, 2, 3, \cdots, n$. We wish to choose the function g so that h_n becomes an optimal partial interpolation for the given sequence $\{w_k\}$, which can be taken to obey $|w_k| \leqq 1$ for all k. This leads us to define the numbers

$$M_n(w) = \inf_{g \in H^\infty} \|B_n R_n - B_n g\|.$$

Moving out to the boundary of the unit circle, and using the fact that $|B_n(z)| = 1$ there, we have

$$M_n(w) = \inf_{g \in H^\infty} \|R_n - g\|.$$

Using the duality theorems and the fact that $H^\infty = (H_1)^\perp$, one finds that

$$M_n(w) = \sup \left| \frac{1}{2\pi} \int_{-\pi}^{\pi} f(e^{i\theta}) R_n(e^{i\theta}) e^{i\theta} \, d\theta \right|,$$

where f ranges over all functions in H_1 with $\|f\| \leqq 1$. If it can be shown that the numbers $M_n(w)$ have a uniform bound M that is independent of n and of the choice of the sequence $w = \{w_k\}$ then $\{z_n\}$ is a sequence in D that admits interpolation. By an elementary estimate, this will follow if it can be shown that there is a finite bound for

$$M = \sup_{\substack{f \in H_1 \\ \|f\| \leqq 1}} \sum_1^\infty |f(z_k)| \, (1 - |z_k|^2).$$

By an elegant simple argument, and another application of the duality theorems, this in turn is shown to be equivalent to an analogous interpolation problem in the space H_2 which can be solved directly. The final result for H^∞ is that a sequence $\{z_n\}$ is a universal interpolation sequence if and only if one can find a constant B, and functions $f_k \in H^\infty$ such that $\|f_k\| \leqq B$ while $f_k(z_n) = \delta_k^n$ for all n and k. (This condition can also be stated in terms of the mutual non-euclidean distances between the points $\{z_n\}$.)

There are many other examples in the literature in which the duality relations are used to *estimate* parameters or to demonstrate *existence* of extremals. It is natural to ask if they can assist us to find or characterize the points in the set

$$B(z) = \{\text{all } x_0 \in M \quad \text{with} \quad \|z - x_0\| = \rho_M(z)\}$$

of *best* approximations in M to z. In the absence of finite dimensionality or special convexity conditions, this set can be empty. It would, therefore, be desirable to have methods for finding "good" approximations, points in the sets

$$B(z, \varepsilon) = \{\text{all } x_0 \in M \quad \text{with} \quad \|z - x_0\| \leqq \rho + \varepsilon\}.$$

These sets are indicated in Figure 1.

In this section, we now show that in theory it is possible to use the duality theorems to obtain the set $B(z)$, and in a later section, that they can be used in a more economical fashion to obtain the sets $B(z, \varepsilon)$, for any $\varepsilon > 0$.

Although, again the critical observation was made independently by others, I. Singer seems to have been the first to state the following result [22]. First, it is convenient to introduce the special set

$$S_M^* = S^* \cap M^\perp$$
$$= \{\text{all } L \in E^* \quad \text{with} \quad \|L\| \leqq 1 \quad \text{and} \quad L = 0 \text{ on } M\}.$$

THEOREM 3. *For any* $z \in E$,

$$B(z) = M \cap \{z + \mathscr{W}\},$$

where

$$\mathscr{W} = \bigcup_{L \in S_M^*} W_L,$$

and, for any L,

$$W_L = \{\text{all } x \in E \quad \text{with} \quad L(x) = \|x\|\}.$$

Some geometric remarks may be helpful. For any $L \in S^*$, the set W_L is a cone with vertex at the origin in E. For any point $x \in E$, $\sup_{L \in S^*} |L(x)| = \|x\|$. Since the

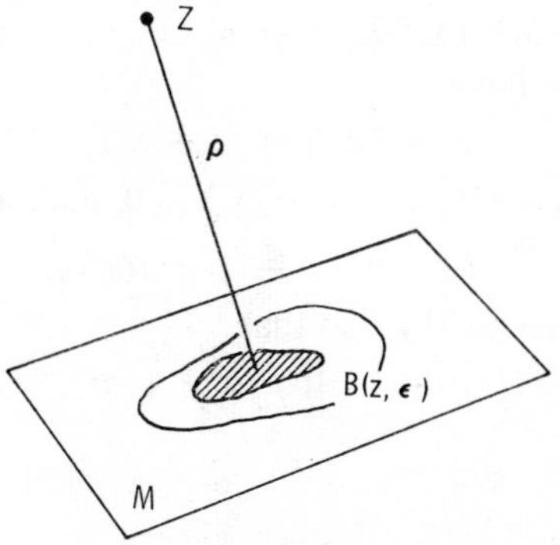

FIGURE 1. Best approximations (shaded), and good approximations to z.

sphere S^* is w^* compact, this supremum is achieved, and there must exist an L with $x \in W_L$. Hence, the whole space E is the union of the cones W_L. In forming $\mathscr{W}$, we take only the cones W_L with $L \in S_M^* \subset S^*$. It is easily seen that this set is symmetric, containing $-x$ when it contains x, but that it need not be convex in general.

The meaning of Theorem 3 is that the set $B(z)$, for any z, can be obtained by translating the set $\mathscr{W}$ to the point z, and then intersecting it with the subspace M; it is easily seen that the resulting set must always be convex, although it may be a single point or indeed empty. This situation is illustrated in Figures 2 and 3, where E has been chosen as the plane, with the l^1-norm, and with M as the subspace generated by the point (1, 1). The shaded set in Figure 2 is $\mathscr{W}$, and in Figure 3, we show the result of translating it to a point z. Indeed, in this case, $\mathscr{W}$ is the union of the two cones W_{L_1} and W_{L_2}, where $L_1(x) = x_1 - x_2$, $L_2 = -L_1$.

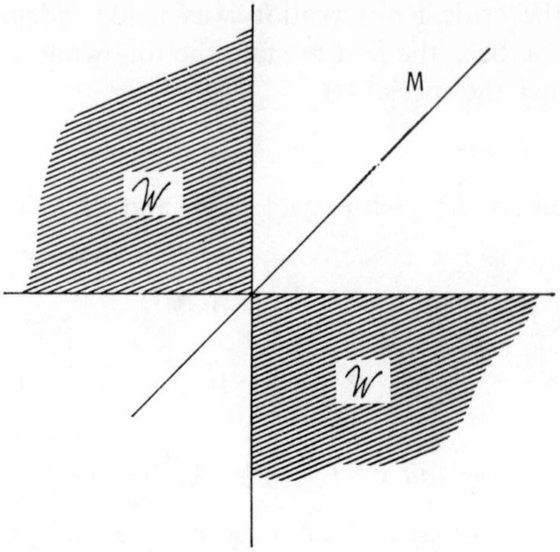

FIGURE 2. Example of $\mathscr{W}$ for the l^1-norm in the plane.

PROOF OF THEOREM 3. For any fixed $z \in E$, let $\rho = \rho_M(z)$. By Theorem 2, there is a functional $L_0 \in S_M^*$ such that $L_0(z) = \rho$. Let x_0 be any point in $B(z)$. Then, $\|z - x_0\| = \rho$, so that we have

$$\rho = L_0(z) = \|z - x_0\|.$$

However, $x_0 \in M$ and $L_0 \in M^\perp$, so that $L_0(x_0) = 0$, and, accordingly,

$$L_0(z - x_0) = \|z - x_0\|.$$

This shows that $z - x_0$ lies in W_{L_0}, so that

$$x_0 \in z - W_{L_0} \subset z + \mathscr{W}.$$

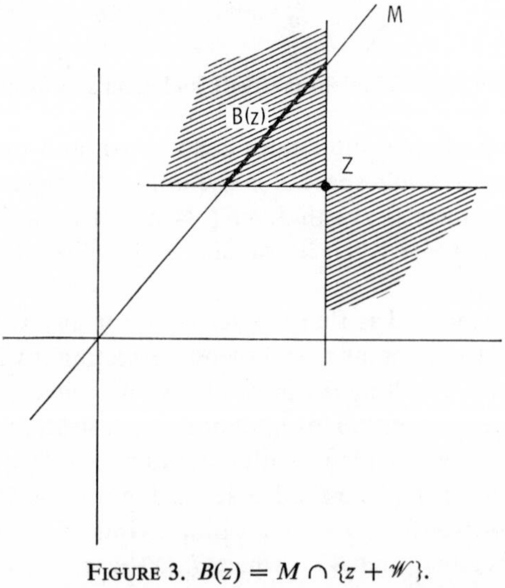

FIGURE 3. $B(z) = M \cap \{z + \mathscr{W}\}$.

Conversely, suppose that x_0 is a point of M that also lies in $z + \mathscr{W}$. Using the symmetry of $\mathscr{W}$, there must exist a functional $L \in S_M^*$ such that $x_0 \in z - W_L$, and thus $z - x_0 \in W_L$, so that

$$L(z - x_0) = \|z - x_0\|.$$

However, $L \in M^\perp$ so that $L(x_0) = 0$ and $L(z - x_0) = L(z)$. However, from Theorem 2, $L(z) \leqq \rho_M(z)$, showing that $\|z - x_0\| = \rho$ and x_0 is a best approximation to z.

This result of Singer's transfers the general problem of determining the set of best approximations of elements of E by elements of M to that of determining all the sets W_L for every functional L in S_M^*, which amounts to knowing the subspace $M^\perp$ explicitly. There are several other ways to arrive at this important set $\mathscr{W}$, as noted, for example, in the survey article by Rivlin and Shapiro **[17]**.

COROLLARY 1. *The set $\mathscr{W}$ is the collection of all points $y \in E$ for which the origin* 0 *is a closest point of M.*

COROLLARY 2. *A point y lies in $\mathscr{W}$ if and only if*

$$\|y - x\| \geqq \|y\|$$

for all points $x \in M$.

The importance of the set $\mathscr{W}$ is further illustrated by the following observation, due to Singer **[23]** and Ptak **[16]**, and throwing light upon the phenomenon of uniqueness in approximation theory.

COROLLARY 3. *The assertion that every point $z \in E$ has at most only one best approximation from the subspace M is equivalent to the geometric condition*

$$\{\mathscr{W} + \mathscr{W}\} \cap M = \{0\}.$$

The proof is immediate. Suppose that a point $z \in E$ has two distinct best approximations x_1 and x_2, in M. By Theorem 3, we must have $x_i = z + y_i$ where $y_i \in \mathscr{W}$. Thus, $x_1 - x_2$, which is not 0, is an element of M that, being equal to $y_1 - y_2$, lies in $\mathscr{W} + \mathscr{W}$. Conversely, suppose that $x_0 \in M$, $x_0 \neq 0$, and $x_0 \in \mathscr{W} + \mathscr{W}$. Writing $x_0 = y_1 + y_2$, we observe that x_0 must be a best approximation to y_1. However, by Corollary 1, y_1 also has 0 as a best approximation. Thus, y_1 is a point of E which has two (and therefore infinitely many) best approximations in M.

We add the remark that the condition involved can be thrown back onto the cones W_L themselves, for it is easily seen that approximation is non-unique if and only if there is some $L \in S_M^*$ such that $W_L - W_L$ contains a non-zero element of M.

3. **Extreme functionals in S_M^*.** As outlined above, it is necessary to work with all the functionals L in $M^\perp$, either to obtain the set $\mathscr{W}$, or to determine the minimum deviation $\rho_M(z)$ from the relation

(3) $$\rho_M(z) = \max_{L \in S_M^*} |L(z)|.$$

However, a considerable simplification is possible. The set S_M^* is obtained as the intersection of the sphere S^* and the subspace $M^\perp$. It is, therefore, a convex set that is w^* closed and compact. In looking for a maximum, on the right side of (3), we are essentially asking for the extreme of a linear function over a convex set. By the Kreĭn-Milman theorem, S_M^* is the closed convex hull of its set of extreme points; denoting this set by $e(S_M^*)$, we see that we can therefore restrict the search to this subset of S_M^*, and have

$$(4) \qquad \rho_M(z) = \sup_{L \in e(S_M)} |L(z)|.$$

(The word "sup" has replaced "max", since the set of extreme points of S_M^* might not be closed.) The effect of this observation is, therefore, to replace the very large set S_M^* by a much smaller subset, which in special cases may turn out to be considerably more manageable.

In the next section, we shall examine how this observation affects the characterization of the sets $B(z)$ of best approximation. In the present section, we summarize some of what is known about the determination of the extreme points of such sets as S_M^*.

First, we recall the fundamental definition.

DEFINITION. *A functional L is an extreme point of a convex set C if it is not possible to represent L in the form*

$$L = \frac{L_1 + L_2}{2}, \qquad L_i \in C,$$

unless $L_1 = L_2 = L$.

Note that it is equivalent to state that L is not extreme if and only if there is a functional θ with $\theta \neq 0$, and such that $L \pm \theta \in C$.

As a preliminary result, we prove the following useful theorem.

LEMMA. *If the set W_L associated with a functional $L \in S^*$ is such that $E = W_L - W_L$, then L is extreme in S^*.*

As defined earlier, the cone W_L is the set of all points $y \in E$ such that $L(y) = \|y\|$. The hypothesis implies that any point $x \in E$ can be expressed as $y_1 - y_2$, for points $y_i \in W_L$. Suppose the functional L were not extreme. We could then find a functional $\theta \neq 0$, so that $\|L \pm \theta\| \leqq 1$. This means that for any $x \in E$,

$$|L(x) \pm \theta(x)| \leqq \|x\|$$

or that

$$-\|x\| \leqq \theta(x) \pm L(x) \leqq \|x\|$$

and

$$|\theta(x)| \leqq \|x\| - L(x)$$

for every point $x \in E$. In particular, if $y \in W_L$, then we see at once that $\theta(y) = 0$.

Since $E = W_L - W_L$, $\theta(x) = 0$ for all $x \in E$, and $\theta = 0$, proving that L is extreme in S^*.

The converse of this result is false. For example, if E is ordinary Euclidean n-space (with the l^2-norm), then S^* is an ordinary ball, and every L of norm 1 is extreme. However, it is easy to see that the cones W_L are each rays, so that the sets $W_L - W_L$ are always one dimensional subspaces of E, and we never have the hypothesis of the Lemma satisfied.

There is, however, a stronger theorem of a similar nature which provides a necessary and sufficient condition for L to be extreme in S^* (Buck [3]).

THEOREM 4. *Let* $\|L\| \leqq 1$ *and set* $H_L = \{\text{all } x \text{ with } \|x\| - L(x) \leqq 1\}$. *Then,* L *is extreme in* S^* *if and only if* $E = H_L - H_L$.

PROOF. As before, if $\|L \pm \theta\| \leqq 1$, then for any $x \in E$,

$$|\theta(x)| \leqq \|x\| - L(x).$$

Hence, for any $x \in H_L$, we have $|\theta(x)| \leqq 1$, and for any point $y \in H_L - H_L$, we have $|\theta(y)| \leqq 2$. If $H_L - H_L$ is all of E (or even dense in E) then $|\theta(y)| \leqq 2$ holds for all points $y \in E$. But, this implies that $|\theta(ny)| \leqq 2$ for $n = 1, 2, 3, \cdots$, so that $\theta(y) = 0$ and L is extreme. Conversely, suppose that $H_L - H_L$ is not dense in E. Since this set is convex and has a non-empty interior (in contrast with the set $W_L - W_L$), there must exist a non-trivial continuous functional θ such that $\theta(x) \leqq 1$ for all $x \in H_L - H_L$. Since this set contains H_L and $-H_L$, we know that

$$|\theta(x)| \leqq 1 \quad \text{for all} \quad x \in H_L.$$

We now discuss two cases.

CASE 1. Suppose $y \in E$ and $\|y\| - L(y) = 0$. Then, $ny \in H_L$ for $n = 1, 2, 3, \cdots$. Since $|\theta(ny)| \leqq 1$, it follows that $\theta(y) = 0$ and in turn that

$$L(y) \pm \theta(y) \leqq \|y\|. \tag{5}$$

CASE 2. Suppose that $y \in E$ and $\|y\| - L(y) = r > 0$. Then, y/r is in H_L so that $|\theta(y/r)| \leqq 1$ or $|\theta(y)| \leqq r$. Hence,

$$L(y) \pm \theta(y) \leqq L(y) + r = \|y\|.$$

This shows that (5) holds in either case, and thus that $\|L \pm \theta\| \leqq 1$. Since θ is not 0, but $2L = (L + \theta) + (L - \theta)$, L is not extreme in S^*.

(The proof given above is a modification of the original proof; it was suggested by R. R. Phelps who has given an extension of this result in the form of a duality theorem for polar convex sets in paired linear spaces [**15**].)

Almost the same proof yields the corresponding result characterizing the extreme points of the convex set $S^*_M = S \cap M^\perp$.

THEOREM 5. *A functional* $L \in M^\perp$ *with* $\|L\| \leqq 1$ *is extreme in* S^*_M *if and only if* $E = M + (H_L - H_L)$.

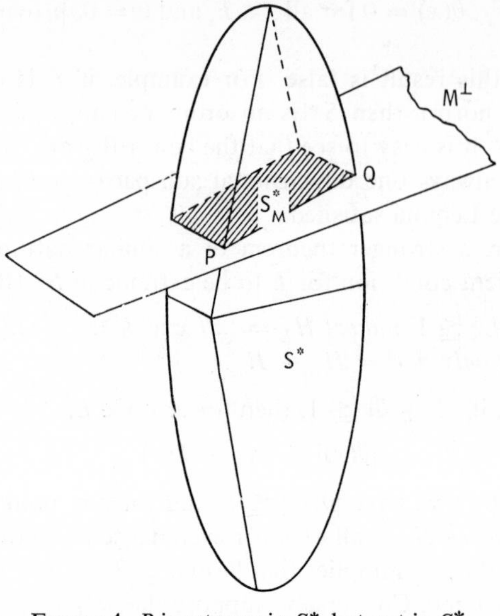

FIGURE 4. P is extreme in S_M^* but not in S^*.

Since S_M^* is a cross section of S^*, any extreme point of S^* that lies in $M^\perp$ will still be an extreme point in S_M^*. (See Figure 4.) One expects that there will be many additional extreme points, and for these, $H_L - H_L$ will be a *proper* subset of E which, however, is sufficiently large to span E when combined with M. This result can be restated in the form of an approximation theorem.

DEFINITION. *For any* $k = 1, 2, 3, \cdots$, *let*

$$H_L^k = \left\{\text{all } y \in E \text{ such that } \|y\| - L(y) \leqq \frac{1}{k}\right\}.$$

COROLLARY. *L is extreme in S_M^* if and only if, for each k,*

$$E = M + (H_L^k - H_L^k).$$

In particular, then, if $L \in e(S_M^*)$, then for any k and any $z \in E$, there exist points $x \in M$ and $y_i \in H_L^k$ with

$$z = x + y_1 - y_2.$$

The previous theorem is a special case of a still stronger result dealing with the local geometric structure of the set S_M^*, and of course applicable to that of S^*. Let L be any functional in $M^\perp$. If $\|L\| = 1$, then it lies on some face G of the convex set S_M^*. Let us say that the order of L is the dimension of the smallest face of S_M^* that contains L. (See Figure 5.) If L has order m, $m < \infty$, then L can be expressed as a convex linear combination of $m + 1$ extreme points of S_M^*. A functional of order 0 is itself extreme. The following result serves to characterize the order of any member of S_M^* (Buck [3]).

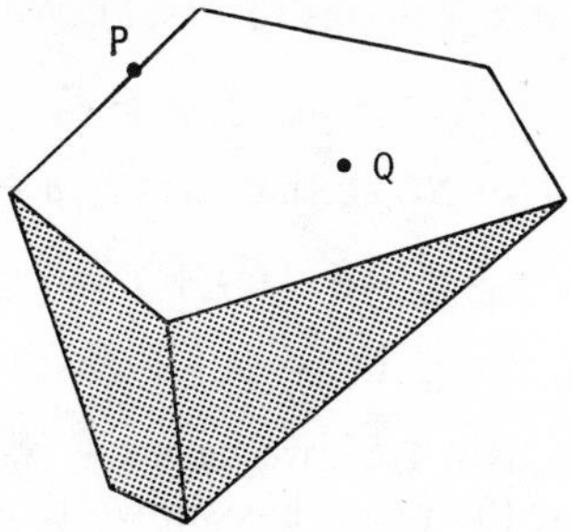

FIGURE 5. P has order 1, Q has order 2.

THEOREM 6. *The order of a functional* $L \in S_M^*$ *is exactly the co-dimension of the closed linear subspace*

$$V = \bigcap_{k=1}^{\infty} \{M + H_L^k - H_L^k\}.$$

4. Characterizations of good approximations. As observed earlier, a knowledge of *all* the sets W_L for $L \in S_M^*$ would allow us to obtain the set $B(z)$ of optimal M approximations for any given $z \in E$. The previous discussion suggests that something similar should hold if we restrict attention to only the extreme points of S_M^*. We cannot use the sets W_L but must instead consider the sets H_L^k; in passing, we note that $W_L = \bigcap_{k=1}^{\infty} H_L^k$, but that it is not in general true that $W_L - W_L = \bigcap_{k=1}^{\infty}(H_L^k - H_L^k)$.

In view of the fact that the set $B(z)$ can sometimes be empty, it is important to observe that the characterization theorem to follow deals with the good approximations sets $B(z, \varepsilon)$; good approximations always exist, and it is usually unnecessary to have an *optimal* approximation to z if it is possible to find one that is *almost* optimal.

We first introduce the analogue of the set $\mathscr{W}$:

DEFINITION. *Let* $\mathscr{H}^k = \bigcup_{L \in e(S_M^*)} H_L^k$.

THEOREM 7. *For any* $z \in E$ *and any* $\varepsilon > 0$, *there exists a pair of integers* k' *and* k'' *such that*

$$M \cap \{z + \mathscr{H}^{k'}\} \subseteq B(z, \varepsilon) \subseteq M \cap \{z + \mathscr{H}^{k''}\}.$$

PROOF. Choose k' and k'' so that $k'' < 1/(2\varepsilon)$ and $1/\varepsilon < k'$. If x_0 belongs to $M \cap \{z + \mathscr{H}^{k'}\}$, then there is an $L \in e(S_M^*)$ such that $x_0 \in M$ and $x_0 \in z - H_L^{k'}$. Hence, there is a $y \in H_L^{k'}$ with $z = x_0 + y$, so that

$$\|z - x_0\| - L(z - x_0) \leqq 1/k'.$$

But, $L \in M^\perp$, so that $L(z - x_0) = L(z)$. As above, we know that $L(z)$ cannot exceed $\rho = \rho_M(z)$, so that we have

$$\|z - x_0\| \leqq \rho + 1/k' < \rho + \varepsilon$$

and $x_0 \in B(z, \varepsilon)$.

Conversely, suppose that x_0 belongs to $B(z, \varepsilon)$. We therefore have

$$\|z - x_0\| \leqq \rho + \varepsilon.$$

Choose an extreme point L of S_M^* so that $L(z) > \rho - \varepsilon$. Then, we must have

$$\|z - x_0\| \leqq \varepsilon + L(z) + \varepsilon = L(z) + 2\varepsilon$$
$$\leqq L(z - x_0) + 2\varepsilon.$$

Recognizing that 2ε is less than $1/k''$, we have $z - x_0 \in H_L^{k''}$, and $x_0 \in z - H_L^{k''}$.

In passing, we note that the proof has shown that $M \cap \{z - H_L^{k'}\}$ is a subset of $B(z, \varepsilon)$, for every choice of L in $e(S_M^*)$, while there must exist at least one choice of L such that $B(z, \varepsilon)$ is contained entirely in $M \cap \{z - H_L^{k''}\}$.

Since the set $B(z, \varepsilon)$ is never empty, we can at once conclude that $E = M + \mathscr{H}^k$, for any $k < 1/(2\varepsilon)$. This may be contrasted with the statement that for any individual choice of $L \in e(S_M^*)$,

$$E = M + H_L^k - H_L^k.$$

5. **Special cases.** Several illustrations of the results of the preceding sections may help to clarify them. First, the sets H_L^k are convex, and contain a neighborhood of the origin. They are parabolic in nature, and $W_L = \bigcap_{k=1}^{\infty} H_L^k$. In Figure 6, we

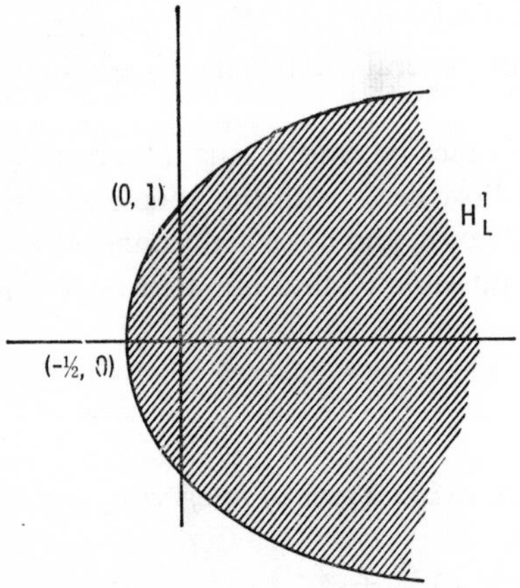

FIGURE 6. $H_L^1 + (-H_L^1) = E$.

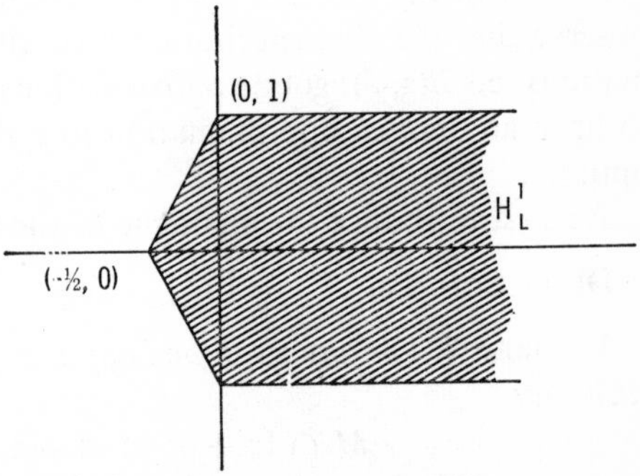

FIGURE 7. $H_L^1 + (-H_L^1) \neq E$.

have shown the set H_L for the choice $E =$ plane, norm $= l^2$, and L given by $L(x_1, x_2) = x_1$. Here, of course, $E = H_L - H_L$, confirming the fact that L is an extreme point of S^*. The result of a change in norm is seen quite clearly from Figure 7, where we have indicated the set H_L for the same choice of L, but with the l^2-norm replaced by the l^1-norm. The functional L is no longer an extreme point in the (new) unit sphere S^*, and it is evident that $H_L - H_L$ is a strip of width 2, and therefore a proper part of E.

When the set E is finite dimensional and the norm spheres S and S^* polyhedral, then the set $e(S_M^*)$ will be finite, and the general results outlined above can be converted into explicit algorithms for calculating $\rho_M(z)$ and the sets $B(z)$ and $B(z, \varepsilon)$. In other cases, it may be possible to obtain enough information about the set $e(S_M^*)$ to derive explicit characterizations of best or good approximations. An example of this is found by taking E to be $C[G]$, the continuous real valued functions on a compact set G. If we take the Chebyshev (uniform) norm, then the dual space E^* will be the space of finite valued signed measures on G, and for any choice of M, $M^\perp$ will be a special family of measures μ, orthogonal to M in the sense that

$$\int_G x(t)\, d\mu(t) = 0$$

for each $x \in M$ and $\mu \in M^\perp$. The extreme points of S_M^* will, in turn, be an even more special class of measures on G, and it is these which we must use to calculate $\rho_M(z)$, and characterize $B(z)$ and $B(z, \varepsilon)$. Their nature, of course, depends strongly upon the choice of M. However, certain general properties must hold in all cases, leading to something like a general alternation theorem.

Let us suppose that the space M contains the constant function 1, and that L is a functional in S_M^*. Suppose further that we can write $L = L_1 - L_2$, where L_1 and L_2 are positive functionals on E, and $\|L\| = \|L_1\| + \|L_2\|$. (This can be done in the case $E = C[G]$ by splitting the measure that represents L into the difference of positive measures.) Since $L \in M$, $L_1 = L_2$ on $M^\perp$, and in particular, $L_1(1) = L_2(1)$. Since these are positive functionals (and assuming that E has 1 as an order unit, again true in our special case), we find that $\|L_1\| = \|L_2\| \leqq \frac{1}{2}$.

Suppose now that x belongs to H_L^k. From the definition, we have at once that

$$\|x\| - 1/k \leqq L_1(x) - L_2(x) \leqq \|x\|$$

and using the fact that $\|L_2\| \leqq \frac{1}{2}$, we find that

$$\|x\| - 2/k \leqq 2L_1(x) \leqq \|x\|.$$

In a similar way, we see that if $x \in H_L^k$, then

$$-\|x\| \leqq 2L_2(x) \leqq -\|x\| + 2/k.$$

In effect, what we have shown is that any function x in H_L^k must be such that $2L_1(x)$ is almost $\|x\|$, and $2L_2(x)$ is almost $-\|x\|$. Suppose now that we represent L_i by a positive measure μ_i, so that

$$L_i(x) = \int_G x(t)\, d\mu_i(t), \qquad x \in E.$$

Let Z be the set of $t \in G$ such that $x(t) < \|x\| - \delta$, for some fixed choice of $x \in H_L^k$. We then have

$$\|x\| - \frac{2}{k} \leqq 2L_1(x) = \int_Z 2x\, d\mu_1 + \int_{G-Z} 2x\, d\mu_1$$

$$< 2(\|x\| - \delta)\mu_1(Z) + 2\,\|x\|\,(\mu_1(G) - \mu_1(Z)).$$

Using the fact that $\mu_1(G) \leqq \frac{1}{2}$, we find at once that $\mu_1(Z) \leqq 1/(k\delta)$. As k increases, for fixed δ, the measure of the corresponding set Z must decrease. Carrying through a similar analysis of the action of L_2, we arrive at the following result. (In this connection, see also Ptak **[16]** and Singer **[23]**, who examined the sets W_L in a similar way.)

LEMMA. *If $x \in H_L^k$, for $L \in S_M^*$, then for any $\delta > 0$, there is a set $Z \subset G$, with $|\mu|(Z) < 2/(k\delta)$, such that $G - Z$ contains two sets, G_1 and G_2, the supports of μ_i, and that:*

(i) on G_1, the values of x lie between $\|x\|$ and $\|x\| - \delta$
(ii) on G_2, the values of x lie between $-\|x\|$ and $-\|x\| + \delta$.

Suppose now that L is an extreme point of S_M^*, and that for this reason, L can be represented by a discrete measure μ, a weighted sum of point measures. For sufficiently large k, we will not be able to have $|\mu|(Z) < 1/(k\delta)$ without having $|\mu|(Z) = 0$. In this case, we would then find that the finite set that is the support of the measure μ falls into two sets G_i, and that any $x \in H_L^k$ is almost its maximum on G_1 and its minimum on G_2. Letting k increase without bound, we find that any function x in W_L must in fact oscillate between $\|x\|$ and $-\|x\|$ on this finite set.

Now, a function x_0 is a best approximation to a given function z if and only if $x_0 \in z + \mathscr{W}$. In particular, this says that there is some $L \in S_M^*$ so that $z - x_0 \in W_L$. Accordingly, x_0 will be a best approximation to z if the deviation function $y = z - x_0$ oscillates in the classical manner between its maximum and minimum values, on the finite set that is the support of the measure representing L.

This gives us some additional insight into the significance of the Chebyshev alternation theorem, and the contrast between polynomial approximation of functions of one variable, and general approximation by arbitrary functions or functions of one or more variables. In the Chebyshev case, one may work with W_L, rather than the sets H_L^K, and the functionals L that arise are indeed finite sums of point measures.

This phenomenon can also occur in other cases. Let G be the plane, and select M as the subspace of continuous functions of the form $x(s, t) = u(s) + v(t)$. Then, as pointed out in **[4]** and **[7]**, there are functionals in S_M^* that are again linear combinations of point measures, and extreme ones arise by choosing the support set as vertices of certain special types of polygons in the plane. The best Chebyshev approximations of a given continuous function by functions $x \in M$, on a rectangle, must again have an alternating property. As an illustration, we include the following very elementary result.

THEOREM 8. *Let $f(s, t) = A(s)B(t)$. Then,*

$$\rho_M(f) = \tfrac{1}{4} \operatorname{osc}(A) \operatorname{osc}(B).$$

Here, we may take G as the unit square, and denote by osc (ϕ) the maximum of $|\phi(t_1) - \phi(t_2)|$. for $0 \leqq t_i \leqq 1$.

Since A and B are assumed to be continuous functions on the interval [0, 1], we may select points t_i and s_i so that

$$\operatorname{osc}(A) = A(s_2) - A(s_1),$$
$$\operatorname{osc}(B) = B(t_2) - B(t_1).$$

Then, it is easily seen that the measure which assigns mass $\frac{1}{4}$ to (s_1, t_1) and (s_2, t_2), and mass $-\frac{1}{4}$ to the points (s_1, t_2) and (s_2, t_1) is in S_M^*. (It can also be shown to be an extreme point.) Applying this functional L to f, we have

$$\begin{aligned} L(f) &= \tfrac{1}{4}\{f(s_1, t_1) - f(s_1, t_2) + f(s_2, t_2) - f(s_2, t_1)\} \\ &= \tfrac{1}{4}\{A(s_2) - A(s_1)\}\{B(t_2) - B(t_1)\} \\ &= \tfrac{1}{4}\operatorname{osc}(A)\operatorname{osc}(B). \end{aligned}$$

This number is therefore a lower estimate for $\rho_M(f)$. To show that it is exact, we construct a best approximating function x. Choose two points s_0 and t_0 in [0, 1] so that

$$A(s_0) = \frac{A(s_1) + A(s_2)}{2},$$

$$B(t_0) = \frac{B(t_1) + B(t_2)}{2}.$$

Then, for any s and t,

$$|A(s) - A(s_0)| \leqq \tfrac{1}{2}\operatorname{osc}(A),$$
$$|B(t) - B(t_0)| \leqq \tfrac{1}{2}\operatorname{osc}(B).$$

Setting

$$x(s, t) = B(t_0)A(s) + A(s_0)B(t) - A(s_0)B(t_0),$$

it is easily verified that

$$f(s, t) - x(s, t) = [A(s) - A(s_0)][B(t) - B(t_0)]$$

and thus

$$\|f - x\| = \tfrac{1}{4}\operatorname{osc}(A)\operatorname{osc}(B).$$

Note that this value is attained with alternating signs at the four points that support the measure L.

To show how critical is the choice of M, one may examine the case in which E is again the space of functions continuous on the unit square, but M is the subspace of functions harmonic in its interior. Here, the extremal functionals are no longer combinations of point masses; instead, for example, we obtain measures whose support consists of a closed curve, together with an isolated point inside the curve. Again, the functions which belong to the cones W_L will achieve their maximum on the curve, and their minimum at the isolated point, so that a form of alternation holds. However, one can expect the nature of the final theory to differ substantially from the simpler classical cases.

I hope by the results and discussion in this paper to have presented a convincing argument that a detailed study of the nature of the extreme points of the convex sets S_M^* will do much to advance our knowledge and understanding of the special problems in approximation of functions by linear classes, and aid in the construction of algorithms for finding both good and best approximations.

REFERENCES

1. S. Banach, *Théorie des opérations linéaires*, Warsawa, 1932.

2. F. F. Bonsall, *Dual extremum problems in the theory of functions*, J. London Math. Soc. **31** (1956), 105–110.

3. R. C. Buck, *A complete characterization for extreme functionals*, Bull. Amer. Math. Soc. **65** (1959), 130–133.

4. R. C. Buck, *Linear spaces and approximation theory*, 11–23, On Numerical Approximation (R. E. Langer ed.), Madison, Wisconsin, 1959.

5. L. Carleson, *An interpolation problem for bounded analytic functions*, Amer. J. Math. **80** (1958), 921–930.

6. M. M. Day, *Normed linear spaces*, Ergeb. der Math. **21** (new series), Springer-Verlag, Berlin, 1958.

7. S. P. Diliberto and E. G. Straus, *On the approximation of a function of several variables by the sum of functions of fewer variables*, Pac. J. Math. **1** (1951), 195–210.

8. S. Ya. Havinson, *On some extremal problems of the theory of analytic functions*, Mosk. Gos. Univ. Ucenye Zap. Mat. **4** (1951), 133–143, 148. Also, in Amer. Math. Soc. Transl. Series 2, **32** (1963), 139–154.

9. W. Hayman, *Interpolation by bounded functions*, Univ. de Grenoble, Ann. Inst. Fourier **13** (1958), 277–290.

10. M. G. Kreĭn (and N. I. Ahiezer), *Some questions in the theory of moments* (Ukr.) in Amer. Math. Soc. Transl. Monographs **2** (1962), 175–204.

11. A. J. MacIntyre and W. W. Rogosinski, *Extremum problems in the theory of analytic functions*, Acta Math. **82** (1950), 275–325.

12. G. Meinardus, *Uber den Haarschen Eindeutigkeitssatz aus der Theorie der linearen Approximationen*, Arch. Mat. **14** (1963), 47–54.

13. D. J. Newman, *Interpolation in* H^∞, Trans. Amer. Math. Soc. **92** (1959), 501–507.

14. S. M. Nikol'skiĭ, *Approximation of functions in the mean by trigonometric polynomials*, Izv. Akad. Nauk. SSSR Mat. **10** (1946), 207–256.

15. R. R. Phelps, *Extreme points of polar convex sets*, Proc. Amer. Math. Soc. **12** (1961), 291–296.

16. V. Ptak, *On approximation of continuous functions in the metric* $\int_a^b |x(t)|\,dt$, Czech. Math. J. **83** (1958), 267–273.

17. T. J. Rivlin and H. S. Shapiro, *A unified approach to certain problems of approximation and minimization*, J. Soc. Indust. Appl. Math. (SIAM) **9** (1961), 67–699.

18. W. W. Rogosinski, *Extremum problems for polynomials and trigonometric polynomials*, J. Lond. Math. Soc. **29** (1954), 259–275.

19. W. W. Rogosinski and H. S. Shapiro, *On certain extremum problems for analytic functions*, Acta Math. **90** (1953), 287–318.

20. H. S. Shapiro, *Applications of normed linear spaces to function-theoretic extremal problems*, in *Lectures On Functions of a Complex Variable* (Kaplan ed.) Univ. of Michigan Press, Ann Arbor, 1955.

21. H. S. Shapiro and A. J. Shields, *On some interpolation problems for analytic functions*, Amer. J. Math. **83** (1961), 513–532.

22. I. Singer, *Caractérisation des éléments de meilleure approximation dans un espace de Banach quelconque*, Acta Sci. Math. Szeged **17** (1956), 181–189.

23. I. Singer, *On a theorem of V. Ptak concerning best approximation*, Czech. Math. J. **85** (1960), 425–431.

24. S. I. Zuhovickii, *On approximation of real functions in the sense of P. L. Cebysev*, Uspehi Mat. Nauk **11** (1956), 125–159.

INCLUSION THEOREMS FOR THE MINIMAL DISTANCE IN RATIONAL TSCHEBYSCHEFF APPROXIMATION WITH SEVERAL VARIABLES[1]

L. COLLATZ

Universität Hamburg, Germany

1. **Introduction.** Suppose a function $f(x)$ of a real variable x in an interval $\mathfrak{F}$ is to be approximated in the sense of Tschebyscheff by functions $w(x)$ of a certain class W. Let $\phi(x)$ be a minimal solution of this problem; then the typical phenomenon is known: the error $\varepsilon = \phi - f$ takes a maximum absolute value ρ_0 at certain successive points $x = x_\nu$ with alternating sign. If one considers not the exact points x_ν, but approximate points ξ_ν, and instead of a minimal solution $\phi(x)$ an approximation w of ϕ, then not all values $|w(\xi_\nu) - f(\xi_\nu)|$ will be equal. However one can in general cases conclude from these values and from the maximum absolute value of ε that there exist bounds for ρ_0 for which one can judge the quality of the approximation w. Frequently one can even choose arbitrary abscissas ξ_ν for testing (provided that the correct number of places is taken); those ξ_ν then form an H-set (see below for definition).

Similar inclusion theorems are also important for several independent variables; however in the case of several variables one can in general not choose arbitrary places ξ_ν for testing, but only H-sets. Present work is concerned with definition of H-sets and with methods of finding H-sets in a systematic way. If the error function ε has the proper sign for all points of an H-set, then there exists an inclusion theorem for the minimal deviation ρ_0. One can judge the quality of the approximation, because one obtains both a lower and an upper bound for ρ_0. If both bounds are close the approximation will be satisfactory; if both bounds coincide then the approximation is even a minimal solution. In this paper examples are given for which one can prove the existence of a minimal solution in this fashion (in one example even the existence of a continuum of minimal solutions is shown).

For the proof that certain sets are H-sets, an algorithm is developed, which has previously [2] been used for linear approximations, and which is now extended also to nonlinear approximation, in particular to rational approximations. A geometric theory of "blocks" permits the construction of H-sets in domains of higher dimension.

A different geometrical method was developed by Newman and Shapiro [4].

---

[1] The preparation of this paper was sponsored in part by the Office of Naval Research, United States Navy, while the author was with Numerical Analysis Research, Univ. of California, Los Angeles.

2. **The basic theorem.** Let B be a given domain in the n-dimensional pointspace R^n of coordinates $x_1, x_2, \cdots, x_n$, written briefly as x; let W be a class of continuous real or complex functions defined on B, and $f(x)$ a given continuous function on B, which does not belong to W. We take as the norm of a function $g(x) \in W$ the term

$$\|g\| = \sup_{x \in B} |g(x)| \, p(x), \tag{2.1}$$

considering only functions for which this term will exist; here $p(x)$ is a given continuous function on B, the values of p are between fixed positive bounds:

$$0 < p_0 \leqq p(x) < p_1 \qquad \text{for } x \in B. \tag{2.2}$$

For many purposes p may be $\equiv 1$. Let

$$\rho_0 = \inf_w \|w - f\|, \tag{2.3}$$

if w runs through all functions of W; a function $\phi(x)$ with

$$\|\phi - f\| = \rho_0 \tag{2.4}$$

is called a minimal solution.

Then the basic theorem (see [**2**], Meinardus [**3**]) holds:

THEOREM 1. (inclusion theorem). *Let w_0 be a fixed element of W and $\varepsilon = w_0 - f$ the "error". Let M be a fixed subset of B with the properties:*

$$|\varepsilon(x)| > 0 \qquad \text{for } x \in M; \tag{2.5}$$

there exists no $q \in W$ with

$$\operatorname{Re}\,[\bar{\varepsilon}(w_0 - q)] > 0 \qquad \text{for } x \in M. \tag{2.6}$$

Then

$$\inf_{x \in M} p \cdot |\varepsilon| \leqq \rho_0 \leqq \|\varepsilon\|. \tag{2.7}$$

PROOF. Let $\sigma = \inf_{x \in M} p\,|\varepsilon|$; then the only fact one has to prove is $\sigma \leqq \rho_0$. If $\sigma > \rho_0$ then there exists a number τ with $\rho_0 < \tau < \sigma$, and an element $w \in W$ with $\|w - f\| \leqq \tau$; in M, $p\,|\varepsilon| \geqq \sigma > \tau \geqq p\,|w - f|$ holds. Therefore

$$|\varepsilon| - |w - f| > 0 \text{ in } M.$$

It follows that

$$w_0 - w = w_0 - f - (w - f) = \varepsilon - (w - f),$$

$$\operatorname{Re}\,[\bar{\varepsilon}(w_0 - w)] = \operatorname{Re}\,[|\varepsilon|^2 - \bar{\varepsilon}(w - f)] \geqq |\varepsilon|^2 - |\varepsilon|\,|w - f|$$

$$= |\varepsilon|\,(|\varepsilon| - |w - f|) > 0 \text{ in } M.$$

This contradicts (2.6) and hence $\sigma > \rho_0$ is impossible.

3. **H-sets and systems of inequalities.** Now let us restrict ourselves to the real domain. We introduce the following hypothesis H: *there exist two fixed sets* M_1,

M_2 of points in B with the property: there exists no pair $w_1, w_2 \in W$ with $w_1 - w_2 > 0$ in M_1, $w_1 - w_2 < 0$ in M_2. A set $M = M_1 \cup M_2$, which satisfies hypothesis *H*, is called an *H*-set.

THEOREM 2. *Let w_0 be a fixed element of W with the "error" $\varepsilon = w_0 - f$. Let the hypothesis H be true. If $\varepsilon > 0$ in M_1 and $\varepsilon < 0$ in M_2 (or $\varepsilon > 0$ in M_2 and $\varepsilon < 0$ in M_1), then the inclusion holds:*

$$m = \inf_{M_1 \cup M_2} p\,|\varepsilon| \leqq \rho_0 \leqq \|\varepsilon\|, \quad \text{where } M = M_1 \cup M_2. \tag{3.1}$$

PROOF. In H we take w_0 as w_1 and write q for w_2; then in W there is no element q with $\varepsilon(w_0 - q) > 0$ in M, and therefore (2.6) is satisfied; so (2.7) yields (3.1).

Now the class of functions W is taken to be the set of functions

$$w = \sum_{\nu=1}^{N} a_\nu \phi_\nu(x_j, b_{\mu\nu}), \tag{3.2}$$

where the ϕ_ν are fixed given functions of their arguments and the a_ν and $b_{\mu\nu}$ (for $\mu = 1, 2, \cdots, m_\nu$) are real constants.

The difference $w_1 - w_2$ of two such functions then has the form

$$w^* = w_1 - w_2 = \sum_{\nu=1}^{k} c_\nu \phi_\nu(x_j, b^*_{\mu\nu}), \tag{3.3}$$

where, in the general case, one may set $k = 2N$ and $\phi_{N+\nu} = \phi_\nu$ for $\nu = 1, \cdots, N$; however, in special cases, one may obtain $k < 2N$ by appropriately collecting terms. Again c_ν and $b^*_{\mu\nu}$ ($\mu = 1, \cdots, m_\nu$) are real constants.

Next a procedure is described that allows a convenient criterion for the validity of hypothesis H in many cases of finite sets M_1 and M_2. Let the set $M = M_1 \cup M_2$ consist of the points P_k ($k = 1, \cdots, s$). For brevity set

$$\phi_{\rho\nu} = \begin{cases} \phi_\nu(P_\rho, b^*_{\mu\nu}), \text{ if } P_k \text{ belongs to } M_1, \\ -\phi_\nu(P_\rho, b^*_{\mu\nu}), \text{ if } P_k \text{ belongs to } M_2. \end{cases} \tag{3.4}$$

It is to be investigated then whether the system of inequalities

$$\sum_{\nu=1}^{k} c_\nu\, \phi_{\rho\nu} > 0, \qquad \rho = 1, \ldots, s \tag{3.5}$$

can be satisfied by real numbers c_ν, $b^*_{\mu\nu}$ or not. If the system (3.5) contains a contradiction, that is, if the system has no solutions, then the hypothesis H is true.

For many practically important cases the system (3.5) can be investigated once and for all. One attempts to reduce the system (3.5) to smaller systems with fewer inequalities and fewer constants c_ν, similar to the procedure of Gauss elimination by forming appropriate linear combinations of inequalities. The inequalities must be multiplied only by positive factors; therefore a factor p, equal to $+1$ or -1 (as given in the scheme) appears in what follows such that the factor multiplying the inequality is positive. For brevity only the matrices $(\phi_{\rho\nu})$ are given in the following schemes; the associated inequalities are numbered by (1), (2), $\cdots$, and in the remaining inequalities the method of construction (the linear combination from preceding inequalities) is indicated. One frequently succeeds in deriving a contradiction by eliminating all c_ν except one, and for that one to derive two inequalities, for which the factors of the coefficients have different signs.

One may further include general rational approximations on the basis of the class W of functions

$$w = \frac{\sum_{\nu=1}^{N} a_\nu \zeta_\nu(x_j, b_{\mu\nu})}{\sum_{\nu=1}^{N'} c_\nu \psi_\nu(x_j, d_{\mu\nu})}, \tag{3.6}$$

where the ζ_ν, ψ_ν are again fixed given functions of their arguments and the a_ν, c_ν, $b_{\mu\nu}$, $d_{\mu\nu}$ are real constants. It is agreed here that only such values of c_ν and $d_{\mu\nu}$ are admitted for which the denominator in (3.6) is positive in all B. The difference between two functions w_1, w_2 of the form (3.6) can be written as

$$w^* = w_1 - w_2 = \frac{1}{D} \sum_{\nu=1}^{k} c_\nu \phi_\nu(x_j, e_{\mu\nu}),$$

where D is the product of the two denominators of w_1 and w_2 and is therefore positive in B. Considering the sign of w^* one may suppress D, each of the φ_ν's being products of a function ζ_ρ and a function ψ_σ; hence the problem is reduced to a problem of the form (3.2) and the above given methods are applicable.

4. Exponential and rational-exponential approximation. The given method is to be carried out first for approximation with exponential functions. For simplicity consider functions $f(x, y)$ of the two variables $x_1 = x$, $x_2 = y$ to be approximated by expressions of the form

$$w = \sum_{\nu=1}^{N} a_\nu e^{\alpha_\nu x + \beta_\nu y}, \tag{4.1}$$

$$\tilde{w} = \frac{\sum_{\nu=1}^{N} a_\nu e^{\alpha_\nu x + \beta_\nu y}}{\sum_{\nu=1}^{N'} c_\nu e^{\gamma_\nu x + \delta_\nu y}}. \tag{4.2}$$

Here all parameters a_ν, α_ν, β_ν, $\cdots$ are variable, α_ν and β_ν are not to be considered as given, the approximation is nonlinear; however the linear case that the a_ν are to be determined for given α_ν, β_ν is included in the following and is also contained in the tables.

In the following it is shown for several choices of the sets M_1 and M_2 that hypothesis H is true. It suffices to bring the points into a special position by an affine transformation so as to obtain simple values for the coordinates. To save indices, a slight change of notation is introduced by writing $a, b, \cdots, \alpha, \beta, \cdots$ instead of $a_1, a_2, \cdots, \alpha_\nu, \beta_\nu$, that is,

$$w = a + be^{\alpha x+\beta y} + ce^{\gamma x+\delta y} + de^{\varepsilon x+\zeta y}. \tag{4.3}$$

In the following Scheme 1 the reduction described in §3 has been performed for several subsets of the points of Figure 1, where a P followed by braces always yields two inequalities which lead to a contradiction upon omission of appropriate coefficients. For example, using only the points (1), (2), (3) and the coefficients a, b, that is, setting $c = d = 0$, inequalities (12), (13) already yield a contradiction.

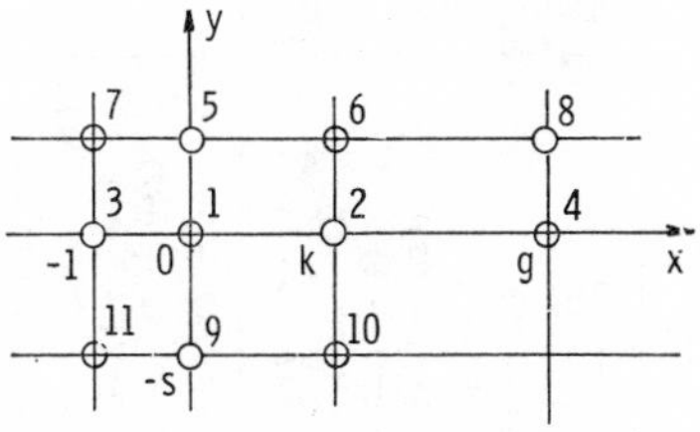

FIGURE 1. Selection of points for exponential approximation.

The big table hence presents a number of configurations which can be used as sets M_1 and M_2. Keeping only a, b, that is, $c = d = 0$, one obtains a contradiction with four points which form an arbitrary convex quadrilateral. Through an affine transformation one can obtain special coordinates for the four points given in Scheme 3.

Here the three numbers $1 - g$, $1 - h$, $g^s h^r - 1$, for $s = k - 1 \geqq 0$, $r \geqq 0$, $g > 0$, $h > 0$, cannot all have the same sign (if one of the three numbers is zero, one also has a contradiction). If $1 - g$ and $1 - h$ have the same sign the third number has the opposite sign. In Figure 2 sets M are given for several assumed functions satisfying hypothesis H. One set is indicated by open circles, the other set by black circles. The sketch shows immediately which lines are parallel. Moreover, if the line segments are required to be equal in length the notation with lower case letters is used.

Almost all pairs P show alternate signs; only for the two pairs in (25), (26) and (27), (28) a slightly longer proof is needed, which is given in the Appendix.

NUMERICAL EXAMPLE. The example is so chosen that the above theorems yield the existence of a continuum of minimal solutions. The function $f(x, y) = x^2 + 3xy^2$ is to be approximated in the sense of Tschebyscheff in the square $|x| \leqq 1$, $|y| \leqq 1$, with weight-function $p \equiv 1$, by a function of the form $w = a + be^{cx+dy}$; for reasons of symmetry d may be set equal to zero. With $a = 2.5 - be^c$ and $b(e^c - e^{-c}) = 3$ one obtains a family of functions $w(c; x, y)$ dependent only on one real parameter c. For $0.382 \leqq c \leqq 1.598$ one obtains functions $w(c; x, y)$, for which maximum deviations $|\varepsilon| = |w - f|$ occur in the following six points:

$$\varepsilon = w - f = 1.5 \quad \text{for} \quad x = -1, y = 0 \quad \text{and for} \quad x = -1, y = \pm 1,$$

$$\varepsilon = w - f = -1.5 \quad \text{for} \quad x = -1, y = 0 \quad \text{and for} \quad x = 1, y = \pm 1.$$

SCHEME 1. $w = a + be^{\alpha x+\beta y} + ce^{\gamma x+\delta y} + de^{\varepsilon x+\zeta y}$.

		a	b	c	d
(1)	$x = 0, \quad y = 0$	1	1	1	1
(2)	$x = k, \quad y = 0, k > 0$	-1	$-e^{k\alpha}$	$-e^{k\gamma}$	$-e^{k\varepsilon}$
(3)	$x = -1, y = 0$	-1	$-e^{-\alpha}$	$-e^{-\gamma}$	$-e^{-\varepsilon}$
(4)	$x = q, \quad y = 0, q > k$	1	$e^{q\alpha}$	$e^{q\gamma}$	$e^{q\varepsilon}$
(5)	$x = 0, \quad y = 1$	-1	$-e^{\beta}$	$-e^{\delta}$	$-e^{\zeta}$
(6)	$x = k, \quad y = 1$	1	$e^{k\alpha+\beta}$	$e^{k\gamma+\delta}$	$e^{k\varepsilon+\zeta}$
(7)	$x = -1, y = 1$	1	$e^{-\alpha+\beta}$	$e^{-\gamma+\delta}$	$e^{-\varepsilon+\zeta}$
(8)	$x = q, \quad y = 1$	-1	$-e^{q\alpha+\beta}$	$-e^{q\gamma+\delta}$	$-e^{q\varepsilon+\zeta}$
(9)	$x = 0, \quad y = -s, s > 0$	-1	$-e^{-\beta s}$	$-e^{-\delta s}$	$-e^{-\zeta s}$
(10)	$x = k, \quad y = -s$	1	$e^{k\alpha-\beta s}$	$e^{k\gamma-\delta s}$	$e^{k\varepsilon-\zeta s}$
(11)	$x = -1, y = -s$	1	$e^{-\alpha-\beta s}$	$e^{-\gamma-\delta s}$	$e^{-\varepsilon-\zeta s}$
(12)	(1) + (2)	0	$P\{1 - e^{k\alpha}$	$1 - e^{k\gamma}$	$1 - e^{k\varepsilon}$
(13)	(1) + (3)	0	$\;\;1 - e^{-\alpha}$	$1 - e^{-\gamma}$	$1 - e^{-\varepsilon}$
(14)	(2) + (4)	0	$e^{q\alpha} - e^{k\alpha}$	$e^{q\gamma} - e^{k\gamma}$	$e^{q\varepsilon} - e^{k\varepsilon}$
(15)	(5) + (6)	0	$P\{e^{\beta}(e^{k\alpha} - 1)$	$e^{\delta}(e^{k\gamma} - 1)$	$e^{\zeta}(e^{k\varepsilon} - 1)$
(16)	(6) + (8)	0	$\;\;e^{\beta}(e^{k\alpha} - e^{q\alpha})$	$e^{\delta}(e^{k\gamma} - e^{q\gamma})$	$e^{\zeta}(e^{k\varepsilon} - e^{q\varepsilon})$
(17)	(5) + (7)	0	$e^{\beta}(e^{-\alpha} - 1)$	$e^{\delta}(e^{-\gamma} - 1)$	$e^{\zeta}(e^{-\varepsilon} - 1)$
(18)	(9) + (10)	0	$P\{e^{-\beta s}(e^{k\alpha} - 1)$	$e^{-\delta s}(e^{k\gamma} - 1)$	$e^{-\zeta s}(e^{k\varepsilon} - 1)$
(19)	(9) + (11)	0	$\;\;e^{-\beta s}(e^{-\alpha} - 1)$	$e^{-\delta s}(e^{-\gamma} - 1)$	$e^{-\zeta s}(e^{-\varepsilon} - 1)$
(20)	$e^{\beta}(12) + (15)$	0	0	$P\{(e^{\delta} - e^{\beta})(e^{k\gamma} - 1)$	$(e^{\zeta} - \varepsilon^{\beta})(e^{k\varepsilon} - 1)$
(21)	$e^{\beta}(14) + (16)$	0	0	$\;\;(e^{\beta} - e^{\delta})(e^{q\gamma} - e^{k\gamma})$	$(e^{\beta} - e^{\zeta})(e^{q\varepsilon} - e^{k\varepsilon})$
(22)	$e^{\beta}(13) + (17)$	0	0	$(e^{\beta} - e^{\gamma})(1 - e^{-\gamma})$	$(e^{\beta} - e^{\zeta})(1 - e^{-\varepsilon})$
(23)	$e^{-\beta s}(12) + (18)$	0	0	$P\{(e^{-\beta s} - e^{-\delta s})(1 - e^{k\gamma})$	$(e^{-\beta s} - e^{-\zeta s})(1 - e^{k\varepsilon})$
(24)	$e^{-\beta s}(13) + (19)$	0	0	$\;\;(e^{-\beta s} - e^{-\delta s})(1 - e^{-\gamma})$	$(e^{-\beta s} - e^{-\zeta s})(1 - e^{-\varepsilon})$
(25)	$p_{\gamma}[(e^{k\gamma} - 1)(21) + (e^{q\gamma} - e^{k\gamma})(20)]$	0	0	0 $(p_{\gamma} = \operatorname{sgn}\gamma)$	$P\{p_{\gamma}(e^{\beta} - e^{\zeta})\Phi(k, q, \gamma, \varepsilon)$
(26)	$p_{\gamma}[(1 - e^{-\gamma})(20) + (e^{k\gamma} - 1)(22)]$	0	0	0	$\;\;p_{\gamma}(e^{\beta} - e^{\zeta})\Phi(-1, k, \gamma, \varepsilon)$
(27)	$p_{\alpha}[(e^{q\alpha} - e^{k\alpha})(12) + (e^{k\alpha} - 1)(14)]$	0	0 $(p_{\alpha} = \operatorname{sgn}\alpha)$	$P\{p_{\alpha}\Phi(k, q, \alpha, \gamma)$	
(28)	$p_{\alpha}[(1 - e^{-\alpha})(12) + (e^{k\alpha} - 1)(13)]$	0	0	$\;\;p_{\alpha}\Phi(-1, k, \alpha, \gamma)$	
(29)	$p_{\beta}[(e^{-\beta s} - e^{-\delta s})(20) + (e^{\gamma} - e^{\beta})(23)]$	0	0	0 $(p_{\beta} = \operatorname{sgn}(\delta - \beta))$	$P\{p_{\beta}(e^{k\varepsilon} - 1)\Psi$
(30)	$p_{\beta}[(e^{-\beta s} - e^{-\delta s})(22) + (e^{\delta} - e^{\beta})(24)]$	0	0	0	$\;\;p_{\beta}(1 - e^{-\varepsilon})\Psi$

$\Phi(u, v, \rho, \sigma) = e^{v\sigma+u\rho} - e^{v\rho+u\sigma} + e^{v\rho} - e^{v\sigma} + e^{u\sigma} - e^{u\rho}$
$\Psi = e^{\zeta-\beta s} - e^{\zeta-\delta s} + e^{-\zeta s+\delta} - e^{-\zeta s+\beta} + e^{-\delta s+\beta} - e^{\delta-\beta s}$

SCHEME 2. $w = a + be^{\alpha x+\beta y} + ce^{\gamma x+\delta y} + de^{\delta x+\zeta y}$.

		a	b	c	d
(1)	$x = 0, \quad y = 0$	1	1	1	1
(2)	$x = 1, \quad y = 0$	-1	$-e^{\alpha}$	$-e^{\gamma}$	$-e^{\varepsilon}$
(3)	$x = -1, y = 0$	-1	$-e^{-\alpha}$	$-e^{-\gamma}$	$-e^{-\varepsilon}$
(4)	$x = 2, \quad y = 0$	1	$e^{2\alpha}$	$e^{2\gamma}$	$e^{2\varepsilon}$
(5)	$x = -2, y = 0$	1	$e^{-2\alpha}$	$e^{-2\gamma}$	$e^{-2\varepsilon}$
(6)	$e^{\alpha}(1) + (e^{\alpha} + 1)(2) + (4)$	0	0	$P\{(e^{\gamma} - e^{\alpha})(e^{\gamma} - 1)$	$(e^{\varepsilon} - e^{\alpha})(e^{\varepsilon} - 1)$
(7)	$(3) + (e^{-\alpha} + 1)(1) + e^{-\alpha}(2)$	0	0	$(e^{-\gamma} - e^{-\alpha})(e^{\gamma} - 1)$	$(e^{-\varepsilon} - e^{-\alpha})(e^{\varepsilon} - 1)$
(8)	$(5) + (e^{-\alpha} + 1)(3) + e^{-\alpha}(1)$	0	0	$(e^{-\alpha} - e^{-\gamma})e^{-\gamma}(e^{\gamma} - 1)$	$(e^{-\alpha} - e^{-\varepsilon})e^{-\varepsilon}(e^{\varepsilon} - 1)$
(9)	$(6) + e^{\alpha+\gamma}(7)$	0	0	0	$P\{Z(e^{\varepsilon} - 1)$
(10)	$(7) + e^{\gamma}(8)$	0	0	0	$-e^{-\alpha-\delta}Z(e^{\varepsilon} - 1)$

$$Z = e^{\varepsilon} + e^{\alpha+\gamma-\varepsilon} - e^{\alpha} - e^{\gamma}$$

SCHEME 3. $w = a + be^{\alpha x+\beta y}$.

		a	b
(1)	$x = 0, y = 0$	1	1
(2)	$x = 1, y = 0$	-1	$-e^{\alpha}$
(3)	$x = 0, y = 1$	-1	$-e^{\beta}$
(4)	$x = k, y = r, k \geqq 1$	1	$e^{k\alpha+r\beta}$
(5)	$(1) + (2), e^{\alpha} = g$	0	$P\{1 - g$
(6)	$(1) + (3), e^{\beta} = h$	0	$1 - h$
(7)	$(2) + (4)$	0	$g[g^{k-1}h^{r} - 1]$

Since these six points are arranged as in Figure 2, the functions $w(c; x, y)$ are minimal solutions for all values of c of the above given interval.

In this way approximations can also be treated by means of other functions. The use of trigonometric functions will be discussed elsewhere; here the case of an approximation by rational functions will be considered because of some special points of view.

5. **Classes of rational functions.** Let $C[k, n]$ be the class of all polynomials of a total degree $\leqq k$ in the variables $x_1, \cdots, x_n$. Further let $K[k, m, n]$ be the class of all quotients Z/N with $Z \in C[k, n]$ and $N \in C[m, n]$, where the case that N is a null-function is excluded. Finally let $W[k/m, n]$ be the subset of those quotients Z/N of $K[k, m, n]$, for which the denominator $N > 0$ in the entire domain B. If the dependence of n is not to be specially emphasized for this class it is briefly written as $[k/m]$. A given function $f(x)$ is to be approximated in B by functions of W. For testing the hypothesis H the difference of two quotients $w_j = Z_j/N_j$ $(j = 1, 2)$ is formed; because of $N_j > 0$ in B, the difference $w_1 - w_2$

Term	Possible situation of points of M
$w = a + be^{\alpha x + \beta y}$ (α, β fixed)	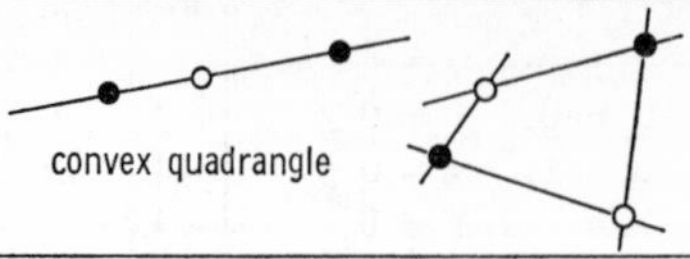
$w = a + be^{\alpha x + \beta y} + ce^{\gamma x + \delta y}$ (α, β, γ, δ fixed) or $w = a + be^{\alpha x + \beta y}$ (a,b, α, β variable)	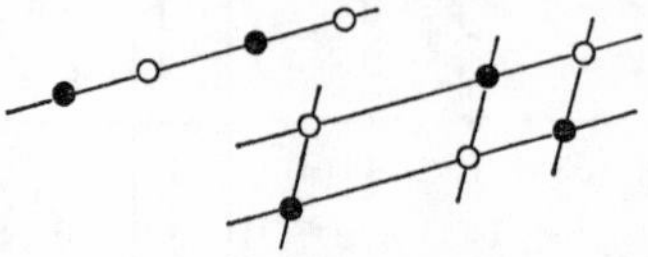
$w = a + be^{\alpha x + \beta y} + ce^{\gamma x + \delta y} + de^{\epsilon x + \phi y}$ (α, β, γ, δ, ϵ, ϕ fixed) or $w = \dfrac{a + be^{\alpha x + \beta y}}{c + de^{\epsilon x + \phi y}}$ (all parameters variable)	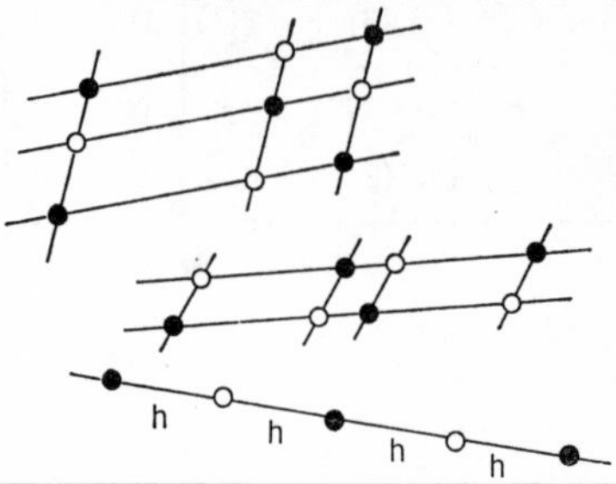

FIGURE 2. *H*-sets for exponential approximations.

has the same sign in B as the polynomial $s(x) = Z_1N_2 - Z_2N_1$; $s(x)$ is an element of $C[k + m, n]$. It is remarkable that for approximation by means of the class $[k/m]$ the sum $r = k + m$ is significant, and in order to apply the above mentioned theorems one has to look for sets $M = M_1 \cup M_2$, such that for no element

$$u \in C[r, n],\ u > 0 \text{ in } M_1,\ u < 0 \text{ in } M_2 \qquad (5.1)$$

is valid.

This question has already been treated earlier, see **[2]**, but will now be treated in such a way as to admit generalization to several dimensions.

6. **The method of blocks.** All the above mentioned classes always contain the function $u \equiv 1$ for all n, therefore it is obvious to try to eliminate the coefficients of the powers $x_1, \cdots, x_n$ by these schemes and to derive a contradiction for the function $u = 1$; that is, to generate within the scheme a pair ± 1 for $u = 1$, the remaining functions having coefficients equal to zero. This suggests the question as to how to obtain blocks, having coefficients $+1$ or -1 for $u = 1$, while the remaining coefficients vanish in the corresponding row.

DEFINITION. *A positive (or a negative) block of class $C[r, n]$ is a set $M = M_1 \cup M_2$ of points in the domain $x_1, \cdots, x_n$ with the following properties: in the expression* (3.2) *one takes as functions ϕ_ν all monomials $x_1^{e_1}x_2^{e_2} \cdots x_n^{e_n}$ with $e_1 + e_2 + \cdots + e_n \leqq r$ and $\phi_1 = 1$ and chooses as points P_k the points of M. In the associated system* (3.5), *with the values $\phi_{\rho\nu}$ given by* (3.4), *it is possible to prove by a linear combination of positive factors that an inequality of the form $c_1 > 0$ (or $c_1 < 0$ for a negative*

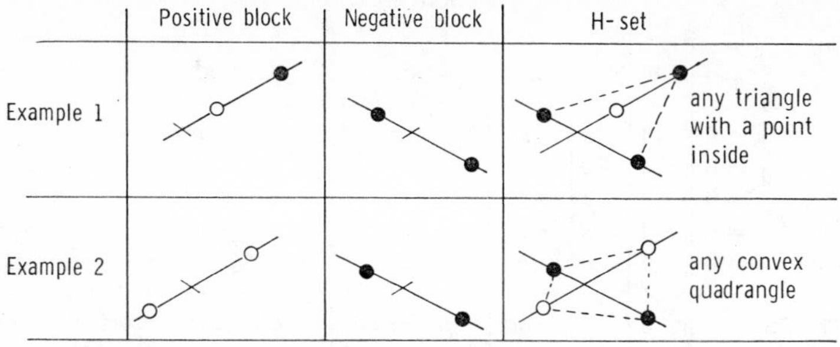

FIGURE 3. Construction of H-sets from positive and negative blocks.

block) results, i.e., the factor of c_1 *equals* $+1$ *(or* -1*), while the remaining factors of all other c's are zero.*

If we exchange the sets M_1 and M_2 a positive block is transformed into a negative one and vice-versa.

Let R_1 be a subspace of points with $x_{l+1} = x_{l+2} = \cdots = x_n = 0$ for a certain l with $1 \leqq l < n$, and let R_2 be the subspace of points with $x_1 = x_2 = \cdots = x_l = 0$. Then the points of a positive block in R_1 and of a negative block in R_2 together yield an H-set, since then a contradiction is contained in the inequalities $c_1 > 0$ and $c_1 < 0$. Here both blocks must belong to the same class $C[r, n]$. Figure 3 gives two examples for this composition of an H-set from two blocks.

For the construction of blocks the schemes 4, 5, 6 which follow have been devised.

SCHEME 4.

		1	x	x^2	x^3	x^4	*Extract positive factor*
(1)	$x = a, y = 0$	1	a	a^2	a^3	a^4	
(2)	$x = b, y = 0$	-1	$-b$	$-b^2$	$-b^3$	$-b^4$	(*Assume*
(3)	$x = c, y = 0$	1	c	c^2	c^3	c^4	$0 < a < b$
(4)	$x = d, y = 0$	-1	$-d$	$-d^2$	$-d^3$	$-d^4$	$< c < d < e$)
(5)	$x = e, y = 0$	1	e	e^2	e^3	e^4	
(6)	$b(1) + a(2)$	1	0	$-ab$	$-a^2b - ab^2$	$-a^3b - a^2b^2 - ab^3$	$b - a$
(7)	$c(2) + b(3)$	-1	0	bc	$b^2c + bc^2$	$b^3c + b^2c^2 + bc^3$	$c - b$
(8)	$d(3) + c(4)$	1	0	$-cd$	$-c^2d - cd^2$	$-c^3d - c^2d^2 - cd^3$	$d - c$
(9)	$e(4) + d(5)$	-1	0	de	$d^2e + de^2$	$d^3e + d^2e^2 + de^3$	$e - d$
(10)	$c(6) + a(7)$	1	0	0	abc	$a^2bc + ab^2c + abc^2$	$c - a$
(11)	$d(7) + b(8)$	-1	0	0	$-bcd$	$-b^2cd - bc^2d - bcd^2$	$d - b$
(12)	$e(8) + c(9)$	1	0	0	cde	$c^2de + cd^2e + cde^2$	$e - c$
(13)	$d(10) + a(11)$	1	0	0	0	$-abcd$	$d - a$
(14)	$e(11) + b(12)$	-1	0	0	0	$bcde$	$e - b$
(15)	$e(13) + a(14)$	1	0	0	0	0	$e - a$

SCHEME 5.

		1	x	x^2	x^3	x^4	Extract positive factor
(1)	$x = a,\ \ y = 0$	1	a	a^2	a^3	a^4	
(2)	$x = -b, y = 0$	1	$-b$	b^2	$-b^3$	b^4	(*Assume*
(3)	$x = c,\ \ y = 0$	-1	$-c$	$-c^2$	$-c^3$	$-c^4$	$0 < a < c < e,$
(4)	$x = -d, y = 0$	-1	d	$-d^2$	d^3	$-d^4$	$0 < b < d)$
(5)	$x = e,\ \ y = 0$	1	e	e^2	e^3	e^4	
(6)	$c(1) + a(3)$	1	0	$-ac$	$-a^2c - ac^2$	$-a^3c - a^2c^2 - ac^3$	$c - a$
(7)	$b(1) + a(2)$	1	0	ab	$a^2b - ab^2$	$a^3b + a^2b^2 + ab^3$	$b + a$
(8)	$d(2) + b(4)$	1	0	$-bd$	$b^2d + bd^2$	$-b^3d - b^2d^2 - bd^3$	$d - b$
(9)	$e(3) + c(5)$	-1	0	ce	$ce^2 + c^2e$	$c^3e + c^2e^2 + ce^3$	$e - c$
(10)	$b(6) + c(7)$	1	0	0	$-abc$	$-a^2bc + ab^2c - abc^2$	$b + c$
(11)	$e(6) + a(9)$	1	0	0	ace	$a^2ce + ac^2e + ace^2$	$e - a$
(12)	$d(7) + a(8)$	1	0	0	abd	$a^2bd - ab^2d - abd^2$	$a + d$
(13)	$e(10) + b(11)$	1	0	0	0	$abce$	$b + e$
(14)	$d(10) + c(12)$	1	0	0	0	$-abcd$	$c + d$
(15)	$d(13) + e(14)$	1	0	0	0	0	$d + e$

In these schemes one can in particular read off the blocks from Figure 4. According to the above mentioned possibility of building up *H*-sets from blocks, the *H*-sets, mentioned in Figure 5, result.

The schemes 4, 5, 6 yield more special blocks; hence *H*-sets can also be constructed for three independent variables.

7. **H-sets on algebraical curves.** More possible *H*-sets can be obtained from simple properties of algebraic curves. An algebraic curve of degree q in the xy-plane and a straight line G in the xy-plane have at most q points in common or all points of G. On the straight line $q + 2$ arbitrary different points P_ν $(\nu = 1, \cdots, q + 2)$ are chosen, numbered successively as they occur when traversing the line in one

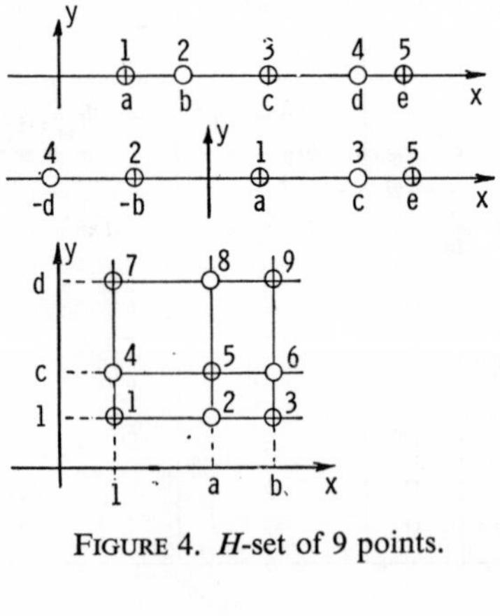

FIGURE 4. *H*-set of 9 points.

SCHEME 6.

		1	x	y	x^2	xy	y^2	x^3	x^2y	xy^2	y^3	*Extract positive factor*
(1)	$x = 1, y = 1$	1	1	1	1	1	1	1	1	1	1	
(2)	$x = a, y = 1$	−1	$-a$	−1	$-a^2$	$-a$	−1	$-a^3$	$-a^2$	$-a$	−1	
(3)	$x = b, y = 1$	1	b	1	b^2	b	1	b^3	b^2	b	1	
(4)	$x = 1, y = c$	−1	−1	$-c$	−1	$-c$	$-c^2$	−1	$-c$	$-c^2$	$-c^3$	(*Let*
(5)	$x = a, y = c$	1	a	c	a^2	ac	c^2	a^3	a^2c	ac^2	c^3	$1 < a < b$,
(6)	$x = b, y = c$	−1	$-b$	$-c$	$-b^2$	$-bc$	$-c^2$	$-b^3$	$-b^2c$	$-bc^2$	$-c^3$	$1 < c < d$)
(7)	$x = 1, y = d$	1	1	d	1	d	d^2	1	d	d^2	d^3	
(8)	$x = a, y = d$	−1	$-a$	$-d$	$-a^2$	$-ad$	$-d^2$	$-a^3$	$-a^2d$	$-ad^2$	$-d^3$	
(9)	$x = b, y = d$	1	b	d	b^2	bd	d^2	b^3	b^2d	bd^2	d^3	
(10)	$a(1) + (2)$	1		1	$-a$		1	$-a^2 - a$	$-a$		1	$a - 1$
(11)	$b(2) + a(3)$	−1		−1	ab		−1	$ab(a + b)$	ab		−1	$b - a$
(12)	$a(4) + (5)$	−1		$-c$	a		$-c^2$	$a^2 + a$	ac		$-c^3$	$a - 1$
(13)	$b(5) + a(6)$	1		c	$-ab$		c^2	$-ab(a + b)$	$-abc$		c^3	$b - a$
(14)	$a(7) + (8)$	1		d	$-a$		d^2	$-a^2 - a$	$-ad$		d^3	$a - 1$
(15)	$b(8) + a(9)$	−1		$-d$	ab		$-d^2$	$ab(a + b)$	abd		$-d^3$	$b - a$
(16)	$c(10) + (12)$	1			$-a$		$-c$	$-a^2 - a$			$-c^2 - c$	$c - 1$
(17)	$d(12) + c(14)$	−1			a		cd	$a^2 + a$			$cd(c + d)$	$d - c$
(18)	$c(11) + (13)$	−1			ab		c	$ab(a + b)$			$c^2 + c$	$c - 1$
(19)	$d(13) + c(15)$	1			$-ab$		$-cd$	$-ab(a + b)$			$-cd(c + d)$	$d - c$
(20)	$b(16) + (18)$	1					$-c$	ab			$-c^2 - c$	$b - 1$
(21)	$b(17) + (19)$	−1					cd	$-ab$			$cd(c + d)$	$b - 1$
(22)	$d(20) + (21)$	1						ab			cd	$d - 1$
(23)	$(16) + (17)$	0				$P\{$	c			$P\{$	$c^2 + cd + c$	$d - 1$
(24)	$(18) + (19)$	0					$-c$				$-c^2 - cd - c$	$d - 1$

direction. If the set M_1 consists of the points P with odd index ν and the set M_2 of the points P_ν with even index, then the points P_ν form an H-set with respect to the class $C[q, 2]$. Let w be a polynomial in x, y of degree $\leqq q$ for which $w > 0$ in M_1 and $w < 0$ in M_2. Then for continuity reasons $w = 0$ for at least $q + 1$ different points of the line G; therefore $w \equiv 0$ on the line G, contradicting $w < 0$ in M_1. Hence no such polynomial w exists.

Now let K be a connected algebraic curve of degree two in the xy-plane. An algebraic curve of degree q has either maximally $2q$ different points in common

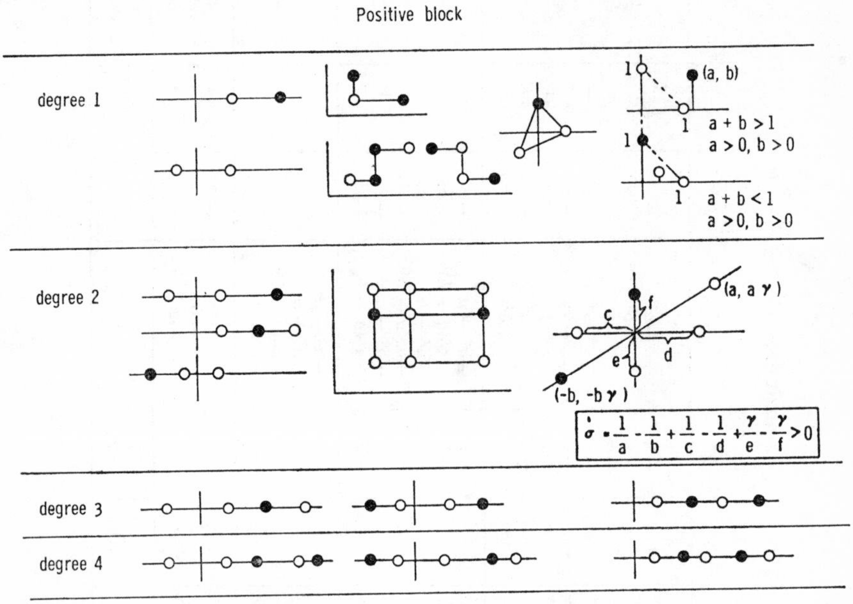

FIGURE 5. Positive blocks for two independent variables.

with K or all points of a branch of K. Next choose $(2q + 2)$ points $P_\nu(\nu = 1, 2, \cdots, 2q + 2)$ on one branch of K where the P_ν are successively numbered in the direction of traversing that branch of K. M_1 again consists of the points P_ν with odd index ν and the set M_2 of the points with even index; then the points P_ν form a H-set with respect to the class $C[q, 2]$. This follows since a polynomial w with the same properties as in the previous discussion would vanish in at least $(2q + 1)$ points of the respective branch K, hence would vanish identically on that branch K; this contradicts the assumption $w > 0$ in M_1.

Figure 6 shows H-sets constructed according to this principle.

EXAMPLE. The function $f(x, y) = |x| \cdot y$ is to be approximated by rational functions in the sense of Tschebyscheff (with weight-function $p \equiv 1$) in the unit circle $x^2 + y^2 \leqq 1$. In the expression $w(x, y) = \alpha y$ the real constant $\alpha = \alpha_0$ can be chosen ($\alpha_0 \approx 0.300$) such that the error $\varepsilon = w - f$ takes on its maximum absolute value at six points of the unit circle, alternating in sign when traversing the unit circle. These six points form an H-set with respect to the class $C[2, 2]$. Therefore $\alpha_0 y$ is a minimal solution in each of the classes $C[1, 2]$, $C[2, 2]$, $W[1/1, 2]$. Thus even in the class $(a_0 + a_1x + a_2y)/(a_3 + a_4x + a_5y)$ there exists no better approximating function then $\alpha_0\, y$.

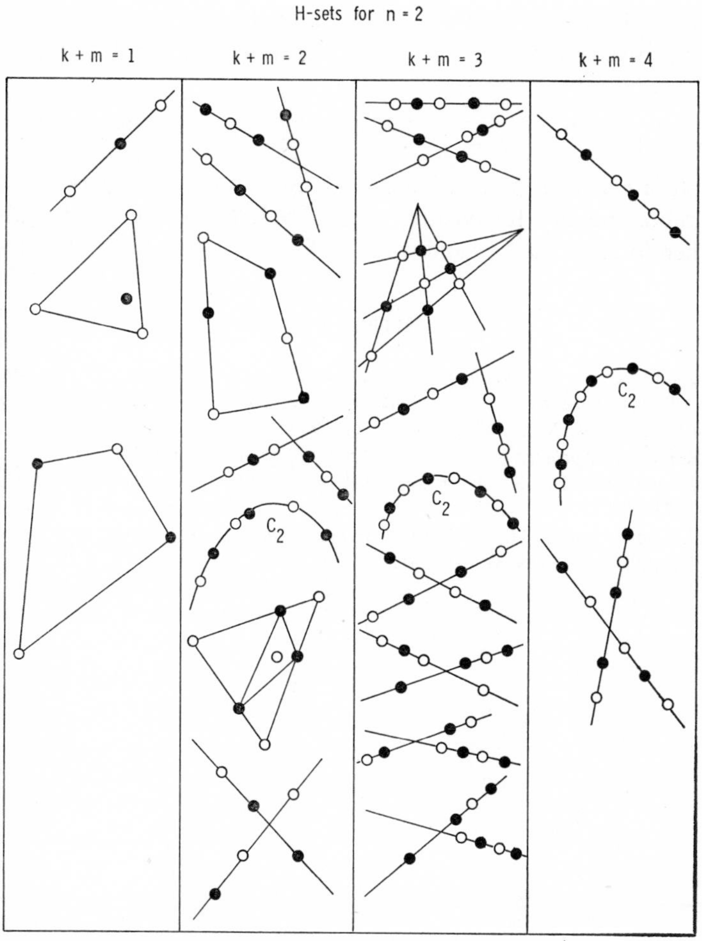

FIGURE 6. H-sets for rational approximation.

Appendix (inequalities). In §4 the expression $\Phi(u, v, \rho, \sigma) = e^{v\sigma+u\rho} - e^{v\rho+u\sigma} + e^{v\rho} - e^{v\sigma} + e^{u\sigma} - e^{u\rho}$ occurred, and it was assumed that $\Phi_1 = \Phi(k, q, \rho, \sigma)$ and $\Phi_2 = \Phi(-1, k, \rho, \sigma)$ for $0 < k < q$ and, for arbitrary real $\rho, \sigma \neq 0$ have different signs (for $\rho = 0$ or $\sigma = 0$ one has $\Phi = 0$ and the respective inequality yields a contradiction). I thank Professor Redheffer, Los Angeles, for the proof that, with $x = e^\sigma$ and $y = e^\rho$, one has

$$\Phi_1 = P_1 - Q_1 \quad \text{with} \quad P_1 = (x^q - 1)(y^k - 1),\ Q_1 = (x^k - 1)(y^q - 1)$$

and

$$\Phi_3 = -xy\Phi_2 = P_3 - Q_3 \quad \text{with} \quad P_3 = (x^{k+1} - 1)(y - 1),$$
$$Q_3 = (y^{k+1} - 1)(x - 1).$$

Hence it is to be shown that $P_1 >$ (or $<$) Q_1 implies $P_3 >$ (or $<$) Q_3. Since x, y, k are positive and $x \neq 1$, $y \neq 1$ this is equivalent to the statement:

$$\frac{x^q - 1}{x^k - 1} > (\text{or} <) \frac{y^q - 1}{y^k - 1} \quad \text{implies} \quad \frac{x^{k+1} - 1}{x - 1} > (\text{or} <) \frac{y^{k+1} - 1}{y - 1}.$$

By assumption $r > 1$ in the relation $q = rk$. Since the function $F(z) = (z^r - 1)/(z - 1)$ is monotone in z for positive z and $r > 1$, $F(x^k) > F(y^k)$ is equivalent to $x^k > y^k$, therefore, with $x > y$ and with $(x^{k+1} - 1)/(x - 1) > (y^{k+1} - 1)/(y - 1)$.

References

1. N. J. Achieser, *Vorlesungen über Approximations-theorie*, Akademie-Verlag, Berlin, 1953.

2. L. Collatz, *Approximation von Funktionen bei einer und bei mehreren unabhängigen Veränderlichen*, Z. angew. Math. Mech. **36** (1956), 198–211.

3. G. Meinardus, *Springer tracts in natural philosophy*, **4** (1964), 1–180.

4. D. J. Newman and H. S. Shapiro, *Some theorems on Cebysev approximation*, Duke Math. J. **30** (1963), 673–682.

5. E. W. Cheney and T. H. Southard, *A survey of methods for rational approximation*, Soc. Indust. Appl. Math. Rev. **5** (1963), 219–231.

RATIONAL APPROXIMATIONS ON FINITE POINT SETS

P. FOX, A. A. GOLDSTEIN[1], AND G. LASTMAN
University of Washington, Seattle

Our object is to establish algorithms for rational approximation which are analogous to those of linear approximation to be found in **[4]** and **[5]**. The setting taken had in mind approximating functions of several variables on a discretized domain; also encompassed, however, is the problem of the smoothing of empirical data. For the latter, the least squares, rather than the uniform criterion we employ, would be preferable. However, at present, the least squares criterion for rational approximation yields an intractable problem.

Other algorithms for our problem are already known, e.g., **[1]**, **[2]**, and **[6]**. These algorithms generate infinite sequences for which the best approximation is a cluster point or possibly a limit point. The algorithms to be given here terminate in a finite number of cycles, the number of cycles depending monotonously on the cardinality of the domain. Unfortunately, the number of operations in each cycle also depends monotonously on the accuracy desired in the computation.

The rational approximation which is obtainable by these algorithms is constrained in the sense that the denominator of the rational fraction is bounded below by, say, $\delta > 0$. With a small additional effort other linear inequalities can be imposed as additional constraints.

If one sets $\delta = 0$, a natural definition can be given for the best rational approximation which is called the "stabilized" best approximation. The existence and characterization of these approximations are discussed in **[2]**. The stabilized approximation may not be practical, however, because it is not necessarily defined throughout the domain of the function to be approximated. If for $\delta > 0$, the magnitude of the deviation of a best approximation from the given function is $M(\delta)$ and $M(0)$ is the magnitude of a stabilized best approximation, then $M(0)$ is the limit of $M(\delta)$ as δ tends positively to 0. Thus for δ sufficiently small the constrained approximation is a satisfactory substitute for the stabilized approximation.

Some information is also given on the approximation of problems on domains which are continua by approximations on domains which are discreta.

1. Let $\hat{I} = \{1, 2, \cdots, m\}$. For $i \in \hat{I}$ let A^i and B^i denote points in E_n, and b^i a real number. Assume that the system $[B^i, x] = \sum_{j=1}^n B_j^i x_j > 0$, all $i \in \hat{I}$, is consistent; equivalently, the origin is disjoint from the convex hull of $\{B^i : i \in \hat{I}\}$. For each x satisfying the above inequalities define

$$F(x) = \max \{|([A^i, x]/[B^i, x]) - b^i| : i \in \hat{I}\}.$$

[1] Paper presented by second author. Location given applies to second author only.

Let $\|x\| = \max \{|x_j|:1 \leqq j \leqq n\}$. Given $\delta > 0$, define $D_1 = \{x \in E_n: \|x\| \leqq 1$ and $[B^i, x] \geqq \delta$ all $i \in \hat{I}\}$. Because $F(\lambda x) = F(x)$ if $\lambda x \neq 0$, we have not lost generality by limiting x to the unit sphere $\|x\| \leqq 1$. Sometimes additional constraints are useful. Let $D_2 = \{x \in E_n:[C^i, x] \leqq d^i:1 \leqq i \leqq k\}$. Here $C^i \in E_n$, d^i is real, and $k \geqq 0$. Let $D = D_1 \cap D_2$. It is clear that a proper choice of points $P^j \in E_n$ and numbers p^j yields $D = \{[P^j, x] \leqq p^j:1 \leqq j \leqq r\}$ with $r = m + 2n + k$. Observe that the set $\{P^j:1 \leqq j \leqq r\}$ is an n-dimensional subset of E_n. The problem to be considered is minimizing F on D. Let $I = \{1, 2, \cdots, 2m\}$ and let $A^{i+m} = -A^i$, $B^{i+m} = B^i$, and $b^{i+m} = -b^i$, for $i \in \hat{I}$. For convenience we write

$$F(x) = \max \{([A^i, x]/[B^i, x]) - b^i:i \in I\}.$$

Observe that F is continuous on D and D is compact; hence there exists $z \in D$ such that $F(z) \leqq F(x)$ for all x in D. Our object will be to construct z.

For $i \in I$ let $R^i(x) = ([A^i, x]/[B^i, x]) - b^i$. Let $J = \{1, \cdots, r\}$.

2. Lemma. *Assume x and $x + h$ belong to D. If $i \in I$, $[A^i, x]/[B^i, x] = [A^i, x + h]/[B^i, x + h]$ if and only if $[A^i - ([A^i, x]/[B^i, x])B^i, h] = 0$.*

Proof. By computation.

3. Theorem. *Take F, D, and R^i as in §1. Let S denote the set of points minimizing F on D. Then:*

(a) *There exists a point y in S such that*

$$\text{(I)} \qquad \begin{cases} R^i(y) = F(y), & i \in I' \subset I, \\ [P^j, y] = p^j, & j \in J' \subset J, \\ R^i(y) < F(y), & i \in I \sim I', \\ [P^j, y] < p^j, & j \in J \sim J'. \end{cases}$$

$I' \cup J'$ contains $n + 1$ points and the set

$$\text{(II)} \qquad \{A^i - (b^i + F(y))B^i:i \in I'\} \cup \{P^j:j \in J'\}$$

is n-dimensional, while the system

$$\text{(III)} \qquad \begin{cases} [A^i - (b^i + F(y))B^i, x] < 0, & i \in I', \\ [P^j, x] \leqq 0, & j \in J', \end{cases}$$

is inconsistent.

(b) *If there exists a point $y \in E_n$ satisfying* (I) *while system* (III) *is inconsistent then y is in S.*

(c) *S is compact and convex.*

Proof (a). That S is non-empty was observed in §1. Take u in S and assume that (III) is consistent with solution h. By the continuity of R^i on D, it is not difficult to see that there exists a number $\lambda > 0$ such that: $[A^i - (b^i + R^i(u + \xi h)B^i, h] < 0$ for all $i \in I'$ and $0 \leqq \xi \leqq \lambda$; $R^i(u + \lambda h) < F(u)$ for $i \in I \sim I'$; and $[P^j, u + \lambda h] \leqq p^j$

for $j \in J$. By the mean value theorem, $R^i(u + \lambda h) = R^i(u) + \lambda[\nabla R^i(u + \xi_i h), h]$ where $\nabla R^i(u + \xi_i h)$ is the gradient of R^i at $u + \xi_i h$ and $0 < \xi_i < \lambda$, whenever $i \in I$. We compute that $\nabla R^i(u + \xi_i h) = (A^i - (b^i + R^i(u + \xi_i h))B^i)/[B^i, u + \xi_i h]$. Since $u + \xi_i h$ is in D, $[B^i, u + \xi_i h] > 0$, all $i \in I$; hence if $i \in I'$, $[\nabla R^i(u + \xi_i h), h] < 0$. Therefore $\max_{i \in I} R^i(u + \lambda h) = F(u + \lambda h) < F(u)$, contradicting that $u \in S$. Thus (III) is inconsistent.

Let Q denote the set $\{A^i - (b^i + F(u))B^i : i \in I'\} \cup \{P^j : j \in J'\}$. Assume that Q is r-dimensional and $r < n$. Choose $h \neq 0$ perpendicular to the span of Q. Choose $\mu \neq 0$, least in magnitude, such that either $R^{i_0}(u + \mu h) = F(u)$ for some i_0 in $I \sim I'$ or $[P^{j_0}, u + \mu h] = p^{j_0}$ for some j_0 in $J \sim J'$. At least one of these must occur because $\{P^j : j \in J\}$ is n-dimensional and D is compact. By §2, $R^i(u + \mu h) = R^i(u)$, if i is in I' and $[P^j, u + \mu h] = [P^j; u]$ if j is in J'. Clearly neither

$$A^{i_0} - (b^{i_0} + F(u))B^{i_0} \quad \text{nor} \quad P^{j_0}$$

will belong to the span of Q. Thus a point u' can be constructed such that Q is at least $(r + 1)$-dimensional. By repeating the above argument, if necessary, we arrive at a point u for which Q is n-dimensional. If Q contains more than n points we are done; otherwise Cramer's rule may be used to show that (III) is consistent. This contradiction establishes (II) of (a). To prove (c), verify by computation that the set $\{x \in D : F(x) \leqq M\}$ is convex for all M, and observe also that this set is closed and bounded. To prove (b) assume (I) and (III) hold. Choose $x \in D$. If J' is non-empty, then $[P^j, x - y] \leqq 0$ for all j in J'. Since (III) is inconsistent, for some i_0 in I', $[A^{i_0} - (b^{i_0} + F(y))B^{i_0}, x - y] \geqq 0$. Since $[A^i - (b^i + F(y))B^i, y] = 0$ for all i in I', $[A^{i_0} - (b^{i_0} + F(y))B^{i_0}, x] \geqq 0$, showing that $F(x) \geqq F(y)$. Thus $y \in S$. A similar theorem may be found in [**1**].

Remark. If $F(y) > 0$ then $i \in I'$ implies $(i + m) \notin I'$.

Proof. If i and $(i + m) \in I'$, a computation shows that $2F(y)[B^i, y] = 0$, a contradiction.

4. **Algorithm.** Assume F, D, and R^i are defined as in §1.

Phase I. Assume x' is given on the boundary of D. Thus $R'(x') \leqq F(x')$ for all $i \in I$, $[P^j, x'] \leqq p^j$ for all $j \in J$, equality obtains for $i \in I'$ and $j \in J'$ respectively, and I' and J' are non-empty. Let $Q' = \{A^i - (b^i + F(x'))B^i : i \in I'\} \cup \{P^j : j \in J'\}$. If the dimension r of Q' is n, go to Phase II; otherwise, choose h perpendicular to Q'; choose λ_i to satisfy $[A^i - (b^i + F(x'))B^i, x' + \lambda_i h] = 0$ for $i \in I \sim I'$ whenever such λ_i exist; similarly, choose λ_j when possible to satisfy $[P^j, x' + \lambda_j h] = p^j$ for $j \in J \sim J'$. Denote by λ that value of λ_j, $j \in J \sim J'$ or λ_i, $i \in I \sim I'$ which is least in magnitude. Define $x'' = x' + \lambda h$. Define I'' and J'' by $R^i(x'') = F(x'')$, $i \in I''$ and $[P^j, x''] = p^j$, $j \in J''$. Define Q'' analogously to Q'. Then dimension $\{Q''\} \geqq r + 1$. If $r + 1 = n$, go to Phase II, setting $I' = I''$, $J' = J''$, and $Q' = Q''$; otherwise go to Phase I, setting $x' = x''$.

PHASE II. Q' has dimension n. If $I' \cup J'$ contains more than n points, set $\bar{\alpha} = 0$ and go to Phase III. Otherwise, let $x(\alpha)$ denote the solution of the system

$$S(\alpha)\begin{cases}[A^i - (b^i + F(x') - \alpha)B^i, x(\alpha)] = 0, & i \in I',\\ [P^j, x(\alpha)] = p^j, & j \in J',\end{cases}$$

for each $\alpha \leqq F(x')$ such that $x(\alpha)$ exists. Let $\mathscr{A} = \{\alpha : x(\alpha)$ satisfies $S(\alpha)$, $x(\alpha) \in D$, and $F(x(\alpha)) = F(x') - \alpha\}$. Let $\bar{\alpha} = \sup \mathscr{A}$. Choose $\bar{x}$ to satisfy $S(\bar{\alpha})$ such that for some $i_0 \in I \sim I'$ or some $j_0 \in J \sim J'$ $[A^{i_0} - (b^{i_0} + F(x') - \alpha)B^{i_0}, \bar{x}] = 0$ or $[P^{j_0}, \bar{x}] = p^{j_0}$, respectively, and

$$C \cup \{A^i - (b^i + F(x') - \bar{\alpha})B^i : i \in I'\} \cup \{P^j : j \in J'\} = C \cup Q(\bar{\alpha})$$

has rank n, where $C = A^{i_0} - (b^{i_0} + F(x') - \bar{\alpha})B^{i_0}$ or P^{j_0}. Augment I' or J' by i_0 or j_0. Go to Phase III.

PHASE III. If the system of inequalities

$$S(\bar{\alpha})\begin{cases}[A^i - (b^i + F(x') - \bar{\alpha})B^i, h] < 0, & i \in I',\\ [P^j, h] \leqq 0, & j \in J',\end{cases}$$

is inconsistent, then $\bar{x}$ is a solution. If, on the other hand, this system is consistent, choose any vector h to satisfy it. Choose λ to be the least positive number satisfying

$$\max\{R^i(\bar{x} + \lambda h) : i \in I \sim I'\} = \max\{R^i(\bar{x} + \lambda h) : i \in I'\} < F(x') - \bar{\alpha}$$

and $[P^j, \bar{x} + \lambda h] \leqq p^j$ for $j \in J \sim J'$. Go to Phase I with $x' = \bar{x} + \lambda h$.

PROOF. The point x' may be taken in D by solving a system of linear inequalities. The existence of λ was discussed in §3. Observe that $F(x') = F(x'')$ in Phase I. This follows by §2. Observe also that the point $x'' \in D$. We now show that $\bar{\alpha}$ and $\bar{x}$ of Phase II, having the stated properties, do indeed exist. Take $\alpha_k \in \mathscr{A}$ such that $\alpha_k \to \bar{\alpha}$ and suppose a subsequence has been chosen so that $x(\alpha_k) \to x(\bar{\alpha})$. Clearly $x(\bar{\alpha})$ satisfies $S(\bar{\alpha})$. If $\delta(\alpha)$ denotes the $n \times n$ determinant of the linear system $S(\alpha)$, then $\delta(\bar{\alpha}) \neq 0$ and $\alpha > \bar{\alpha}$ implies that either $x(\alpha) \notin D$ or $F(x(\alpha)) > F(x') - \alpha$. Otherwise, for some $\alpha > \bar{\alpha}$, $\delta(\alpha) \neq 0$, and $\alpha \in \mathscr{A}$, a contradiction. In this case, therefore, $\bar{x} = x(\bar{\alpha})$. If $\delta(\bar{\alpha}) = 0$, choose $h \perp Q(\bar{\alpha})$. Arguing as before, for some $\mu \neq 0$, $(x(\bar{\alpha}) + \mu h) \in D$ and $Q(\bar{\alpha})$ is augmented by at least one point. If $Q(\bar{\alpha})$ now has rank n, set $\bar{x} = x(\bar{\alpha}) + \mu h$; otherwise, the above process may be repeated if necessary until $Q(\bar{\alpha})$ is n-dimensional. This must happen eventually because $\{P^j : j \in J\}$ is n-dimensional.

In Phase III, if $S(\bar{\alpha})$ is inconsistent then by §3, $\bar{x}$ is a solution. Otherwise, we have $[A^i - (b^i + F(x') - \bar{\alpha})B^i, \bar{x} + \lambda h] < 0$ for $i \in I'$, which implies $R^i(\bar{x} + \lambda h) < F(x') - \bar{\alpha}$ for $i \in I'$; while by our choice of λ, $F(\bar{x} + \lambda h) = \max_{i \in I'} R^i(\bar{x} + \lambda h)$, and $\bar{x} + \lambda h$ belongs to D. Thus $F(\bar{x} + \lambda h) < F(x') - \bar{\alpha}$, with $\bar{x} + \lambda h$ in D.

Recall that at the outset of Phase III one has on hand an index set $I' \cup J'$ of $n + 1$ or more indices such that the system

$$(S)\begin{cases}[A^i - (b^i + F(\bar{x}))B^i, \bar{x}] = 0, & i \in I',\\ [P^j, \bar{x}] = p^j, & j \in J',\end{cases}$$

is consistent. In what follows we shall assume that the index set $I' \cup J'$ contains precisely $n + 1$ points. For the general case the reasoning is similar. Set $\{i_1, \cdots, i_r\} = I'$ and $\{j_1, \cdots, j_s\} = J'$. Since the system (S) is consistent, the determinant whose kth column, $1 \leqq k \leqq n$, and whose $(n + 1)$st column are, respectively,

$$\begin{bmatrix} A_k^{i_1} - (b^{i_1} + F(\bar{x}))B_k^{i_1} \\ \cdot \\ \cdot \\ \cdot \\ A_k^{i_r} - (b^{i_r} + F(\bar{x}))B_k^{i_r} \\ P_k^{j_1} \\ \cdot \\ \cdot \\ \cdot \\ P_k^{j_s} \end{bmatrix}, \quad \begin{bmatrix} 0 \\ \cdot \\ \cdot \\ \cdot \\ 0 \\ p^{j_1} \\ \cdot \\ \cdot \\ \cdot \\ p^{j_s} \end{bmatrix},$$

has the value 0. This determinant is a polynomial of degree at most n in $F(\bar{x}) = F(x') - \bar{\alpha}$. Because the system (S) is inconsistent if $\bar{\alpha}$ is slightly decreased, the coefficients of this polynomial cannot be identically 0. Thus, corresponding to the pair (I', J'), there are at most n values that $F(\bar{x})$ can assume for which the system (S) is consistent.

Observe now that the numbers $F(x') - \bar{\alpha}$ generated by the algorithm form a decreasing sequence, and the number of possible pairs (I', J') are finite. Since each pair (I', J') can arise in Phase (III) at most n-times the algorithm must eventually terminate, the termination occurring if and only if the system $S(\bar{\alpha})$ is inconsistent.

5. **Alternate algorithm ("vertex to vertex").** In this variation, Phase I and Phase II are used only once and we proceed to:

PHASE III'. If the system of inequalities $S(\bar{\alpha})$ of Phase III is inconsistent, then $\bar{x}$ is a solution. Otherwise, given $\alpha > 0$ choose $h(\alpha)$, if possible, to satisfy $T(\alpha)$ below, with equality at some subset of n indices of $I' \cup J'$.

$$T(\alpha)\begin{cases}[A^i - (b^i + F(\bar{x}) - \alpha)B^i, h(\alpha)] \leqq -\alpha[B^i, \bar{x}], & i \in I',\\ [P^j, h(\alpha)] \leqq 0, & \in J'.\end{cases}$$

Find the least $\bar{\alpha} > 0$ such that either $T(\bar{\alpha})$ is inconsistent or for some $i \in I \sim I'$ or $j \in J \sim J'$, $[A^i - (b^i + F(\bar{x}) - \alpha)B^i, \bar{x} + h(\alpha)] = 0$ or $[P^j, \bar{x} + h(\alpha)] = p^j$, respectively. Go to phase III′ setting the value of $\bar{x}$ in $T(\alpha)$ to $\bar{x} + h(\bar{\alpha})$.

Proof. Let $S(\alpha)$ denote the system

$$S(\alpha)\begin{cases}[A^i - (b^i + F(\bar{x}) - \alpha)B^i, u(\alpha)] < 0, & i \in I', \\ [P^j, u(\alpha)] \leqq 0, & j \in J'.\end{cases}$$

Then $S(\alpha)$ is consistent if and only if $T(\alpha)$ is consistent. Clearly $S(\alpha)$ is consistent for small positive α. If $T(\bar{\alpha})$ is inconsistent, then so is $S(\bar{\alpha})$ and $\bar{x} + h(\bar{\alpha})$ is a solution. If $h(\alpha)$ satisfies $T(\alpha)$ then since the system S in the proof of §4 is satisfied, we have that $[A^i - (b^i + F(\bar{x}) - \alpha)B^i, \bar{x} + h(\alpha)] \leqq 0$, and $[P^j, \bar{x} + h(\alpha)] \leqq p^j$ for $i \in I'$ and $j \in J'$. Because some subset n of the indices of $I' \cup J'$ holds with equality in these inequalities the situation at the beginning of Phase III′ will again arise when $\alpha = \bar{\alpha}$. The remainder of the proof is as before.

6. **Remarks on solving inequalities.** To implement the algorithms a method for solving linear inequalities is required. Usually it will be necessary to solve an $r \times n$ system of inequalities with $r = n + 1$. When $r > n + 1$, it is convenient to resort to the perturbation technique of linear programming. This is accomplished by small positive displacements to appropriate components of $\{b^i\}$ so that $r = n + 1$. When the solution is obtained to the perturbed system, one starts afresh with this solution going to Phase (I) with the original unperturbed system. See for example [**5**, p. 418].

To solve the $(n + 1) \times n$ system of inequalities the following lemma from [**5**, p. 420] is useful.

Lemma. *Let $\{A^i : 1 \leqq i \leqq n + 1\}$ be a subset of E_n of rank n. Let u be chosen in E_{n+1} so that $\sum_{i=1}^{n+1} u_i A^i = 0$, $u \neq 0$, and $(u, b) \geqq 0$. Then:*

(1) The system of inequalities $[A^i, x] \leqq b_i$ $(1 \leqq i \leqq n + 1)$ is consistent if and only if either $[u, b] = 0$ or u exhibits a positive component.

(2) If $[u, b] > 0$ and $u_j > 0$, then $\{A^i : i \neq j\}$ has full rank. Let x satisfy $[A^i, x] = b_i$ $(1 \leqq i \leqq n + 1, i \neq j)$. Then $[A^j, x] \leqq b_j$. If $[u, b] = 0$ the system $[A^i, x] = b_i$, $(1 \leqq i \leqq n)$, is consistent.

Proof. [**2**, p. 240].

Remark. The solution of the inequalities is effected with n equalities as required by Phase III′ of §5.

7. **Numerical example.** We wrote several programs to implement the algorithms. The details of these programs will be described in a report which will be available at the Computation Center of the University of Texas.

The first computations were recalculations of results obtained by H. Loeb [**6**] by other methods. The results to be reported here are concerned with the approximation of

$$\operatorname{Re}\left\{\int_{a+ib}^{\infty} (e^{-z}/z)\,dz\right\} = f(a, b)$$

on the square $\{(a, b): 0 \leqq a \leqq 1, 0 \leqq b \leqq 1\}$, where $f(0, 0) = \infty$. The next 5 examples will approximate f on various subsets of the square with various polynomials.

EXAMPLE 1. In this example we have 25 data points as follows:

$$0.2 \leqq a \leqq 1.0 \text{ in steps of } 0.2,$$

$$0.2 \leqq b \leqq 1.0 \text{ in steps of } 0.2.$$

Let

$$x = a - 0.6,$$

$$y = b - 0.6.$$

On these 25 points $f(a, b)$ is to be approximated by:

$$\frac{c_0 + c_1 y + c_2 x + c_3 xy + c_4 y^2 + c_5 x^2}{d_0 + d_1 y + d_2 x + d_3 xy + d_4 y^2 + d_5 x^2}.$$

The coefficients yielding a best approximation are:

$$\begin{aligned} c_0 &= 0.0996511681 & d_0 &= 0.5901378263 \\ c_1 &= -0.2679841565 & d_1 &= 0.5790828697 \\ c_2 &= 0.1038722831 & d_2 &= 1.000000000 \\ c_3 &= 0.0791500540 & d_3 &= 0.0864687953 \\ c_4 &= -0.2278015383 & d_4 &= 0.3753406864 \\ c_5 &= -0.0868051600 & d_5 &= 0.7019570201 \end{aligned}$$

The maximum error over all 25 points is 2.886199×10^{-3}.

EXAMPLE 2. We now add two terms thusly:

$$\frac{c_0 + c_1 y + c_2 x + c_3 xy + c_4 y^2 + c_5 x^2 + c_6 x^2 y}{d_0 + d_1 y + d_2 x + d_3 xy + d_4 y^2 + d_5 x^2 + d_6 x^2 y}$$

and obtain:

$$\begin{aligned} c_0 &= 0.0837914633 & d_0 &= 0.5032968598 \\ c_1 &= -0.1640272544 & d_1 &= 0.8973700662 \\ c_2 &= 0.0891182027 & d_2 &= 0.8928419099 \\ c_3 &= 0.1204883022 & d_3 &= 1.000000000 \\ c_4 &= -0.3867638268 & d_4 &= 0.4322944985 \\ c_5 &= -0.0701517797 & d_5 &= 0.6495118685 \\ c_6 &= -0.0289637846 & d_6 &= 0.7869549905 \end{aligned}$$

Maximum error $= 1.4388298 \times 10^{-3}$ over the same 25 points as Example 1.

EXAMPLE 3. We add two more terms:

$$\frac{c_0 + c_1y + c_2x + c_3xy + c_4y^2 + c_5x^2 + c_6x^2y + c_7y^3}{d_0 + d_1y + d_2x + d_3xy + d_4y^2 + d_5x^2 + d_6x^2y + d_7y^3}$$

and obtain:

$c_0 = 0.0921088117$ $d_0 = 0.5497567936$
$c_1 = -0.2849268231$ $d_1 = 0.3741778896$
$c_2 = 0.1005021254$ $d_2 = 1.000000000$
$c_3 = -0.0003441744$ $d_3 = -0.0212117468$
$c_4 = -0.1459524922$ $d_4 = 0.0257847905$
$c_5 = -0.0828488206$ $d_5 = 0.6919862405$
$c_6 = 0.1047913742$ $d_6 = -0.0217499310$
$c_7 = 0.1995149649$ $d_7 = -0.1748834438$

Maximum error $= 6.78750 \times 10^{-4}$ over the same 25 points as Example 1.

EXAMPLE 4. Again adding two more terms:

$$\frac{c_0 + c_1y + c_2x + c_3xy + c_4y^2 + c_5x^2 + c_6x^2y + c_7y^3 + c_8xy^2}{d_0 + d_1y + d_2x + d_3xy + d_4y^2 + d_5x^2 + d_6x^2y + d_7y^3 + d_8xy^2}$$

we obtain

$c_0 = 0.0960041046$ $d_0 = 0.5718305472$
$c_1 = -0.2406299991$ $d_1 = 0.7357740426$
$c_2 = 0.0998915478$ $d_2 = 1.00000000$
$c_3 = 0.0867557146$ $d_3 = 0.5014273072$
$c_4 = -0.2499496967$ $d_4 = 0.7704642845$
$c_5 = -0.0854718254$ $d_5 = 0.7047651776$
$c_6 = 0.0283182696$ $d_6 = 0.1880050704$
$c_7 = -0.1066314166$ $d_7 = 0.1740235386$
$c_8 = 0.0820618837$ $d_8 = 0.6828501570$

Maximum error $= 1.837059 \times 10^{-4}$ over the same 25 points as Example 1.

EXAMPLE 5. There are 100 data points as follows:

$$0.1 \leqq a \leqq 1.0, \text{ in steps of } 0.1,$$
$$0.1 \leqq b \leqq 1.0, \text{ in steps of } 0.1.$$

Let $x = a - 0.55$, $y = b - 0.55$. We use the approximating function of Example 4 and obtain:

$c_0 = 0.1157842294$ $d_0 = 0.5559147072$
$c_1 = -0.1925531085$ $d_1 = 0.9885289044$
$c_2 = 0.1144356251$ $d_2 = 1.000000000$
$c_3 = 0.1098909731$ $d_3 = 0.7230335039$
$c_4 = -0.4242775100$ $d_4 = 0.8556143567$
$c_5 = -0.1153246269$ $d_5 = 0.6618566410$
$c_6 = 0.0077507759$ $d_6 = 0.2155059213$
$c_7 = -0.1422053729$ $d_7 = 0.2096329609$
$c_8 = 0.2198488738$ $d_8 = 0.4174542178$

Maximum error $= 1.251383 \times 10^{-3}$ over all 100 points. The residuals are:

Residuals × 1000

b										
1.0	−1.251383	−1.251383	−0.857142	−0.461648	−0.137079	0.127431	0.338485	0.480278	0.520143	0.422815
	0.972071	0.791550	0.861584	0.925732	0.992959	1.089683	1.194469	1.251285	1.196651	0.973399
0.8	1.251383	1.251383	1.159842	1.017065	0.967007	1.042297	1.171992	1.251383	1.177108	0.880268
	0.329415	0.825764	0.627700	0.330560	0.260328	0.422740	0.669380	0.826905	0.762570	0.396933
0.6	−0.845907	0.310718	−0.104025	−0.576745	−0.605262	−0.288979	0.105777	0.337079	0.252014	−0.223394
	−1.251383	0.391542	−0.523399	−1.203256	−1.136113	−0.646782	−0.145280	0.083028	−0.108834	−0.772595
0.4	−0.241333	1.137293	−0.508196	−1.251383	−0.995291	−0.371125	0.125348	0.224350	−0.185664	−1.120887
	1.251383	1.251383	−0.487483	−0.749815	−0.201189	0.448140	0.797949	0.661417	−0.024133	−1.251383
0.2	−1.251382	−1.251383	−0.781262	−0.162767	0.505738	1.049588	1.251383	0.965452	0.131137	−1.251383
	−1.251381	1.251383	−0.194969	−1.251383	−1.045162	−0.314517	0.286787	0.405125	−0.101597	−1.251383
a	0.1	0.2	0.3	0.4	0.5	0.6	0.7	0.8	0.9	1.0

Each residual was computed by

$$R^i(x) = \frac{[A^i, x]}{[B^i, x]} - b^i \qquad 1 \leqq i \leqq 100.$$

The values of f on the grid are[1]:

b \ a	0.1	0.2	0.3	0.4	0.5	0.6	0.7	0.8	0.9	1.0
1.0	−0.260102	−0.196048	−0.144211	−0.103189	−0.071395	−0.047222	−0.029174	−0.015940	−0.006419	0.000282
	−0.197141	−0.133831	−0.084691	−0.047765	−0.020895	−0.001986	0.010826	0.019096	0.024061	0.026676
0.8	−0.118431	−0.057358	−0.012925	0.017703	0.037524	0.049293	0.055315	0.057387	0.056853	0.054674
	−0.020740	0.035871	0.072667	0.093931	0.103914	0.106235	0.103674	0.098224	0.091240	0.083607
0.6	0.100448	0.149070	0.173775	0.181324	0.177820	0.167924	0.154817	0.140517	0.126221	0.112594
	0.251763	0.286357	0.291899	0.279505	0.257866	0.232626	0.207020	0.182721	0.160481	0.140547
0.4	0.443503	0.452751	0.427474	0.386389	0.341112	0.297441	0.257770	0.222784	0.192393	0.166192
	0.692608	0.652965	0.577505	0.496487	0.422211	0.357993	0.303718	0.258208	0.220102	0.188148
0.2	1.027547	0.884824	0.730009	0.598490	0.492769	0.408461	0.340883	0.286251	0.241692	0.205051
	1.478689	1.113268	0.855048	0.673991	0.541967	0.442372	0.365257	0.304338	0.255453	0.215370

[1] *Tables of the exponential integral for complex arguments*, Nat. Bur. Standards Applied Math. Series **51**, 1958.

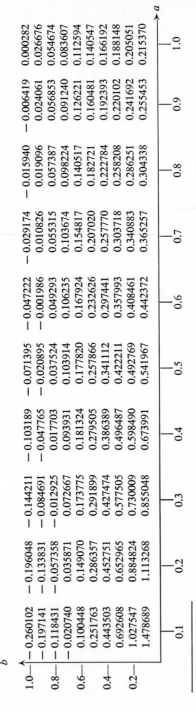

8. Let T denote a metric compactum, and $C(T)$ the Banach space of real-valued continuous functions on T with norm, $\max_{t\in T} |f(t)| = \|f\|$. Let A and B denote continuous maps from T to E_n and let $D = \{x \in E_n : [B(t), x] \geqq \mu > 0$, all $t \in T$ and $\|x\|_\infty \leqq 1\}$. Let $f_x(t) = [A(t), x]/[B(t), x]$ and $M = \{f_x : x \in D\}$. By virtue of the continuity of A and B, the compactness of D, and because $[B(t), x]$ is bounded below, the set M is equicontinuous. Let S denote a finite subset of T and define on $C(T)$ the semi-norm $\|f\|_S = \max_{t\in S} |f(t)|$. Let g be a given point in $C(T)$. By means of §4 we are able to construct x_0 in D to minimize $\|g - f_x\|_S$. Furthermore, for an appropriate S, x_0 does more.

THEOREM. *Given* $\varepsilon > 0$, *choose* δ *such that* $\delta < \varepsilon/3$, $|f_x(t_1) - f_x(t_2)| < \varepsilon/3$ *and* $|g(t_1) - g(t_2)| < \varepsilon/3$, *whenever* $d(t_1, t_2) < \delta$. *Assume that S satisfies* $\inf_{s\in S} d(s, t) < \delta$ *for all* $t \in T$. *Then* $\|f_{x_0} - g\| \leqq \inf\{\|f_x - g\| : x \in D\} + \varepsilon$.

PROOF. See [3, p. 267].

ACKNOWLEDGMENTS. The authors are grateful for use of the computing machinery at the Massachusetts Institute of Technology and at the University of Texas. The second-named author acknowledges support from grant AF-AFOSR-62-348 and from the General Motors Research Laboratories.

REFERENCES

1. E. W. Cheney and H. L. Loeb, *Two algorithms for rational approximation*, Numer. Math. **3** (1961), 72–75.

2. A. A. Goldstein, *On the stability of rational approximation*, Numer. Math. **5** (1963), 431–438.

3. E. W. Cheney and A. A. Goldstein, *Newton's method for convex programming and Tchebycheff approximation*, Numer. Math. **1** (1959), 253–268.

4. ———, *Note on a paper by Zuhovickii concerning the Tchebycheff problem for linear equations*, J. Soc. Indust. Appl. Math. **6** (1958), 233–239.

5. ———, *A finite algorithm for the solution of consistent linear equations and inequalities and for the Tchebycheff approximation of inconsistent linear equations*, Pacific J. Math. **8** (1958), 415–427.

6. H. L. Loeb, *Algorithms for Cebysev approximation using the ratio of linear forms*, J. Soc. Indust. Appl. Math. **8** (1960), 458–465.

PHASE METHODS FOR POLYNOMIAL APPROXIMATION

E. STIEFEL
Eidgenössische Technische Hochschule, Zürich, Switzerland

1. **Introduction of the phase function.** Our problem is to approximate a given function $f(x)$ on the interval $-1 \leqq x \leqq 1$ by a polynomial $P_n(x)$ of given degree n. Let φ be the Tchebycheff *angular variable* defined by $x = \cos \varphi$ and varying from 0 to π (see Figure 1). In order to solve this approximation problem we try to construct a phase function $\varepsilon_n(\varphi)$ subjected to $\varepsilon_n(0) = 0$, $\varepsilon_n(\pi) = 0$, an amplitude λ, and a polynomial $P_n(\cos \varphi)$ such that

$$f(\cos \varphi) = P_n(\cos \varphi) + \lambda \cos [(n + 1)\varphi + \varepsilon_n(\varphi)]. \tag{1}$$

THEOREM 1. *If this relation is satisfied for* $0 \leqq \varphi \leqq \pi$, *then* P_n *is the polynomial of best fit.*

PROOF. It follows that

$$|f(\cos \varphi) - P_n(\cos \varphi)| \leqq |\lambda|. \tag{2}$$

Thus the approximation error is everywhere less than $|\lambda|$.

The points φ where this maximum is attained can be constructed as follows (see Figure 2, $n = 2$). The phase curve $y = \varepsilon_n(\varphi)$ is plotted in a φ, y-coordinate system and intersected with the straight lines

$$y = j\pi - (n + 1)\varphi, \qquad j = 0, 1, \cdots, (n + 1). \tag{3}$$

On each line there is at least one point φ_j of intersection. In particular we may choose $\varphi_0 = 0$, $\varphi_{n+1} = \pi$.

From

$$i\pi - (n + 1)\varphi_j = \varepsilon_n(\varphi_j) \tag{4}$$

and (1) it follows that

$$f(\cos \varphi_j) - P_n(\cos \varphi_j) = \lambda \cos j\pi = (-1)^j\lambda.$$

At the corresponding abscissas $x_j = \cos \varphi_j$ the maximal error λ is therefore attained with alternating signs; the $(n + 2)$ abscissas x_j build the famous *Tchebycheff alternant*. Some remarks should be added to this proof.

Our discussion contains a graphical construction of the alternant if the phase-curve is known. With increasing n the lines (3) become steeper and steeper. If

$\varepsilon_n(\varphi)$ remains bounded for $n \to \infty$, the φ_j will be for large n very close to the values

(5) $$\varphi_j = \frac{j\pi}{n+1}\,.$$

The corresponding abscissas $x_j = \cos\,\varphi_j$ are known as *Tchebycheff abscissas*. This remark shows that the asymptotical behavior of the phase function for

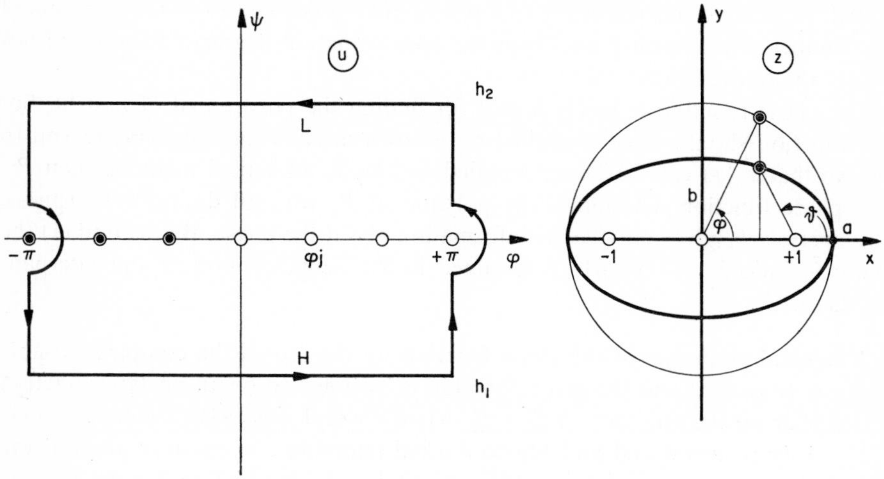

FIGURE 1. Conformal mapping $z = \cos u$.

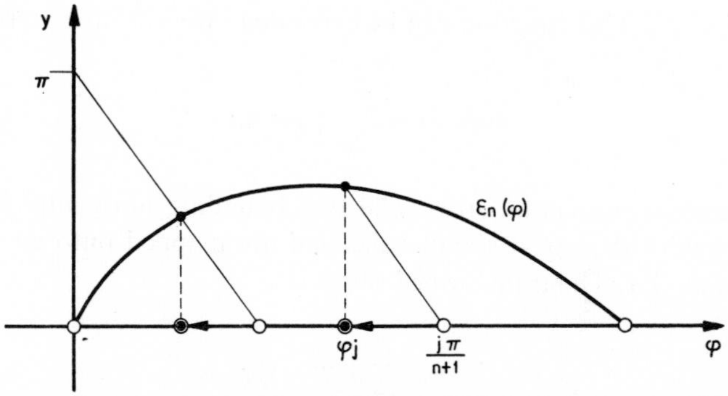

FIGURE 2. Phase-curve ($n = 2$).

large n is very important for the theoretical investigation of approximation problems.

Our construction has produced an alternant x_j containing the endpoints $x_0 = +1$, $x_{n+1} = -1$ of the given interval. It is very well known that the Tchebycheff alternant of the polynomial of best approximation does not necessarily have this property. Thus our construction is not always possible. In this connection we may mention the following fact.

If the $(n + 1)$st derivative of $f(x)$ does not vanish for $-1 \leqq x \leqq 1$, the end-points $x = \pm 1$ are members of the alternant. This is easy to prove. In such a case our construction can be recommended. Let us assume for instance that $f(x)$ is an even function. The approximating polynomial should of course also be even, and therefore one is tempted to choose n as an even integer. But this leads to failure because the $(n + 1)$st derivative of f vanishes at $x = 0$. Only the choice of an odd n is good for establishing relation (1), and the corresponding polynomial P_n will be reduced automatically to a polynomial of degree $(n - 1)$. The excess of the number of alternant points over the approximation degree is then 3 and not 2 as in the normal case.

The phase function is so far a tool for finding the polynomial of best fit, but this function should also be studied on its own merits. There is some reason to believe that $\varepsilon_n(\varphi)$ can be better handled by classic analytical methods than P_n. The phase function determines the polynomial P_n with all desirable sharpness, but inversely P_n gives only vague information about the phase. By relation (1) the phase is indeed only poorly determined in the neighborhood of the alternant points φ_j.

2. **General properties of the phase function.** In the sequel the complex variable $z = x + iy$ is used and the given function is assumed to be an analytic function $f(z)$ regular on the interval $-1 \leqq x \leqq +1$ of the real axis. Also a complex angle $u = \varphi + i\psi$ is introduced and the conformal mapping $z = \cos u$ of the u-plane (called "parameter-plane") onto the z-plane is established (see Figure 1). The transformed function $f(\cos u)$ is an even analytic function of u regular on the real axis with period 2π. This function can be expanded into a Fourier series

$$(\cos u) = \sum_{n=0}^{\infty} a_n \cos nu \tag{6}$$

convergent inside a horizontal strip. The two bounding horizontal lines of this strip pass through the nearest singularities and are mapped onto an ellipse with foci at the points ± 1. The transformed series is

$$f(z) = \sum_{n=0}^{\infty} a_n T_n(z), \tag{7}$$

where $T_n(z)$ is the nth Tchebycheff polynomial. The series converges in the interior of this "*ellipse of convergence*", and finally the ellipse passes through the nearest singularity of $f(z)$. There are some functions $f(x)$ with explicitly known phase function. A famous example is

$$f(x) = \frac{1}{a - x} = \frac{1}{a - \cos \varphi}, \qquad a > 1. \tag{8}$$

The corresponding ellipse of convergence passes through the point a on the x-axis. S. Bernstein [**1**, p. 120] has proved that the phase is

$$\varepsilon_n(\varphi) = \vartheta(\varphi) - \varphi, \tag{9}$$

where ϑ is the angle shown in Figure 1. (Astronomers call ϑ the "true" and φ the "eccentric" anomaly of a point moving on the ellipse.)

PROOF. Let a, b be the semi-axes of the ellipse ($a^2 - b^2 = 1$). A point on the ellipse has the coordinates $a \cos \varphi$, $b \sin \varphi$; hence its focal distance is

$$r^2 = (a \cos \varphi - 1)^2 + b^2 \sin^2 \varphi, \qquad r = a - \cos \varphi,$$

$$\cos \vartheta = \frac{a \cos \varphi - 1}{a - \cos \varphi}, \qquad \sin \vartheta = \frac{b \sin \varphi}{a - \cos \varphi}. \tag{10}$$

According to (1) the expression

$$f(\cos \varphi) - \lambda \cos [(n+1)\varphi + \varepsilon_n(\varphi)] = f(\cos \varphi) - \lambda \cos (n\varphi + \vartheta)$$

$$= \frac{1 - \lambda(a \cos \varphi - 1) \cos n\varphi + \lambda b \sin \varphi \sin n\varphi}{a - \cos \varphi}$$

should be a polynomial $P_n(\cos \varphi)$. The numerator is a polynomial of degree $(n + 1)$ in $\cos \varphi = x$. Thus the quotient is a polynomial of degree n if and only if the numerator vanishes for $\cos \varphi = a$. Taking into account

$$\sin \varphi = \sqrt{1 - a^2} = ib,$$

this furnishes the condition

$$\lambda b^2(\cos n\varphi - i \sin n\varphi) = 1,$$

$$\lambda = \frac{e^{ni\varphi}}{b^2} = \frac{1}{b^2}(\cos \varphi + i \sin \varphi)^n = \frac{(a-b)^n}{b^2}.$$

With this value of λ the relation (1) is satisfied and Bernstein's result is established. The maximal deviation of the polynomial of best fit is

$$\lambda = \frac{(a-b)^n}{b^2}.$$

Thus P_n converges linearly to f with increasing n; the factor of convergence is $(a - b)$. In this example a complex phase function $\varepsilon_n(u)$ can be defined by

$$\varepsilon_n(u) = \vartheta(u) - u, \qquad \cos \vartheta = \frac{a \cos u - 1}{a - \cos u}, \qquad \sin \vartheta = \frac{b \sin u}{a - \cos u}, \tag{11}$$

as follows from (9) and (10). Our restrictions $\varepsilon_n(0) = 0$, $\varepsilon_n(\pi) = 0$ ensure that this function is a single-valued analytic and odd function of the variable u with period 2π. Its only singularity is the pole $\cos u = a$ of the given function. But the most surprising fact is the *independence* of the phase function *of the degree n* of approximation. Therefore it is trivial that a limiting phase function

$$\varepsilon(u) = \lim \varepsilon_n(u), \qquad n \to \infty$$

exists and is given by

$$\varepsilon(u) = \vartheta(u) - u. \tag{12}$$

Next we consider an analytic function $f(z)$ having on its ellipse of convergence only a single pole of first order at $x = a > 1$. Outside the ellipse any kind of singularity may occur. Then the corresponding phase function $\varepsilon_n(u)$ is no longer independent of n, but has as its limit for $n \to \infty$ the function $\varepsilon(u)$ defined above. This is to say that the limiting phase function is determined by this dominant pole. This result was obtained by F. Schläpfer (forthcoming thesis) by using techniques developed by Bernstein. He proved also the following theorem. Let $f(z)$ be an entire function of exponential type. There is a sequence of degrees $n_1, n_2, \cdots, n_k, \cdots$ with $n_k \to \infty$ for $k \to \infty$ such that

$$\lim \varepsilon_{n_k}(\varphi) = 0, \qquad k \to \infty. \tag{13}$$

This statement is intimately connected with Bernstein's investigations on the approximation of entire functions by their truncated Tchebycheff expansion (7).

From such results and other experiences we may conjecture that an analytic function $f(z)$ regular on the interval $-1 \leqq x \leqq 1$ of the real axis has always a corresponding limiting phase function $\varepsilon(u)$ if $f(z)$ is not a polynomial, and furthermore that $\varepsilon(u)$ is determined by the position and nature of the singularities on the ellipse of convergence of $f(z)$. But we are far from proving statements of this general type. Of course a preliminary study of the assumptions on $f(z)$ must be made in order to make sure the existence of a sequence n_k such that the corresponding phase functions do exist. Mr. Schläpfer's thesis contains also theorems concerning the existence of the phase function $\varepsilon_n(\varphi)$.

The limiting phase function $\varepsilon(\varphi)$ is a measure for the deviation of $f(z)$ from an entire function and also for the fitness of $f(z)$ for polynomial approximation.

3. **An integral equation.** In this section we work in the complex z-plane as well as in the parameter plane $u = \varphi + i\psi$. We need the interpolation formula for the Tchebycheff abscissas

$$x_j = \cos \varphi_j, \qquad \varphi_j = \frac{j\pi}{n+1}, \qquad j = 0, 1, \cdots, (n+1) \tag{14}$$

as interpolating nodes. The polynomial $Q_{n+1}(z)$ interpolating given functional values $f(x_j)$ at those nodes is

$$Q_{n+1}(\cos u) = \frac{\sin u \sin (n+1)u}{2(n+1)} \sum_{j=0}^{n+1} (-1)^j p_j \frac{f(\cos \varphi_j)}{\cos \varphi_j - \cos u}. \tag{15}$$

The p_j are the trapezoidal weights

$$(16) \qquad p_0 = 1, \quad p_1 = p_2 = \cdots = p_n = 2, \quad p_{n+1} = 1.$$

The coefficient of the highest term $\cos(n+1)u$ in this polynomial is

$$(17) \qquad \frac{1}{2(n+1)}\Delta, \quad \text{where} \quad \Delta = \sum_{j=0}^{n+1}(-1)^j p_j f(\cos\varphi_j).$$

A special case of (15) is used below. Let in particular the function $\cos(n+1)\varphi$ to be interpolated. The corresponding functional values are

$$\cos(n+1)\varphi_j = \cos j\pi = (-1)^j;$$

thus (15) is reduced to the identity

$$(18) \qquad \cos(n+1)u = \frac{\sin u \sin(n+1)u}{2(n+1)} \sum_{j=0}^{n+1} \frac{p_j}{\cos\varphi_j - \cos u}.$$

Let now $f(z)$ be an analytic function regular in the interior and on an ellipse with foci at ± 1 ("*ellipse of regularity*"). Our goal is to establish an integral equation for the corresponding phase function $\varepsilon_n(u)$ with that ellipse as path of integration. It is a little more convenient to map the situation into the parameter plane. The ellipse of regularity is mapped onto a horizontal segment H below the φ-axis, φ varying from $(-\pi)$ to $(+\pi)$ (Figure 1, $n = 2$). The corresponding function $f(\cos u)$ is regular in the infinite strip bounded by the horizontal lines h_1, h_2.

THEOREM 2. *Let $Q_{n+1}(\cos u)$ be the polynomial interpolating $f(\cos\varphi)$ at the Tchebycheff nodes φ_j. Let furthermore $\varepsilon_n(u)$ be an analytic odd function regular in the strip mentioned above and on its boundary. Also $\varepsilon_n(u)$ is assumed to have the period 2π. If $\varepsilon_n(u)$ satisfies the integral equation*

$$(19) \qquad \sin\varepsilon_n(u) = \frac{Q_{n+1}(\cos u) - f(\cos u)}{\lambda \sin(n+1)u} - \frac{\sin u}{2\pi i}\int_{(H)} \frac{\cos\varepsilon_n(v) - \cos\varepsilon_n(u)}{\cos v - \cos u} \times \operatorname{cotg}(n+1)v\, dv$$

on the segment H, it is the phase function corresponding to $f(\cos u)$.

The value of λ will be determined below.

PROOF. The polynomial appearing in relation (1) has at the nodes φ_j the values

$$f(\cos\varphi_j) - (-1)^j\lambda\cos\varepsilon_n(\varphi_j), \qquad j = 0, 1, \cdots, (n+1).$$

Therefore we construct a polynomial by interpolation from those functional values. In general it has the degree $(n+1)$, but by appropriate choice of λ the degree can be reduced to n. By annihilating the highest coefficient the condition

$$\sum_{j=0}^{n+1}(-1)^j p_j[f(\cos\varphi_j) - (-1)^j\lambda\cos\varepsilon_n(\varphi_j)] = 0$$

is obtained. This follows from the general formula (17). Hence

$$\lambda = \frac{\Delta}{\sum_{j=0}^{n+1} p_j\cos\varepsilon_n(\varphi_j)}, \qquad \Delta = \sum_{j=0}^{n+1}(-1)^j p_j f(\cos\varphi_j). \tag{20}$$

From (15) it follows that the constructed polynomial is

$$P_n(\cos u) = \frac{\sin u\sin(n+1)u}{2(n+1)}\sum_{j=0}^{n+1}(-1)^j p_j\frac{f(\cos\varphi_j) - (-1)^j\lambda\cos\varepsilon_n(\varphi_j)}{\cos\varphi_j - \cos u}$$

or

$$P_n(\cos u) = Q_{n+1}(\cos u) - \lambda\frac{\sin u\sin(n+1)u}{2(n+1)}\sum_{j=0}^{n+1} p_j\frac{\cos\varepsilon_n(\varphi_j)}{\cos\varphi_j - \cos u}, \tag{21}$$

as follows from (15).

Next the integral $\mathfrak{J}$ in formula (19) is computed. The integrand is an odd periodic function of v. Its singularities in our strip are the points $j\pi/(n+1)$ where j runs through all integers. In particular our Tchebycheff nodes φ_j of (14) are poles of first order. We may replace the segment H of integration by the closed rectangular loop $\mathscr{L}$ of Figure 1, taking into account the oddness and periodicity of the integrand of

$$\mathfrak{J} = \frac{1}{2}\int_{\mathscr{L}}\frac{\cos\varepsilon_n(v) - \cos\varepsilon_n(u)}{\cos v - \cos u}\operatorname{cotg}(n+1)v\,dv.$$

The poles in the interior of the loop are the points $j\pi/(n+1)$ with j running from $(-n)$ to $(n+1)$. By residual integration and uniting two terms arising from symmetric poles the result

$$\mathfrak{J} = \frac{\pi i}{n+1}\sum_{j=0}^{n+1} p_j\frac{\cos\varepsilon_n(\varphi_j) - \cos\varepsilon_n(u)}{\cos\varphi_j - \cos u}$$

is obtained. Or we have

$$\mathfrak{J}\sin u\sin(n+1)u = \frac{\pi i}{n+1}\sin u\sin(n+1)u\sum_{j=0}^{n+1} p_j\frac{\cos\varepsilon_n(\varphi_j)}{\cos\varphi_j - \cos u}$$
$$- 2\pi i\cos\varepsilon_n(u)\cos(n+1)u,$$

as follows from (18).

Finally the integral equation (19) is used. By multiplication with $\lambda\sin(n+1)u$ it may be written

$$\lambda\sin\varepsilon_n(u)\sin(n+1)u = Q_{n+1}(\cos u) - f(\cos u) + \lambda\cos\varepsilon_n(u)\cos(n+1)u$$
$$- \frac{\lambda}{2(n+1)}\sin u\sin(n+1)u\sum_{j=0}^{n+1} p_j\frac{\cos\varepsilon_n(\varphi_j)}{\cos\varphi_j - \cos u}.$$

On the right side the polynomial (21) appears, hence

$$\lambda \sin \varepsilon_n(u) \sin (n+1)u = P_n(\cos u) - f(\cos u) + \lambda \cos \varepsilon_n(u) \cos (n+1)u,$$

or

$$f(\cos u) = P_n(\cos u) + \lambda \cos [(n+1)u + \varepsilon_n(u)].$$

Thus the basic relation (1) is satisfied on the segment H, and by analytic continuation it follows that it holds true on the real φ-axis. Also the boundary conditions $\varepsilon_n(0) = \varepsilon_n(\pi) = 0$ are satisfied because $\varepsilon_n(u)$ is odd and periodic. Therefore $\varepsilon_n(\varphi)$ is the phase function and $P_n(x)$ the polynomial of best approximation as follows from Theorem 1.

Some additional remarks are in order.

(1) The numerator in the first term of the integral equation is the interpolation error.

(2) The quantity λ should be removed from the integral equation in order to have only the phase as the unknown function in the equation. This can be performed as follows. By residual integration the formula

$$\int_{(H)} \cos \varepsilon_n(v) \operatorname{cotg} (n+1)v \, dv = \frac{\pi i}{n+1} \sum_{j=0}^{n+1} p_j \cos \varepsilon_n(\varphi_j)$$

is obtained. From (20) it follows that

$$\frac{1}{\lambda} = \frac{n+1}{\pi i \Delta} \int_{(H)} \cos \varepsilon_n(v) \operatorname{cotg} (n+1)v \, dv. \tag{22}$$

By inserting this into (19) a new integral equation is produced containing only given data and the phase function. Δ is determined by (17). This quantity is also the value of the $(n+1)$st derivative of $f(x)$ at some unspecified abscissa in the interval $-1 \leqq x \leqq 1$ (up to a numerical factor). If this derivative does not vanish in the interval, Δ is $\neq 0$ and therefore the denominator Δ in (22) is harmless. This hypothesis on the $(n+1)$st derivative was also discussed in §1.

(3) The integral equation (19) is non-linear. For small phases $\varepsilon_n(\varphi)$ it can be solved by iteration starting from $\varepsilon_n(\varphi) \equiv 0$ and the corresponding value of λ taken from formula (20):

$$\lambda = \Delta/2(n+1).$$

New values of the phase are then computed by (19) and a new value of λ by (22), and so on.

But the integral equation is not well suited for numerical quadrature because of the undetermined form of the integrand at the value $v = u$ of the integration variable. Therefore a modified method for iterative construction of the phase function using complex integration was proposed in [**2**]. We describe it briefly. Let $\varepsilon_n(\varphi_j)$ be initial values of the phase at the Tchebycheff nodes. From the basic relation (1) the values $P_n(\cos \varphi_j)$ are computed using the expression (20) for λ.

Next $P_n(\cos u)$ is evaluated on the horizontal segment H by application of the general interpolation formula (15):

$$P_n(\cos u) = \frac{\sin u \sin (n+1)u}{2(n+1)} \sum_{j=0}^{n+1} (-1)^j p_j \frac{P_n(\cos \varphi_j)}{\cos \varphi_j - \cos u}.$$

The basic relation (1) is used again on H and furnishes on that line the function $\varepsilon_n(u)$. Finally new values of $\varepsilon_n(\varphi_j)$ are computed by Cauchy's integral formula

$$\sin \varepsilon_n(\varphi_j) = \frac{\sin \varphi_j}{2\pi i} \int_{(H)} \frac{\sin \varepsilon_n(v)}{\cos \varphi_j - \cos v} \, dv.$$

This iteration must be repeated until a final function $\varepsilon_n(\varphi)$ is obtained.

EXAMPLE. To approximate

$$f(x) = \frac{1}{1.25 - x}$$

by a parabola ($n = 2$). This is a rather difficult case because the singularity of the function is close to the endpoint $x = 1$ of the approximation interval. The major semi-axis of the ellipse of integration was chosen to be $a = \cosh 0.4 = 1.0811$. For numerical integration the segment H was divided into 48 equal parts. Starting from $\varepsilon_n(\varphi_j) = 0$ six iterations produced the phase function with 5 correct significant decimals.

4. **Discretization.** From a practical viewpoint complex integration is not an agreeable tool. In this section methods are developed operating on the real φ-axis and thus avoiding this difficulty.

In the sequel $f(x)$ is *assumed* to be a *polynomial* of degree $m > n + 1$:

$$f(\cos \varphi) = \sum_{k=0}^{m} a_k \cos k\varphi. \tag{23}$$

If such a polynomial is interpolated at the Tchebycheff nodes $\varphi_j = j\pi/(n+1)$, a polynomial $P_{n+1}(\cos \varphi)$ is obtained. Denoting the difference of degrees by $d = m - (n+1)$, we record the following well-known fact. The interpolation error has the form

$$f(\cos \varphi) - P_{n+1}(\cos \varphi) = \sin (n+1)\varphi \sum_{l=1}^{d} b_l \sin l\varphi, \tag{24}$$

where the b_l are linear combinations of the higher coefficients $a_{n+2}, \cdots, a_m$; thus

$$b_l = \sum_{\rho=1}^{d} K_{l\rho} a_{n+\rho+1}, \qquad l = 1, 2, \cdots, d. \tag{25}$$

The K_{l_ρ} are numerical constants and many among them are zero. They can be computed in the following way. Write

$$\sum_{k=0}^{m} a_k \cos k\varphi - P_{n+1}(\cos \varphi) = \frac{1}{2} \sum_{l=1}^{d} b_l [\cos (n - l + 1)\varphi - \cos (n + l + 1)\varphi].$$

Both sides of this relation are polynomials of degree m in $\cos \varphi$. By comparing the coefficients of $\cos (n+2)\varphi, \cdots, \cos m\varphi$ a system of linear equations for the b_l is obtained.

EXAMPLE. $n = 2, m = 12, d = 9$. The linear transformation is $b_1 = -2(a_4 + a_{10})$, $b_2 = -2(a_5 + a_{11})$, $b_3 = -2(a_6 + a_{12})$, $b_4 = -2a_7$, $b_5 = -2a_8$, until $b_9 = -2a_{12}$. After this preliminary remark we are going to establish the basic relation (1). It may be written

$$(26) \quad [f(\cos \varphi) - \lambda \cos (n+1)\varphi \cos \varepsilon_n(\varphi)] - P_n(\cos \varphi) = -\lambda \sin (n+1)\varphi \sin \varepsilon_n(\varphi).$$

At the Tchebycheff abscissas φ_j this is reduced to

$$(27) \qquad P_n(\cos \varphi_j) = [f(\cos \varphi_j) - \lambda \cos (n+1)\varphi_j \cos \varepsilon_n(\varphi_j)];$$

thus $P_n(\cos \varphi)$ interpolates the function

$$(28) \qquad f(\cos \varphi) - \lambda \cos (n+1)\varphi \cos \varepsilon_n(\varphi)$$

at the Tchebycheff nodes. The interpolation error is

$$(29) \qquad -\lambda \sin (n+1)\varphi \sin \varepsilon_n(\varphi),$$

as follows from (26). Because the interpolating polynomial is of degree n and not of degree $(n+1)$, we have for λ the same condition as in §3 and λ is determined by (20).

In order to take advantage of this interpolation property the following discretization is proposed. The interval $0 \leqq \varphi \leqq \pi$ of the φ-axis is divided into m equal parts, and φ *will no longer denote* in the sequel any point of this interval but *one of the partition points.*

Our next step is to carry out the harmonic cosine analysis of the function (28) at the partition points, thus obtaining the finite expansion

$$(30) \qquad f(\cos \varphi) - \lambda \cos (n+1)\varphi \cos \varepsilon_n(\varphi) = \sum_{k=0}^{m} \alpha_k \cos k\varphi.$$

Because the interpolation error is given by (29) our general formula (24) for such errors furnishes the result

$$-\lambda \sin (n+1)\varphi \sin \varepsilon_n(\varphi) = \sin (n+1)\varphi \sum_{l=1}^{d} \beta_l \sin l\varphi,$$

where

$$(31) \qquad \beta_l = \sum_{\rho=1}^{d} K_{l\rho}\alpha_{n+\rho+1};$$

hence

$$\sin \varepsilon_n(\varphi) = -\frac{1}{\lambda}\sum_{l=1}^{d} \beta_l \sin l\varphi.$$

By collecting the formulae (17) (30) (20) (31) the following set of *guiding rules* appears.

1. $$\Delta = \sum_{j=0}^{n+1} (-1)^j p_j f(\cos \varphi_j), \qquad \varphi_j = (j\pi)/(n+1),$$

(p_j = trapezoidal weights).

2. Cosine analysis:

$$f(\cos \varphi) - \lambda \cos (n+1)\varphi \cos \varepsilon_n(\varphi) = \sum_{k=0}^{m} \alpha_k \cos k\varphi.$$

3. $$\lambda = \frac{\Delta}{\sum_{j=0}^{n+1} p_j \cos \varepsilon_n(\varphi_j)}.$$

4. $$\sin \varepsilon_n(\varphi) = -\frac{1}{\lambda} \sum_{l=1}^{d} \beta_l \sin l\varphi, \qquad d = m - (n+1),$$

$$\beta_l = \sum_{\rho=1}^{d} K_{l\rho} \alpha_{n+\rho+1}.$$

This set is, in itself, an iterative method for computing the phase. The partition of the interval $0 \leqq \varphi \leqq \pi$ should be made in such a way that the Tchebycheff nodes are partition points, that is to say that m must be a multiple of $(n + 1)$. With starting values of $\varepsilon_n(\varphi)$ the harmonic analysis of Rule 2 is carried out, and then Rules 3, 4 yield new values of the phases. This process is repeated successively. Finally the polynomial $P_n(x)$ of approximation is computed by (27):

(32) $$P_n(\cos \varphi_j) = f(\cos \varphi_j) - \lambda(-1)^j \cos \varepsilon_n(\varphi_j)$$

and interpolation.

This procedure converges if the phase is not too large. The final phase and polynomial satisfy the basic relation (1) at the partition points but not necessarily elsewhere.

5. **The phase equations.** Let us consider the following special case of the method just described. We choose $m = 2(n + 1)$, that is to say the partition points are the Tchebycheff nodes and their midpoints. Let

(33) $$f(\cos \varphi) = \sum_{k=0}^{2(n+1)} a_k \cos k\varphi$$

be the cosine analysis of $f(x)$ at the partition points. In order to perform the analysis of Rule 2 above we introduce the cosine analysis of $\cos \varepsilon_n(\varphi)$ at the Tchebycheff nodes

(34) $$\cos \varepsilon_n(\varphi_j) = \sum_{l=0}^{n+1} p_l \gamma_l \cos l\varphi_j, \qquad j = 0, 1, \cdots, n+1,$$

where

(35) $$\gamma_l = \frac{1}{2(n+1)} \sum_{k=0}^{n+1} p_k \cos \varepsilon_n(\varphi_k) \cos l\varphi_k.$$

With this auxiliary expansion the cosine analysis of Rule 2 may be written

$$f(\cos\varphi) - \lambda\cos(n+1)\varphi\cos\varepsilon_n(\varphi)$$
$$= \sum_{k=0}^{2(n+1)} a_k \cos k\varphi - \lambda\cos(n+1)\varphi \sum_{l=0}^{n+1} p_l\gamma_l \cos l\varphi.$$

This is indeed correct at the Tchebycheff nodes but it also holds true at the midpoints, because $\cos(n+1)\varphi$ vanishes there. Thus the higher coefficients in the expansion of Rule 2 are

$$\alpha_{n+l+1} = a_{n+l+1} - \frac{\lambda}{2} p_l\gamma_l, \qquad l = 1, 2, \cdots, (n+1).$$

In the special case at hand the linear transformation (25) is $b_l = -2a_{n+l+1}$. Therefore we have, according to Rule 4, $\beta_l = -2\alpha_{n+l+1}$ and

$$\text{(36)}\qquad \begin{aligned} \sin\varepsilon_n(\varphi) &= \frac{2}{\lambda}\sum_{l=1}^{n+1}\alpha_{n+l+1}\sin l\varphi \\ &= \frac{2}{\lambda}\sum_{l=1}^{n+1} a_{n+l+1}\sin l\varphi - \sum_{l=1}^{n+1} p_l\gamma_l \sin l\varphi. \end{aligned}$$

If we use this formula only at the Tchebycheff nodes, the summation stops at the index n; thus

$$\text{(37)}\qquad \sin\varepsilon_n(\varphi_j) = \frac{2}{\lambda}\sum_{l=1}^{n} a_{n+l+1}\sin l\varphi_j - 2\sum_{l=1}^{n}\gamma_l\sin l\varphi_j.$$

Finally (35) is inserted into the last sum:

$$\begin{aligned} \sum_{l=1}^{n}\gamma_l\sin l\varphi_j &= \frac{1}{2(n+1)}\sum_{l=1}^{n}\sin l\varphi_j \sum_{k=0}^{n+1} p_k\cos\varepsilon_n(\varphi_k)\cos l\varphi_k \\ &= \frac{1}{2(n+1)}\sum_{k=0}^{n+1} p_k\cos\varepsilon_n(\varphi_k)\sum_{l=1}^{n}\sin l\varphi_j\cos l\varphi_k. \end{aligned}$$

The last sum can be evaluated in closed form:

$$\sum_{l=1}^{n}\sin l\varphi_j\cos l\varphi_k = \frac{\sin\varphi_j}{\cos\varphi_k - \cos\varphi_j}$$

if $k \not\equiv j \pmod 2$. For $k \equiv j \pmod 2$ the sum vanishes.

By collecting all this the *phase equations* are obtained:

$$\text{(38)}\qquad \sin\varepsilon_n(\varphi_j) = \frac{2}{\lambda}\sum_{l=1}^{n} a_{n+l+1}\sin l\varphi_j - \frac{\sin\varphi_j}{n+1}\sum_{(k)} p_k \frac{\cos\varepsilon_n(\varphi_k)}{\cos\varphi_k - \cos\varphi_j},$$

where k runs through the integers from 0 to $(n+1)$ which are $\not\equiv j \pmod 2$.

As usual some remarks are added.

1. The coefficient of $\cos(n+1)\varphi$ in the harmonic cosine analysis of f at the partition points is the same as in the analysis at the Tchebycheff nodes. Thus

formula (17) yields

$$\Delta = 2(n+1)a_{n+1}$$

and Rule 4 of §4 is reduced to

$$\frac{1}{\lambda} = \frac{1}{2(n+1)a_{n+1}} \sum_{j=0}^{n+1} p_j \cos \varepsilon_n(\varphi_j),$$

or

$$\frac{1}{\lambda} = \frac{1}{(n+1)a_{n+1}} \left[1 + \sum_{j=1}^{n} \cos \varepsilon_n(\varphi_j) \right]. \tag{39}$$

If this result is inserted into the phase equations (38) a system of n equations of the type

$$\sin \varepsilon_n(\varphi_j) = c_j + \sum_{(k)} c_{jk} \cos \varepsilon_n(\varphi_k), \qquad j = 1, 2, \cdots, n, \tag{40}$$

is obtained with certain known coefficients c_j, c_{jk} depending only on the higher coefficients $a_{n+1}, a_{n+2}, \cdots, a_{2n+1}$ in the Tchebycheff expansion of $f(x)$. The last coefficient a_{2n+2} does not influence the phase values at the Tchebycheff nodes φ_j.

2. For phases of modest size the equations (40) can be solved by iteration. With $\varepsilon_n(\varphi_j) = 0$ as starting values the first approximation is

$$\sin \varepsilon_n(\varphi) = \frac{2}{\lambda} \sum_{l=1}^{n+1} a_{n+l+1} \sin l\varphi, \qquad \lambda = a_{n+1}, \tag{41}$$

as follows from (36) and (39). For larger phases the method of Newton-Raphson is available for solving the non-linear equations (40). After having determined the values $\varepsilon_n(\varphi_j)$ the coefficients γ_l are computed by cosine analysis. At last the phase function is given by the finite Fourier expansion (36). Due to our discretization this is of course only an approximation of the true phase function.

3. The phase equations (38) may be interpreted as a discretization of the integral equation (19). If the iterative solution of (19) is started with the initial values $\varepsilon_n(\varphi) = 0$ the first approximation is

$$\sin \varepsilon_n(\varphi) = \frac{Q_{n+1}(\cos \varphi) - f(\cos \varphi)}{\lambda \sin (n+1)\varphi}.$$

By taking into account our discussion of an interpolation error, it turns out that this coincides with (41), if $f(x)$ is a polynomial of degree $2(n+1)$ as was assumed. Thus the expression

$$\sin \varepsilon_n(\varphi) = 2 \sum_{l=1}^{n+1} \frac{a_{n+l+1}}{a_{n+1}} \sin l\varphi \tag{42}$$

is a rough approximation to the phase and is easily available. This expression shows clearly how the size of the phase depends on the rate of decrease of the coefficients in the Tchebycheff expansion of $f(x)$.

4. The Tchebycheff alternant (see §1) is computed as follows. Write the sine-expansion (36) of the phase

(43) $$\sin \varepsilon_n(\varphi) = \sum_{l=1}^{n+1} c_l \sin l\varphi,$$

where

$$c_l = \frac{2}{\lambda} a_{n+l+1} - p_l \gamma_l.$$

The condition (4) for the alternant furnishes the equation

$$\varepsilon_n(\varphi) = j\pi - (n+1)\varphi;$$

thus

$$\sin \varepsilon_n(\varphi) = \sum_{l=1}^{n+1} c_l \sin l\varphi = -(-1)^j \sin (n+1)\varphi.$$

By division with $\sin \varphi$ the algebraic equation

(44) $$\sum_{l=1}^{n+1} c_l U_{l-1}(x) + (-1)^j U_n(x) = 0$$

is obtained. $U_k(x)$ is the Tchebycheff polynomial of second kind and degree k.

EXAMPLE. To approximate

$$f(x) = \frac{1}{1.25 - x}$$

by a parabola ($n = 2$). This example was already discussed in §3. By cosine analysis at the points $\varphi = 0°, 30°, \cdots, 180°$ the coefficients a_3, a_4, a_5, a_6 were computed and the phase equations established. They are

$$\sin \varepsilon(60) = -0.097734 + 0.47962 \cos \varepsilon(60) + 1.05697 \cos \varepsilon(120),$$

$$\sin \varepsilon(120) = 0.70171 - 0.45299 \cos \varepsilon(60) + 0.12436 \cos \varepsilon(120).$$

Because the pole $x = 1.25$ of $f(x)$ is very close to the approximation interval, the phase is large and iteration of the phase equations does not converge. By Newton's method the solutions

$$\varepsilon(60) = 66.84°, \qquad \varepsilon(120) = 38.39°$$

were obtained. This yields $\lambda = 0.46662$. The corresponding sine-expansion (36) of the phase is

$$\sin \varepsilon(\varphi) = 0.8893 \sin \varphi + 0.1722 \sin 2\varphi + 0.04844 \sin 3\varphi.$$

In the first line of the following table the corresponding phase values are listed. The second line contains the true values (see §2). All values are in degrees.

30°	60°	90°	120°	150°
39.96	66.84	57.23	38.39	20.12
47.58	60.00	53.14	38.22	19.78

As can be seen, the method furnishes only a rough approximation of the phase. The points of the Tchebycheff alternant, computed from (44), turn out to be

$$x_0 = -1, \qquad x_1 = -0.2401, \qquad x_2 = 0.7422, \qquad x_3 = 1.$$

The exact values are:

$$x_0 = -1, \qquad x_1 = -0.25, \qquad x_2 = 0.75, \qquad x_3 = 1.$$

We observe that the points of the alternant are shifted far away from the Tchebycheff abscissas

$$x_0 = -1, \qquad x_1 = -0.5, \qquad x_2 = 0.5, \qquad x_3 = 1.$$

It may be mentioned that our rough phase produces a rather good approximation of the alternant.

References

1. S. Bernstein, *Lecons sur les propriétés extrémales et la meilleure approximation des fonctions analytiques*, Gauthier-Villars, Paris, 1926.

2. E. Stiefel, *Methods—old and new—for solving the Tchebycheff approximation problem*, J. Soc. Indust. Appl. Math. Ser. B, Numerical Analysis, **1** (1964), 164–176.

OPTIMAL AND NEARLY-OPTIMAL LINEAR APPROXIMATIONS

MICHAEL GOLOMB
Purdue University, Lafayette, Indiana

0. How close can linear approximation come to best approximation is the general theme of my lecture. Since the definition of a linear approximation procedure presupposes a linear manifold of functions to be approximated, my inquiry is directed not toward the approximation of individual functions, but of various linear classes of functions. In most cases I deal with continuous (complex-valued) functions of period 2π, whose class shall be denoted as $\mathring{\mathscr{C}}$. Throughout we are interested in Chebyshev approximation and for this purpose we introduce the norm $\|x\| = \sup_t |x(t)|$ for the elements $x \in \mathring{\mathscr{C}}$, which with the usual interpretation makes $\mathring{\mathscr{C}}$ into a Banach space. $E(x, y) = \|x - y\|$ is the distance of x, y in $\mathring{\mathscr{C}}$, interpreted as the error in the approximation of x by y. More generally,

$$E(x, \mathscr{P}) = \inf_{y \in \mathscr{P}} E(x, y)$$

is the optimal error in the approximation of x by elements of $\mathscr{P} \subset \mathring{\mathscr{C}}$, and

$$E(\mathscr{S}, \mathscr{P}) = \sup_{x \in \mathscr{S}} E(x, \mathscr{P}) = \sup_{x \in \mathscr{S}} \inf_{y \in \mathscr{P}} E(x, y)$$

is the maximal optimal error in the approximation of elements of a class $\mathscr{S} \subset \mathring{\mathscr{C}}$ by elements of $\mathscr{P}$.

A linear approximation procedure is defined by a linear transformation L (we always assume, without explicit mention, that L is bounded and denote its norm by $\|L\|$), whose domain includes the set $\mathscr{S}$ of functions to be approximated, and whose range includes $\mathscr{P}$, the set of approximants. In many cases the set of approximants is $\mathring{\mathscr{P}}_n$, the class of trigonometric polynomials of degree $\leqq n$, which can be thought of as the subspace of $\mathring{\mathscr{C}}$ that is spanned by the functions e^{ikt} $(k = 0, \pm 1, \cdots, \pm n)$.

1. As a first question one may ask: Is there a linear transformation $L: \mathring{\mathscr{C}} \to \mathring{\mathscr{P}}_n$, such that

$$E(x, Lx) = E(x, \mathring{\mathscr{P}}_n)$$

for every $x \in \mathring{\mathscr{C}}$? The answer is clearly no, as the simplest examples show.

2. Next we ask: Is there a linear transformation $\mathring{\mathscr{C}} \to \mathring{\mathscr{P}}_n$, and a constant C_n such that

$$E(x, Lx) \leqq C_n E(x, \mathring{\mathscr{P}}_n) \tag{2.1}$$

for every $x \in \mathring{\mathscr{C}}$? Such a transformation must be a projection, i.e. $L^2 = L$, since (2.1) implies $Lx = x$ if $x \in \mathring{\mathscr{P}}_n$. We shall denote the class of these projections by

$\mathring{\mathscr{L}}_n$. Any $L \in \mathring{\mathscr{L}}_n$ satisfies (2.1) with $C_n = 1 + \|L\|$. Indeed, if $y_* \in \mathring{\mathscr{P}}_n$ is such that $E(x, y_*) = E(x, \mathring{\mathscr{P}}_n)$ then

$$\begin{aligned} E(x, Lx) &= E(x - y_*, \ L(x - y_*)) \\ &\leqq (1 + \|L\|) \, \|x - y_*\| \\ &= (1 + \|L\|) \, E(x, \mathring{\mathscr{P}}_n). \end{aligned} \tag{2.2}$$

One version of the well known Lozinskiĭ-Haršiladze theorem (see, for example, [**1**, Chapter 15] or [**2**, Appendix 3]; in the sequel it will be referred to as L.H. theorem) is that the constant $\|L\|$ is the smallest if $L = \mathring{S}_n$, where $\mathring{S}_n x$ represents the nth partial sum in the Fourier series expansion of x:

$$\mathring{S}_n x(t) = \sum_{k=-n}^{n} \alpha_k e^{ikt}, \qquad \alpha_k = \frac{1}{2\pi} \int_0^{2\pi} x(t) e^{-ikt} \, dt. \tag{2.3}$$

In this case, $\|\mathring{S}_n\| = \lambda_n$, the classical nth Lebesgue constant, given by (see, e.g. [**1**, Chapter 12])

$$\begin{aligned} \lambda_n &= \frac{2}{\pi} \int_0^{\pi/2} \left| \frac{\sin (2n + 1)t}{\sin t} \right| dt \\ &= \frac{4}{\pi^2} \log n + O(1). \end{aligned} \tag{2.4}$$

That $C_n = 1 + \lambda_n$ is the best possible constant in (2.1) is expressed by the relation

$$\inf_{L \in \mathring{\mathscr{L}}_n} \sup_{x \in \mathring{\mathscr{C}}} \frac{E(x, Lx)}{E(x, \mathring{\mathscr{P}}_n)} = \sup_{x \in \mathring{\mathscr{C}}} \frac{E(x, \mathring{S}_n x)}{E(x, \mathring{\mathscr{P}}_n)} = 1 + \lambda_n, \tag{2.5}$$

which is proved in essentially the same way as the L.H. inequality $\|L\| \leqq \|\mathring{S}_n\|$.

The conclusion $\|L - 1\| \geqq 1 + \lambda_n$ follows from the single hypothesis $Ly - y = 0$ for all $y \in \mathring{\mathscr{P}}_n$. We observe that the weaker hypothesis $\|Ly - y\| \leqq c \, \|y\|$ for all $y \in \mathring{\mathscr{P}}_n$ implies the inequality $\|L - 1\| \geqq 1 + \lambda_n(1 - c)$. This is a simple extension of the L.H. inequality (Sapogov [**3**]).

Let $\mathring{\mathscr{C}}$ be replaced by $\mathscr{C} = \mathscr{C}(I)$, the class of functions continuous on I: $-1 \leqq t \leqq 1$, $\mathring{\mathscr{P}}_n$ by $\mathscr{P}_n$, the algebraic polynomials of degree $\leqq n$, and $\mathring{\mathscr{L}}_n$ by $\mathscr{L}_n$, the class of projections of $\mathscr{C}$ onto $\mathscr{P}_n$. Which $L \in \mathscr{L}_n$ is of minimum norm? To deal with this question we map $\mathscr{C}$ isomorphically and isometrically onto $\tilde{\mathring{\mathscr{C}}}$ and $\mathscr{P}_n$ onto $\tilde{\mathring{\mathscr{P}}}_n$, where the superscript $\sim$ refers to the fact that only even functions in the respective classes are considered. The map which associates $x \in \mathscr{C}$ with $\mathring{x} \in \tilde{\mathring{\mathscr{C}}}$ is defined by the relation $x(\cos t) = \mathring{x}(t)$. The projection S_n of $\mathscr{C}$ onto $\mathscr{P}_n$ which corresponds to $\mathring{S}_n$ in this case is the nth partial sum in the Chebyshev series expansion:

$$\begin{aligned} S_n x(t) &= \tfrac{1}{2}\alpha_0 + \sum_{k=1}^{n} \alpha_k T_k(t), \\ \alpha_k &= \frac{2}{\pi} \int_{-1}^{1} (1 - t^2)^{-1/2} x(t) T_k(t) \, dt = \frac{1}{\pi} \int_{-\pi}^{\pi} \mathring{x}(t) \cos kt \, dt. \end{aligned} \tag{2.6}$$

A modification of Berman's proof for the L.H. theorem gives

$$\|\tilde{L}\| \geqq \tfrac{1}{2}\|\mathring{S}_0 + \mathring{S}_n\| \geqq \frac{2}{\pi^2}\log n + O(1) \tag{2.7}$$

for any projection $\tilde{L}$ of $\tilde{\mathring{\mathscr{C}}}_n$ onto $\tilde{\mathring{\mathscr{P}}}_n$. The lower bound for $\|\tilde{L}\|$ and the projection for which it is attained are apparently not known. For $n = 1$, the bound in (2.7) is 1, which is the exact lower bound since the linear transformation which associates with $x \in \tilde{\mathring{\mathscr{C}}}$ its interpolant with nodes at 0 and π is a projection of norm 1. On the other hand, $\|\mathring{S}_1\| = \lambda_1 = 1.43\cdots$, which shows that $\mathring{S}_n$ is, in general, not the projection of lowest norm of $\tilde{\mathring{\mathscr{C}}}$ onto $\tilde{\mathring{\mathscr{P}}}_n$. Correspondingly, the Chebychev expansion S_n is, in general, not the projection of lowest norm of $\mathscr{C}$ onto $\mathscr{P}_n$. For $n = 1$, the interpolant

$$I_1x(t) = \tfrac{1}{2}x(-1)(1 + t) + \tfrac{1}{2}x(1)(1 - t) \tag{2.8}$$

is the projection of minimum norm, $\|I_1\| = 1$.

3. The constant C_n in (2.1) depends on n. The question whether there exists a sequence $\mathscr{N}$ of increasing natural numbers, a linear transformation $L_n\colon \mathring{\mathscr{C}} \to \mathring{\mathscr{P}}_n$ for each $n \in \mathscr{N}$, and a constant C such that

$$E(x, L_nx) \leqq CE(x, \mathring{\mathscr{P}}_n) \tag{3.1}$$

for each $x \in \mathring{\mathscr{C}}$, $n \in \mathscr{N}$, is seen to have a negative answer. By §2, C is at least λ_n, which is asymptotically equal to $4\pi^{-2}\log n$.

4. If we allow dependence of C on x in (3.1) the answer is still negative. Indeed, the inequality

$$E(x, L_nx) \leqq C_xE(x, \mathring{\mathscr{P}}_n) \leqq C_x\,\|x\|$$

for each $x \in \mathring{\mathscr{C}}$ and $n \in \mathscr{N}$ would imply, by the uniform boundedness theorem, the boundedness of the numbers $\|L_n\|$, $n \in \mathscr{N}$.

We may ask whether

$$E(x, L_nx) \leqq C_xE(x, \mathring{\mathscr{P}}_n) \tag{4.1}$$

is possible for each $n \in \mathscr{N}$ and each x of some subclass of $\mathring{\mathscr{C}}$. We first consider $\mathring{\mathscr{C}}^{(r)}$, the subclass of functions $x \in \mathring{\mathscr{C}}$ which have a continuous rth derivative D^rx. We show that for this case, too, (4.1) is impossible. Indeed, if (4.1) were valid for each $x \in \mathring{\mathscr{C}}^{(r)}$ then by a theorem of Freud ([**4**], see also Garkavi [**5**]) on simultaneous best-order approximation of derivatives

$$E(D^rx, D^rL_nx) \leqq C_{D^rx}E(D^rx, \mathring{\mathscr{P}}_n). \tag{4.2}$$

Now let $M_n = D^rL_nD^{-r}$, which is a linear transformation $\mathring{\mathscr{C}} \to \mathring{\mathscr{P}}_n$, and (4.2) implies

$$E(y, M_ny) \leqq C_yE(y, \mathring{\mathscr{P}}_n)$$

for each $y \in \mathring{\mathscr{C}}$, $n \in \mathscr{N}$. This was seen above to be impossible.

Even if the subset to be approximated is the narrow class $\mathring{\mathscr{A}}_\alpha$ of functions $x(s) = x(t + i\tau)$ of period 2π, real for real s, analytic in the open strip $|\tau| < \alpha$ and continuous in the closed strip, inequality (4.1) is impossible. This is seen by considering the operator B, which is defined by $Bx(t) = x(t + i\alpha)$. One verifies readily that, for $x \in \mathring{\mathscr{A}}_\alpha$, best $\mathring{\mathscr{P}}_n$ approximation gives simultaneously best-order $\mathring{\mathscr{P}}_n$ approximation of Bx, so that (4.1) implies

$$E(Bx, BL_n x) \leqq C_{Bx} E(Bx, \mathring{\mathscr{P}}_n). \tag{4.3}$$

Using the inverse operator B^{-1} (which produces the function $y(s)$ in $\mathring{\mathscr{A}}_\alpha$ from the boundary values $y(t + i\alpha)$), we put $M_n = BL_n B^{-1}$, which is a linear transformation: $\mathring{\mathscr{C}} \to \mathring{\mathscr{P}}_n$, and obtain from (4.3)

$$E(y, M_n y) \leqq C_y E(y, \mathring{\mathscr{P}}_n)$$

for each $n \in \mathscr{N}$, $y \in \mathring{\mathscr{C}}$, once more a contradiction.

However, there are subclasses of $\mathring{\mathscr{C}}$ for which the question raised by (4.1) has an affirmative answer. Choose a sequence $\mathscr{N}$, and let $\mathring{\mathscr{B}}_{\mathscr{N}}$ denote the class of function $x \in \mathring{\mathscr{C}}$ with an absolutely convergent Fourier series expansion, $x(t) = \sum_{|k| \geqq 0} \alpha_k e^{ikt}$, where

$$\sum_{|k| > n} |\alpha_k| = O(\sup_{|k| > n} |\alpha_k|) \tag{4.4}$$

for $n \in \mathscr{N}$, $n \to \infty$. If $x \in \mathring{\mathscr{B}}_{\mathscr{N}}$ then

$$E(x, \mathring{S}_n x) \leqq \sum_{|k| > n} |\alpha_k|,$$

while on the other hand (see [**1**, Chapter 8])

$$E(x, \mathring{S}_n x) \geqq \sup_{|k| > n} |\alpha_k|.$$

Thus, by (4.4),

$$E(x, \mathring{S}_n x) = O(E(x, \mathring{\mathscr{P}}_n)) \tag{4.5}$$

uniformly for $n \in \mathscr{N}$.

As a special case, suppose x is some arbitrary analytic function in $\mathring{\mathscr{C}}$, $x(t) = \sum \alpha_k e^{ikt}$. Then there exist a sequence $\mathscr{N}_x$ and a constant C_x such that

$$\sum_{|k| > n} |\alpha_k| \leqq C_x \sup_{|k| > n} |\alpha_k|$$

and, therefore,

$$E(x, \mathring{S}_n x) \leqq C_x E(x, \mathring{\mathscr{P}}_n) \tag{4.6}$$

for each $n \in \mathscr{N}_x$. If x is an entire function then $\mathscr{N}_x$ may be so chosen that we have asymptotically

$$\sum_{|k| > n} |\alpha_k| \sim \sup_{|k| > n} |\alpha_k|.$$

In this case, we obtain the asymptotic equality

$$(4.7) \qquad E(x, \mathring{S}_n x) \sim E(x, \mathring{\mathscr{P}}_n)$$

for $n \in \mathscr{N}_x$, $n \to \infty$.

We remark that the above positive results (except (4.7)) remain valid if the Fourier sum $\mathring{S}_n x$ is replaced by the interpolant $\mathring{I}_n x \in \mathring{\mathscr{P}}_n$, which interpolates x at the equidistant points $k\pi/(n+1)$ $(k = 0, 1, \cdots, 2n)$. Indeed we need only to observe that if $x(t) = \Sigma \alpha_k e^{ikt}$ then (see Zygmund [6, Chapter 10])

$$(4.8) \qquad E(x, \mathring{I}_n x) \leqq 2 \sum_{|k|>n} |\alpha_k|.$$

Analogous results hold for the approximation of functions on the interval I by polynomials. Corresponding to the class $\mathring{\mathscr{A}}_\alpha$ we have the class of functions analytic in the ellipse with foci at the endpoints of I and sum of semiaxes equal to e^α. The Fourier sums $\mathring{S}_n x$ are replaced by the Chebyshev sums $S_n x$, and the trigonometric interpolants $\mathring{I}_n x$ are replaced by the algebraic interpolants $I_n x$ with the Chebyshev nodes $\cos k\pi/(2n+1)$ $(k = 0, 1, \cdots, 2n)$.

5. Next we ask, how close can linear approximation by polynomials of degree $n-1$ come to best approximation by polynomials of degree $m < n$? Thus, we are looking for a linear transformation $L\colon \mathring{\mathscr{C}} \to \mathring{\mathscr{P}}_{n-1}$ and a constant C such that

$$(5.1) \qquad E(x, Lx) \leqq CE(x, \mathring{\mathscr{P}}_m)$$

for each $x \in \mathring{\mathscr{C}}$. This requires L to leave the points of $\mathring{\mathscr{P}}_m$ invariant, $Ly = y$ for each $y \in \mathring{\mathscr{P}}_m$. Let the class of these transformations be denoted by $\mathring{\mathscr{L}}_{mn}$. If $L \in \mathring{\mathscr{L}}_{mn}$ then (5.1) holds with $C = 1 + \|L\|$.

A transformation in the class $\mathring{\mathscr{L}}_{mn}$ is given by the De La Vallée-Poussin sum

$$(5.2) \qquad \mathring{V}_{mn} x = \frac{1}{n-m}(\mathring{S}_m + \mathring{S}_{m+1} + \cdots + \mathring{S}_{n-1})$$

$$= \frac{n}{n-m}\mathring{F}_n x - \frac{m}{n-m}\mathring{F}_m x,$$

where $\mathring{F}_n x$ is the Fejér sum, $\mathring{F}_n = \mathring{V}_{0n}$. Since $\|\mathring{F}_n\| = 1$, one has immediately

$$(5.3) \qquad \|\mathring{V}_{mn}\| \leqq \frac{n+m}{n-m}.$$

More precisely, Stečkin [7] has proved that

$$(5.4) \qquad \|\mathring{V}_{mn}\| = \lambda_{m/(n-m)}$$

if $m(n-m)^{-1}$ is an integer (the λ in (5.4) stands again for the classical Lebesgue constant). Stečkin also has shown monotonicity: $\|\mathring{V}_{m+p,n+p}\| > \|\mathring{V}_{mn}\|$ $(p = 1, 2, \cdots)$. Thus, we obtain the rather accurate bounds for arbitrary $m < n$:

$$(5.5) \qquad \lambda_{[m/(n-m)]} \leqq \|\mathring{V}_{mn}\| < \lambda_{[m/(n-m)]+1}.$$

Using the upper bound $3 + 4\pi^{-2} \log k$ for λ_k one then arrives at the inequality

$$E(x, \mathring{V}_{mn}x) < \left(4 + \frac{4}{\pi^2} \log \frac{n}{n-m}\right) E(x, \mathring{\mathscr{P}}_m) \tag{5.6}$$

for each $x \in \mathring{\mathscr{C}}$.

Is $L = \mathring{V}_{mn}$ a transformation in the class $\mathring{\mathscr{L}}_{mn}$ for which $1 + \|L\|$ is minimal? To answer this question we use the method that Berman used **[8]** for a similar problem, and that he had introduced for the proof of the L.H. theorem. Let T_h be the shift operator: $T_h x(t) = x(t + h)$, and A the averaging (with respect to h) operator: $Ax = (2\pi)^{-1}\int_0^{2\pi} x\, dh$. Then if $j_k(t) = e^{ikt}$ $(k = 0, \pm 1, \pm 2, \cdots)$ one verifies easily for $L \in \mathring{\mathscr{L}}_{mn}$:

$$\begin{aligned} AT_{-h}LT_h j_k &= j_k, & |k| &\leqq m, \\ &= \gamma_k j_k, & m < |k| &< n, \\ &= 0, & n &\leqq |k|, \end{aligned} \tag{5.7}$$

where the γ_k are constants dependent on L. Since all the operators involved are continuous, one concludes that for any $x \in \mathring{\mathscr{C}}$ with Fourier coefficients α_k

$$AT_{-h}LT_h x = \sum_{|k| \leqq m} \alpha_k j_k + \sum_{m<|k|<n} \gamma_k \alpha_k j_k. \tag{5.8}$$

Thus, the operator $AT_{-h}LT_h$ is a convolution operator

$$AT_{-h}LT_h x = l * x \tag{5.9}$$

where l is the polynomial

$$l(t) = \sum_{|k| \leqq m} e^{ikt} + \sum_{m<|k|<n} \gamma_k e^{ikt}$$

and $l * x$ denotes the convolution

$$l * x(t) = \frac{1}{2\pi} \int_0^{2\pi} l(t-s)x(s)\, ds.$$

From (5.9) one derives

$$\|l * x\| \leqq \|L\|\, \|x\| \tag{5.10}$$

for each $x \in \mathring{\mathscr{C}}$. The norm of the transformation: $x \to l * x$ is the L_1 norm of l:

$$\begin{aligned} \|l\|_1 &= \frac{1}{2\pi} \int_0^{2\pi} |l(t)|\, dt \\ &= \frac{1}{2\pi} \int_0^{2\pi} \left| \sum_{|k| \leqq m} e^{ikt} + \sum_{m<|k|<n} \gamma_k e^{ikt} \right| dt \end{aligned} \tag{5.11}$$

and it is minimal if the γ_k are so chosen as to minimize the right-hand term of (5.11). Let the minimizing coefficients be denoted as $\gamma_{mn,k}$ (clearly $\gamma_{mn,k} = \gamma_{mn,-k}$ real) and put

$$l_{mn}(t) = \sum_{|k| \leqq m} e^{ikt} + \sum_{m<|k|<n} \gamma_{mn,k} e^{ikt},$$

$$\overset{*}{L}_{mn} x = l_{mn} * x, \qquad \|\overset{*}{L}_{mn}\| = \lambda_{mn}.$$

Clearly, L^*_{mn} is in the class $\mathring{\mathscr{L}}_{mn}$. The problem of finding the minimizing $\gamma_{mn,k}$ is that of determining the linear combination of $\cos(m+1)t, \cos(m+2)t, \cdots, \cos(n-1)t$ which approximates the Dirichlet kernel

$$\mathring{D}_m(t) = \tfrac{1}{2} + \cos t + \cdots + \cos mt$$

best in the L_1 norm.

We have proved that *among all transformations L in the class* $\mathring{\mathscr{L}}_{mn}$ *the convolution transform* L^*_{mn} *is one of the minimum norm* λ_{mn}.

The De La Vallée-Poussin sum $\mathring{V}_{mn}x$ is also a convolution, $\mathring{V}_{mn}x = v_{mn} * x$, where

$$v_{mn}(t) = \sum_{|k|\leq m} e^{ikt} + \sum_{m<|k|<n} \frac{n-|k|}{n-m} e^{ikt}. \tag{5.12}$$

In general $\|\mathring{V}_{mn}\| = \|v_{mn}\|_1$ is close to the optimal $\|L^*_{mn}\| = \|l_{mn}\|_1$. Berman has proved [8] that $\|\mathring{V}_{mn}\| = \|L^*_{mn}\|$ if and only if $n - m$ divides $2m$. If we put $m = qn$, this gives for q one of the numbers $0, \frac{1}{3}, \frac{2}{4}, \frac{3}{5}, \cdots$.

That $\lambda_{mn} = \|L^*_{mn}\|$ is minimal among $\|L\|$, $L \in \mathring{\mathscr{L}}_{mn}$, does not yet prove that $\|1 - L^*_{mn}\|$ is also minimal among $\|1 - L\|$, $L \in \mathring{\mathscr{L}}_{mn}$. However, this can be proved by a slight modification of the above proof, and one also obtains easily $\|1 - L^*_{mn}\| = 1 + \lambda_{mn}$. Thus we have arrived at the relation

$$\inf_{L\in\mathring{\mathscr{L}}_{mn}} \sup_{x\in\mathring{\mathscr{C}}} \frac{E(x, Lx)}{E(x, \mathring{\mathscr{P}}_m)} = \sup_{x\in\mathring{\mathscr{C}}} \frac{E(x, \overset{*}{L}_{mn}x)}{E(x, \mathring{\mathscr{P}}_m)} = 1 + \lambda_{mn}. \tag{5.13}$$

We also have seen that *if m is one of the numbers* $0, \frac{1}{2}n, \frac{2}{3}n, \frac{3}{4}n, \cdots$ *then* L^*_{mn} *may be replaced by* $\mathring{V}_{mn}$, *and* λ_{mn} *coincides with the classical Lebesgue constant* $\lambda_{m/(n-m)}$. Of special interest is the case $m = 0$:

Of all linear transformations $\mathring{\mathscr{C}} \to \mathring{\mathscr{P}}_{n-1}$ *which leave the constant functions invariant the Fejér sum* F_n *is of minimum norm,* $\|F_n\| = 1$.

Among the transformations of class $\mathring{\mathscr{L}}_{mn}$ there are also generalized interpolations. We consider only the case $n \leqq 2m$ and put

$$\mathring{J}_{mn} = \frac{1}{2n - 2m - 1} \sum_{k=2m-n+1}^{k=n-1} \mathring{I}_{mk},$$

where $\mathring{I}_{mm}x = \mathring{I}_m x$ is the interpolant of x with equidistant nodes $k\pi/(m+1)$ $(k = 0, 1, \cdots, 2m)$, which may be written as a Stieltjes convolution integral

$$\mathring{I}_m x(t) = \frac{1}{2\pi} \int_0^{2\pi} \mathring{D}_m(t-s)x(s)\, dw(s),$$

and $\mathring{I}_{mk}x$ is a sort of partial sum

$$\mathring{I}_{mk}x(t) = \frac{1}{2\pi} \int_0^{2\pi} \mathring{D}_k(t-s)x(s)\, dw(s).$$

Clearly, $\mathring{I}_{mk}x \in \mathring{\mathscr{P}}_k$, hence $\mathring{J}_{mn}x \in \mathring{\mathscr{P}}_{n-1}$. Also one can show (see Zygmund **[6**,

Chapter 10]) that $\mathring{J}_{mn}x$ interpolates x at $2m + 1$ equidistant nodes so that $\mathring{J}_{mn}y = y$ for each $y \in \mathring{\mathscr{P}}_m$. It is not hard to prove that

$$\|\mathring{J}_{mn}\| \leqq \frac{2m+1}{2n-2m-1}, \tag{5.14}$$

and much better bounds can be given. For reference we record

$$E(x, \mathring{J}_{mn}x) \leqq \frac{2n}{2n-2m+1} E(x, \mathring{\mathscr{P}}_m x). \tag{5.15}$$

6. We now consider the asymptotic error in the approximation of $x \in \mathring{\mathscr{C}}$ by Lx, $L \in \mathring{\mathscr{L}}_{mn}$. We ask is there a sequence $\mathscr{N}$, a number $m = m(n)$, $m \to \infty$ as $n \to \infty$, a transformation $L_{mn} \in \mathring{\mathscr{L}}_{mn}$ for each $n \in \mathscr{N}$, as well as a constant C such that

$$E(x, L_{mn}x) \leqq CE(x, \mathring{\mathscr{P}}_m) \tag{6.1}$$

for each $x \in \mathring{\mathscr{C}}$, $n \in \mathscr{N}$? We prove that this is the case if and only if

$$\overline{\lim}\, \frac{m(n)}{n} < 1. \tag{6.2}$$

It is well known (see, for example, [**1**, Chapter 15]) that if (6.2) is satisfied then (6.1) holds with $L_{mn} = \mathring{V}_{mn}$ and $\mathscr{N}$ the sequence of all integers. Thus the sufficiency of condition (6.2) is established. That (6.2) is also necessary has been proved (see [**1**, Chapter 15]) for the case $L_{mn} = \mathring{V}_{mn}$. Since the latter need not be the transformations in $\mathring{\mathscr{L}}_{mn}$ of minimal norm the necessity of (6.2) remains to be demonstrated.

By a method similar to that used by Stečkin [7] to prove $\|\mathring{V}_{m+p,n+p}\| > \|\mathring{V}_{mn}\|$ one proves $\lambda_{m+p,n+p} > \lambda_{mn}$ $(p = 1, 2, \cdots)$. Now assume $\overline{\lim}\, m/n = 1$; then for each positive integer r there is some $n \in \mathscr{N}$ such that

$$\frac{n}{n-m} = r + \frac{k}{n-m}$$

for some integer $k \geqq 0$. Then

$$\begin{aligned} \|L_{mn}\| \geqq \|\overset{*}{L}_{mn}\| = \lambda_{mn} \geqq \lambda_{m-k,n-k} \\ = \lambda_{r(n-m),(1+r)(n-m)}, \end{aligned} \tag{6.3}$$

and, by §5, the final term of (6.3) equals $\lambda_r \sim 4\pi^{-2} \log r$. *Thus the numbers* $\|L_{mn}\|$, $n \in \mathscr{N}$, *are not bounded and* (6.1) *is impossible if* $\overline{\lim}\, m/n = 1$.

7. We turn to the approximation of the derivative $D^r x$ for a given $x \in \mathring{\mathscr{C}}^{(r)}$ by some Lx, where L is a linear transformation: $\mathring{\mathscr{C}} \to \mathring{\mathscr{P}}_{n-1}$. We seek: given r, n and

$m \leqq n$, to determine the linear transformation $L: \mathring{\mathscr{C}} \to \mathring{\mathscr{P}}_{n-1}$ such that

$$E(D^r x, Lx) \leqq CE(D^r x, \mathring{\mathscr{P}}_m) \tag{7.1}$$

for each $x \in \mathring{\mathscr{C}}^{(r)}$, with a constant C as small as possible. Clearly, (7.1) requires $Ly = D^r y$ for each $y \in \mathring{\mathscr{P}}_m$. We denote by $\mathring{\mathscr{L}}^{(r)}_{mn}$ the class of linear transformations $L: \mathring{\mathscr{C}} \to \mathring{\mathscr{P}}_{n-1}$ such that $Ly = D^r y$ for each $y \in \mathring{\mathscr{P}}_m$. For any $L \in \mathring{\mathscr{L}}^{(r)}_{mn}$, (7.1) will be seen to hold with

$$C = 1 + \|k_r\|_1 \, \|L\|, \tag{7.2}$$

where

$$k_r(t) = \sum_{|l| \geqq 1} \frac{e^{ilt}}{(il)^r}.$$

A simple bound for $\|k_r\|_1$ is $\pi^r/2$.

To prove (7.1), (7.2) we first observe that if $D^r z \in \mathring{\mathscr{C}}$ and $\int_0^{2\pi} z = 0$ then

$$\|z\| \leqq \|k_r\|_1 \, \|D^r z\|. \tag{7.3}$$

Indeed it is well known (see, for example, [**1**, Chapter 9] or [**9**], §88]) that $z = k * D^r z$, whence (7.3) follows immediately. Now choose $y \in \mathring{\mathscr{P}}_m$ with $\int_0^{2\pi} y = \int_0^{2\pi} x$ such that

$$E(D^r x, D^r y) = E(D^r x, \mathring{\mathscr{P}}_m) = d.$$

Then since $Ly = D^r y$

$$\begin{aligned} E(D^r x, Lx) &\leqq E(D^r x, D^r y) + E(Ly, Lx) \\ &\leqq d + \|L\| \, E(x, y), \end{aligned}$$

and, because of $\|D^r(x - y)\| = d$, we have by (7.3), $E(x, y) \leqq \|k_r\|_1 \, d$, hence

$$E(D^r x, Lx) \leqq (1 + \|k_r\|_1 \, \|L\|) \, d,$$

or

$$E(D^r x, Lx) \leqq (1 + \|k_r\|_1 \, \|L\|) E(D^r x, \mathring{\mathscr{P}}_m). \tag{7.4}$$

For the special case $L = D^r \mathring{V}_{mn} = \mathring{V}_{mn} D^r$ we get, using the Bernstein inequality $\|D^r y\| \leqq n^r \, \|y\|$ for $y \in \mathring{\mathscr{P}}_n$,

$$\|Lx\| = \|D^r \mathring{V}_{mn} x\| \leqq n^r \, \|\mathring{V}_{mn} x\|,$$

$$\|L\| \leqq n^r \, \|\mathring{V}_{mn}\| < n^r \lambda_{[m/(n-m)]+1}. \tag{7.5}$$

Thus, we have derived

$$E(D^r x, D^r \mathring{V}_{m,n} x) \leqq [1 + \|k_r\|_1 \, n^r \lambda_{[m/(n-m)]+1}] E(D^r x, \mathring{\mathscr{P}}_m) \tag{7.6}$$

for each $x \in \mathring{\mathscr{C}}^{(r)}$.

To obtain a transformation $L = L_*$ in $\mathring{\mathscr{L}}^{(r)}_{mn}$ for which $\|L_*\|$ is minimal we proceed as in §5 and see that L_* is a convolution transform, $L_* x = l_{mn,r} * x$, $\|L_*\| = \|l_{mn,r}\|_1$ where

$$l_{mn,r}(t) = \sum_{|k| \leqq m} (ik)^r e^{ikt} + \sum_{m < |k| < n} \delta_k e^{ikt} \tag{7.7}$$

with the δ_k chosen so that $\|l_{mn,r}\|_1$ is minimal. Thus, if r is even, the minimizing δ_k are found by determining the linear combination of $\cos(m+1)t, \cdots,$ $\cos(n-1)t$, which approximates the differentiated Dirichlet kernel $\mathring{D}_m^{(r)}(t)$ best in the L_1-norm.

8. We now compare the error by linear approximation with the maximum error by optimal approximation in the class of functions to be approximated. Given a subset $\mathscr{S}$ of $\mathring{\mathscr{C}}$ and given n, we ask: Is there a linear transformation

$$L = L(\mathscr{S}): \mathscr{C} \to \mathring{\mathscr{P}}_{n-1}$$

such that

$$\sup_{x\in\mathscr{S}} E(x, Lx) = E(\mathscr{S}, \mathring{\mathscr{P}}_{n-1})? \tag{8.1}$$

If this is the case we call $L(\mathscr{S})$ an optimal approximator of $\mathscr{S}$.

We first consider the set, for $r \geqq 1$,

$$\mathring{\mathscr{S}}^{(r)} = \{x \in \mathring{\mathscr{C}}^{(r)} : \|D^r x\| \leqq 1\}.$$

For this set we know

$$E(\mathring{\mathscr{S}}^{(r)}, \mathring{\mathscr{P}}_{n-1}) = \mu_r n^{-r} \tag{8.2}$$

(see [**8**, Chapter 9] or [**9**, §88]) and it is also known that there is a convolution transformation $L(\mathring{\mathscr{S}}^{(r)})$ that is an *optimal approximator* (see [**10**, §5.5]). To describe it and other convolutions $L: \mathring{\mathscr{C}} \to \mathring{\mathscr{P}}_{n-1}$, we use the following conventions. If $x \in \mathring{\mathscr{C}}$ has the Fourier coefficients α_k $(k = 0, \pm 1, \pm 2, \cdots)$ then the convolution transform Lx has the Fourier coefficients $\lambda_k \alpha_k$, where $\lambda_0 = 1$, $\lambda_k = \lambda_{-k}$, and $\lambda_k = 0$ for $|k| \geqq n$. We shall call the λ_k the *multipliers* of the convolution transform, and in order to describe L we shall only give the λ_k for $k = 1, 2, \cdots, n-1$.

The optimal approximator $L(\mathring{\mathscr{S}}^{(r)})$ is a convolution with multipliers

$$\begin{aligned}\lambda_k &= (-1)^{r/2}\left[1 - k^r \sum_{l=1}^{\infty} (-1)^{l+1}\{(2ln-k)^{-r} + (2ln+k)^{-r}\}\right], \quad r \text{ even},\\ &= (-1)^{(r-1)/2}\left[1 - k^r \sum_{l=1}^{\infty} \{(2ln-k)^{-r} - (2ln+k)^{-r}\}\right], \quad r \text{ odd}.\end{aligned} \tag{8.3}$$

One can show, using Jackson's uniqueness theorem for L_1-approximation (see [**1**, Chapter 7], [**9**, §49]) that among convolution transformations the above is the only optimal approximator of $\mathring{\mathscr{S}}^{(r)}$.

Next consider the class $\mathring{\mathscr{A}}_\alpha$ of functions $x(s) = x(t + i\tau)$ of period 2π, real for real s, analytic in the open strip $|\tau| < \alpha$, and continuous in the closed strip $|\tau| \leqq \alpha$, with $\sup_t |\mathrm{Re}\, x(t + i\tau)| \leqq 1$. The error

$$E(\mathring{\mathscr{A}}_\alpha, \mathring{\mathscr{P}}_{n-1}) = \mu_\alpha(n) \tag{8.4}$$

is known explicitly (see [**1**, Chapter 9], [**9**, §94]). This class also has an optimal approximator $L(\mathring{\mathscr{A}}_\alpha)$ which is a convolution. The multipliers are

$$\lambda_k = 1 - \cosh k\alpha \sum_{l=1}^{\infty} (-1)^{l+1}\{\mathrm{sech}\,(2ln-k)\alpha + \mathrm{sech}\,(2ln+k)\alpha\}. \tag{8.5}$$

Here we also wish to consider the space $\mathscr{C} = \mathscr{C}(I_\infty)$ of (complex-valued) functions x, continuous and bounded on $I_\infty: -\infty < t < \infty$, with norm $\|x\| = \sup_t |x(t)|$. The appropriate approximants for these functions are entire functions of exponential order, and we denote the class of these functions of exponent $\leqq \nu$ by $\mathscr{E}_\nu$. For the set

$$\mathscr{S}^{(r)} = \{x, Dx, \cdots, D^r x \in \mathscr{C}: \|D^r x\| \leqq 1\}$$

one knows (see [**1**, Chapter 10], [**9**, §87])

$$E_-(\mathscr{S}^{(r)}, \mathscr{E}_\nu) = \mu_r \nu^{-r} \tag{8.6}$$

where μ_r is the same number as in (8.2) (the precise meaning of the left-hand term of (8.6) is $\lim_{u\to\nu-0} E(\mathscr{S}^{(r)}, \mathscr{E}_u)$; correspondingly, the approximants to be chosen will be of the form $\lim_{u\to\nu-0} L_u x$). $\mathscr{S}^{(r)}$ has an optimal approximator $L(\mathscr{S}^{(r)})$ which is a convolution transformation. To describe the convolution transform Lx for $x \in \mathscr{C}(I_\infty)$ we give the multiplier $\lambda(u)$, whose meaning is that if the Fourier transform of x is $\alpha(u)(-\infty < u < \infty)$ then the Fourier transform of Lx is $\lambda(u)\alpha(u)$ where $\lambda(u) = \lambda(-u)$ and $\lambda(u) = 0$ for $|u| \geqq \nu$. The optimal approximator $L(\mathscr{S}^{(r)})$ is a convolution with multiplier $\lambda(u)$, see (8.3) where k is replaced by the continuous variable u.

For the subset $\mathscr{A}_\alpha$ of $\mathscr{C}(I_\infty)$, defined like $\mathring{\mathscr{A}}_\alpha$ except that the condition of periodicity is dropped, one also knows

$$E_-(\mathscr{A}_\alpha, \mathscr{E}_\nu) = \mu_\alpha(\nu) \tag{8.7}$$

(see [**1**, Chapter 10], [**9**, §94]). Again there is an optimal approximator $L(\mathscr{A}_\alpha)$ which is a convolution transformation with multiplier $\lambda(u)$; see (8.5) with k replaced by u.

For the Lipschitz class $(0 < \alpha < 1)$

$$\mathring{\mathscr{S}}^{(\alpha)} = \{x \in \mathring{\mathscr{C}}: \|T_h x - x\| \leqq h^\alpha\}$$

Korneĭčuk [**11**] has found the maximal optimal error

$$E(\mathring{\mathscr{S}}^{(\alpha)}, \mathring{\mathscr{P}}_{n-1}) = \frac{1}{2}\left(\frac{\pi}{n}\right)^\alpha, \tag{8.8}$$

and he has also shown that no linear transformation $L: \mathring{\mathscr{C}} \to \mathring{\mathscr{P}}_{n-1}$ realizes this error, but for each $L: \mathring{\mathscr{C}} \to \mathring{\mathscr{P}}_{n-1}$ the inequality

$$\sup_{x \in \mathring{\mathscr{S}}^{(\alpha)}} E(x, Lx) \geqq \frac{1}{2}\left(\frac{\pi}{n}\right)^\alpha + \frac{1}{2}\frac{1-\alpha}{1+\alpha}\left(\frac{\pi}{n}\right)^\alpha \tag{8.9}$$

holds. Korneĭčuk [**11**] has also determined

$$E(\mathring{\mathscr{S}}^{(\omega)}, \mathring{\mathscr{P}}_{n-1}) = \tfrac{1}{2}\omega\left(\frac{\pi}{n}\right), \tag{8.10}$$

where $\mathring{\mathscr{S}}^{(\omega)}$ is the continuity class

$$\mathring{\mathscr{S}}^{(\omega)} = \{x \in \mathring{\mathscr{C}}, \|T_h x - x\| \leqq \omega(h)\} \tag{8.11}$$

and ω is any modulus of continuity (not linear). For this case, too, no $L:\mathring{\mathscr{C}} \to \mathring{\mathscr{P}}_{n-1}$ attains (8.10) since one can show

$$(8.12) \qquad \sup_{x\in\mathring{\mathscr{S}}^{(\omega)}} E(x, Lx) \geqq \frac{n}{\pi}\int_0^{\pi/n} \omega(h)\,dh > \tfrac{1}{2}\omega\left(\frac{\pi}{n}\right).$$

Therefore, no optimal approximators exist for either $\mathring{\mathscr{S}}^{(\alpha)}$ or $\mathring{\mathscr{S}}^{(\omega)}$, and the same is probably true for

$$\mathring{\mathscr{S}}^{(r+\alpha)} = \{x \in \mathring{\mathscr{C}}^{(r)}: D^r x \in \mathring{\mathscr{S}}^{(\alpha)}\} \quad \text{and} \quad \mathring{\mathscr{S}}^{(r,\,\omega)} = \{x \in \mathring{\mathscr{C}}^{(r)}: D^r x \in \mathring{\mathscr{S}}^{(\omega)}\}.$$

9. The sets $\mathring{\mathscr{S}}^{(r)}$, $\mathring{\mathscr{A}}_\alpha$ considered in the preceding section are special members of a class of sets which have optimal approximators given by convolution transformations.

Let K be an integrable function of period 2π, either even or odd with Fourier coefficients γ_l ($l = 0, \pm 1, \pm 2, \cdots$), $\gamma_l \neq 0$ for $l \neq 0$. Suppose $Q_K \in \mathring{\mathscr{P}}_{n-1}$ interpolates K at the points $m\pi/n$ ($m = 1, 2, \cdots, n-1$) if K is odd; and at the points $(m + 1/2)\,\pi/n$ ($m = 0, 1, \cdots, n-1$) if K is even. We also suppose that $K - Q_K$ changes sign at the above points and no other point in $(0, \pi)$. If these conditions are satisfied we call K an approximation kernel (this is a special case of an M. Kreĭn kernel, see [**9**, §85]). It is readily seen (see [**1**, p. 68]) that

$$(9.1) \qquad \|K - Q_K\|_1 = \left|\frac{1}{\pi}\int_0^\pi K(t)\operatorname{sgn}\sin nt\,dt\right|, \qquad K \text{ odd,}$$

$$= \left|\frac{1}{\pi}\int_0^\pi K(t)\operatorname{sgn}\cos nt\,dt\right|, \qquad K \text{ even.}$$

In terms of the Fourier coefficients γ_k we have:

$$(9.2) \qquad \mu_K(n) \equiv \|K - Q_K\|_1$$

$$= \left|\frac{4}{\pi}\sum_{l=0}^{\infty} \frac{\gamma_{(2l+1)n}}{2l+1}\right|, \qquad K \text{ odd,}$$

$$= \left|\frac{4}{\pi}\sum_{l=0}^{\infty} (-1)^l\frac{\gamma_{(2l+1)n}}{2l+1}\right|, \qquad K \text{ even.}$$

We now consider the subset $\mathring{\mathscr{S}}_K$ of $\mathring{\mathscr{C}}$ defined by

$$\mathring{\mathscr{S}}_K = \left\{x = K * y\colon\ y \in \mathring{\mathscr{C}},\ \int_0^{2\pi} y = 0,\ \|y\| \leqq 1\right\}.$$

We call this the *approximation class* generated by K. We observe that if $x \in \mathring{\mathscr{S}}_K$ and α_l ($l = \pm 1, \pm 2, \cdots$) are the Fourier coefficients of x, then $x = K * y$ and y is the uniquely determined element of $\mathring{\mathscr{C}}$ whose Fourier coefficients are $\alpha_l\gamma_l^{-1}$. Thus y is a convolution transform of x, and we write $y = K^{-1} * x$. We now prove:

Each approximation class $\mathring{\mathscr{S}}_K$ has an optimal approximator $L(\mathring{\mathscr{S}}_K) = L_K$ which is a convolution transformation, $L_K x = (Q_K * K^{-1}) * x$:

$$(9.3) \qquad \sup_{x\in\mathring{\mathscr{S}}} E(\alpha, L_K x) = E(\mathring{\mathscr{S}}_K, \mathring{\mathscr{P}}_{n-1}) = \mu_K(n).$$

For the proof we first observe that there is a natural extension of L_K to every function $x \in \overset{\circ}{\mathscr{C}}$ for which $\int_0^{2\pi} x = 0$. If $\int_0^{2\pi} x \neq 0$ then we write $x = \alpha_0 + y$ where $\int_0^{2\pi} y = 0$, and put $L_K x = \alpha_0 + L_K y$. Then L_K is defined on $\overset{\circ}{\mathscr{C}}$ and one sees readily that $L_K : \overset{\circ}{\mathscr{C}} \to \overset{\circ}{\mathscr{P}}_{n-1}$.

Now suppose $x \in \overset{\circ}{\mathscr{S}}_K$, $x = K * y$. Then

$$E(x, Lx) = \|(K - Q_K) * y\| \leqq \|K - Q_K\|_1 = \mu_K(n)$$

and, therefore,

$$\sup_{x \in \overset{\circ}{\mathscr{S}}_K} E(x, L_K x) \leqq \mu_K(n). \tag{9.4}$$

Now assume K odd and put $y(t) = \operatorname{sgn} \sin t$, $x_K = K * y$. Then by (9.1)

$$\|x_K\| = |x_K(0)| = \left| \frac{1}{\pi} \int_0^{\pi} K(t) \operatorname{sgn} \sin nt \, dt \right|$$

$$= \mu_K(n)$$

and

$$x_K(0) = -x_K\left(\pm \frac{\pi}{n}\right) = +x_K\left(\pm \frac{2\pi}{n}\right) = \cdots.$$

It follows that $E(x_K, \overset{\circ}{\mathscr{P}}_{n-1}) \geqq \mu_K(n)$. $x_K = K * y$ is not in $\overset{\circ}{\mathscr{S}}_K$ since y is not continuous, but it is clear that x_K belongs to the closure of $\overset{\circ}{\mathscr{S}}_K$ in $\overset{\circ}{\mathscr{C}}$. Hence,

$$E(\overset{\circ}{\mathscr{S}}_K, \overset{\circ}{\mathscr{P}}_{n-1}) \geqq \mu_K(n), \tag{9.5}$$

and this inequality is proved in a similar fashion if K is even. (9.4) and (9.5) together prove (9.3).

We observe that the hypothesis $\gamma_l \neq 0$ for $l \neq 0$ is not essential. If some (possibly infinitely many) of the Fourier coefficients of K are 0 then $\overset{\circ}{\mathscr{S}}_K$ lies in a certain subspace $\overset{\circ}{\mathscr{C}}_K$ of $\overset{\circ}{\mathscr{C}}$. The operator L_K is then extended only to a linear transformation $\overset{\circ}{\mathscr{C}}_K \to \overset{\circ}{\mathscr{P}}_{n-1}$. Otherwise there is no change.

Explicit expressions for the optimal approximator L_K are obtained for the following special kernels (compare [**9**, §86]). For the case of odd K with Fourier expansion $\sum_{l=1}^{\infty} \beta_l \sin lt$ assume the sequence $\{\beta_l\}$ is doubly monotone, say $\beta_l \geqq 0$, $\Delta\beta_l \leqq 0$, $\Delta^2\beta_l \geqq 0$. Then we define

$$b_l = \sum_{k=1}^{\infty} (\beta_{2kn-l} - \beta_{2kn+l}), \qquad l = 1, 2, \cdots, n-1,$$

$$Q_K(t) = \sum_{l=1}^{n-1} (\beta_l - b_l) \sin lt,$$

and obtain

$$K(t) - Q_K(t) = \sum_{l=1}^{n-1} b_l \sin lt + \sum_{l=n}^{\infty} \beta_l \sin lt \tag{9.6}$$

$$= \sum_{l=1}^{\infty} \sum_{k=1}^{\infty} (\beta_{|n-l|+(2k-1)n} - \beta_{n+l+(2k-1)n}) \sin lt$$

$$= \lim_{N\to\infty} 2 \sin nt \sum_{m=0}^{\infty} \left[\sum_{k=1}^{N} \beta_{m+(2k-1)n} \right] \cos mt.$$

The numbers in brackets form themselves a doubly monotone sequence. Therefore, by a well known theorem, $\sum_{m=0}^{\infty} [\ ] \cos mt \geqq 0$, and we have proved

$$\operatorname{sgn} [K(t) - Q_K(t)] = \operatorname{sgn} \sin nt.$$

Thus, K is an approximation kernel and $\mathring{\mathscr{S}}_K$ is an approximation class, whose optimal approximator L_K is given by $L_K x = (Q_K * K^{-1}) * x$. This means $L_K x$ is a convolution transform of x with the explicitly given multipliers $\lambda_l = 1 - \beta_l/b_l$.

If K is even with Fourier expansion $\sum_{l=1}^{\infty} \alpha_l \cos lt$ we assume the sequence $\{\alpha_l\}$ is triply monotone and define

$$a_l = \sum_{k=1}^{\infty} (-1)^{k-1} (\alpha_{2kn-l} + \alpha_{2kn+l}), \qquad l = 1, 2, \cdots, n-1,$$

$$Q_K(t) = \sum_{l=1}^{n-1} (\alpha_l - a_l) \cos lt.$$

We prove as before that K is an approximation kernel generating the approximation class $\mathring{\mathscr{S}}_K$ whose optimal approximator L_K is a convolution transformation with multipliers $\lambda_l = 1 - \alpha_l/a_l$.

In a similar way one can construct approximation classes in $\mathring{\mathscr{C}}(I_\infty)$ and corresponding optimal approximators. However, the examples $\mathscr{S}^{(r)}$, $\mathscr{A}_\alpha$ in §8 are considered sufficient.

10. As we have seen, there are some important subsets $\mathscr{S}$ of $\mathring{\mathscr{C}}$ which have no optimal approximator $L: \mathring{\mathscr{C}} \to \mathring{\mathscr{P}}_{n-1}$ for which (8.1) holds. Also, where optimal approximators exist, they may be impractical. We now seek, given $\mathscr{S} \subset \mathring{\mathscr{C}}$, to determine for each n (or at least for all sufficiently large n) a linear transformation $L_n: \mathring{\mathscr{C}} \to \mathring{\mathscr{P}}_{n-1}$ such that

$$\sup_{x\in\mathscr{S}} E(x, L_n x) = O(E(\mathscr{S}, \mathring{\mathscr{P}}_{n-1})), \qquad n \to \infty. \tag{10.1}$$

If L_n satisfies (10.1) we call it an *asymptotically optimal approximator* of $\mathscr{S}$.

We first consider the case $\mathscr{S} = \mathring{\mathscr{S}}^{(r)}$ again. Among the convolution transformations $\mathring{\mathscr{C}} \to \mathring{\mathscr{P}}_{n-1}$ there are many asymptotically optimal approximators. The Fourier partial sums $L_n = \mathring{S}_{n-1}$ (multipliers $\lambda_k = 1$) do not quite qualify since

$$\sup_{x\in\mathring{\mathscr{S}}^{(r)}} E(x, \mathring{S}_{n-1} x) = O(n^{-r} \log n), \qquad n \to \infty. \tag{10.2}$$

A simple and useful asymptotically optimal approximator of $\mathring{\mathscr{S}}^{(r)}$ is the Zygmund sum $Z_{n,p}$ with $p \geqq 2[0.5(r+1)]$, which is a convolution transformation with the multipliers

$$\lambda_k = 1 - \left(\frac{k}{n}\right)^p \tag{10.3}$$

(see [**1**, Chapter 12], [**9**, §8.7]). $Z_{n,p}$ is also asymptotically optimal in $\mathring{\mathscr{S}}^{(r,\omega)}$ if $p \geqq r+1$.

Timan has proved (see [**10**, §8.5]) that if the convolution $L_n:\mathring{\mathscr{C}} \to \mathring{\mathscr{P}}_{n-1}$ is an asymptotically optimal approximator of $\mathring{\mathscr{S}}^{(r)}$ then its multipliers λ_k must satisfy the condition

$$\sum_{k=1}^{n-1} \frac{1-\lambda_k}{k^r(n-k)} - \frac{\log n}{n^r} = O(n^{-r}), \qquad n \to \infty. \tag{10.4}$$

If $\Delta^2 k^{-r}(1-\lambda_k) \geqq 0$ (or $\leqq 0$) for $k = 1, 2, \cdots, n-1$ (here one sets $\lambda_{-1} = 0$, $\lambda_0 = 1$) then (10.4) is also sufficient in the case of even r, and is sufficient in the case of odd r if moreover $1 - \lambda_1 = O(n^{-r-1})$. In the case of odd r, the last conditions also imply that L_n is an asymptotically optimal approximator of $\mathring{\mathscr{S}}^{(r+\alpha)}$ $(0 < \alpha < 1)$, that is

$$\sup_{x \in \mathring{\mathscr{S}}^{(r+\alpha)}} E(x, L_n x) = O(n^{-r-\alpha}). \tag{10.5}$$

For the class $\mathring{\mathscr{A}}_\alpha$ where we have

$$E(\mathring{\mathscr{A}}_\alpha, \mathring{\mathscr{P}}_{n-1}) = \mu_\alpha(n) \sim \frac{8}{\pi} e^{-\alpha n}, \qquad n \to \infty, \tag{10.6}$$

we assert that the *Fourier sum* S_{n-1} *is an asymptotically optimal approximator*. To prove this we refer to the fact that the convolution transformation $L(\mathring{\mathscr{A}}_\alpha)$ with the multipliers λ_k (see (8.5)) is an optimal approximator of $\mathring{\mathscr{A}}_\alpha$. Thus there is a constant C such that

$$E(x, L(\mathring{\mathscr{A}}_\alpha)x) \leqq Ce^{-n\alpha} \tag{10.7}$$

for each n and each $x \in \mathring{\mathscr{A}}_\alpha$. If we put $x_\alpha(t) = x(t + i\alpha)$ then $L(\mathring{\mathscr{A}}_\alpha)x$ can also be written as a convolution transform of x_α: $L(\mathring{\mathscr{A}}_\alpha)x = Mx_\alpha$. The corresponding multipliers are (this follows easily from the representation $x = k_\alpha * x_\alpha$ given in [**1**, §11]):

$$\mu_k = \lambda_k \operatorname{sech} \alpha k. \tag{10.8}$$

Similarly, $\mathring{S}_{n-1}x$ can also be written as a convolution transform of $x_\alpha : \mathring{S}_{n-1}x = Rx_\alpha$, with multipliers

$$\rho_k = \operatorname{sech} \alpha k. \tag{10.9}$$

Since $\|x_\alpha\| \leqq 1$ we have

$$
\begin{aligned}
(10.10) \qquad \|L(\mathring{\mathscr{A}}_\alpha x) - S_{n-1}x\| &= \|(M - R)x_\alpha\| \\
&\leqq \left\| 2\sum_{k=1}^{n-1} (\mu_k - \rho_k) \cos kt \right\|_1 \\
&\leqq 2\sum_{k=1}^{n-1} |\lambda_k - 1| \operatorname{sech} \alpha k \\
&= 2\sum_{k=1}^{n-1} \left| \sum_{l=1}^{\infty} (-1)^{l+1} \{\operatorname{sech}(2ln - k)\alpha + \operatorname{sech}(2ln + k)\alpha\} \right| \\
&\leqq 2\sum_{k=1}^{n-1} \{\operatorname{sech}(2n - k)\alpha + \operatorname{sech}(2n + k)\alpha\} \\
&< 4\sum_{k=1}^{n-1} \{e^{-(2n-k)\alpha} + e^{-(2n+k)\alpha}\} \\
&= 4e^{-2n\alpha}\left\{\frac{e^{n\alpha} - 1}{1 - e^{-\alpha}} + \frac{e^{-n\alpha} - 1}{1 - e^{\alpha}}\right\} \\
&= O(e^{-n\alpha}).
\end{aligned}
$$

Together with (10.7) this gives

$$
(10.11) \qquad E(x, \mathring{S}_{n-1}x) = O(e^{-n\alpha}),
$$

which proves our assertion.

We finally remark that there are asymptotically optimal approximators L_n of $\mathring{\mathscr{S}}^{(r)}$, $\mathring{\mathscr{S}}^{(r,\omega)}$, $\mathring{\mathscr{A}}_\alpha$ having the desirable property that $L_n x$ is obtained from the values of x at $2n - 1$ equidistant points ("generalized interpolators"). One can obtain such approximators by replacing the above convolution transformations, which are formed with respect to uniform measure, by convolution transformations with respect to the measure dw_n, which has its mass concentrated at the points

$$
2k\pi/(2n - 1) \quad (k = 1, 2, \cdots, 2n - 1).
$$

Work has been done in this direction by Pogodičeva and Timan (see **[12]**, also **[10**, §8.5]) and Ganzburg **[13]**.

11. In §8 we have seen that there exist optimal approximators of the classes $\mathring{\mathscr{S}}^{(r)}$ and $\mathscr{A}_\alpha$. One may ask whether there is a transformation $L: \mathring{\mathscr{C}} \to \mathring{\mathscr{P}}_{n-1}$, that is an optimal approximator of each of the classes $\mathring{\mathscr{S}}^{(1)}$, $\mathring{\mathscr{S}}^{(2)}$, $\mathring{\mathscr{S}}^{(3)}$, $\cdots$. The answer to this question is almost certainly no, since optimal approximators are most likely convolutions and we have found that among convolutions the optimal approximator of $\mathscr{S}^{(r)}$ is unique and it depends on r.

However, there are transformations $L_n: \mathring{\mathscr{C}} \to \mathring{\mathscr{P}}_{n-1}$ which are asymptotically optimal approximators of each $\mathring{\mathscr{S}}^{(r)}$ $(r = 1, 2, \cdots)$. Indeed, *the De La Vallée-Poussin sum* $\mathring{V}_{[qn],n}$ *is, for each* $0 < q < 1$, *such a universal approximator*, as we shall now show. We assert

$$\sup_{x\in\mathring{\mathscr{C}}^{(r)}} E(x, \mathring{V}_{[qn],n}x) = O(E(\mathring{\mathscr{C}}^{(r)}, \mathring{\mathscr{P}}_{n-1})), \qquad n \to \infty \tag{11.1}$$

for each $r = 1, 2, \cdots$. Indeed, by (5.6) and (8.2) we have

$$\begin{aligned} E(x, \mathring{V}_{[qn],n}x) &< \left[4 - \frac{4}{\pi^2}\log(1-q)\right]E(x, \mathring{\mathscr{P}}_{[qn]}) \\ &\leqq \left[4 - \frac{4}{\pi^2}\log(1-q)\right]\mu_r q^r n^{-r} \end{aligned} \tag{11.2}$$

for each $x \in \mathring{\mathscr{C}}^{(r)}$, and this implies (11.1). Also the modified interpolator $\mathring{J}_{[qn],n}$ is an asymptotically optimal approximator in the above sense. Indeed, by (5.15) and (8.2) one obtains

$$\sup_{x\in\mathring{\mathscr{C}}^{(r)}} E(x, \mathring{J}_{[qn],n}x) \leqq \frac{q^r}{1-q}\mu_r n^{-r}. \tag{11.3}$$

Clearly, both $\mathring{V}_{[qn],n}$ and $\mathring{J}_{[qn],n}$ are asymptotically optimal approximators of each class $\mathring{\mathscr{S}} \subset \mathring{\mathscr{C}}$ for which

$$E(\mathring{\mathscr{S}}, \mathring{\mathscr{P}}_{[qn]})/E(\mathring{\mathscr{S}}, \mathring{\mathscr{P}}_n) = O(1), \qquad n \to \infty. \tag{11.4}$$

Such classes are not only $\mathring{\mathscr{S}}^{(r)}$, but also $\mathring{\mathscr{S}}^{(r+\alpha)}$, $\mathring{\mathscr{S}}^{(r,\omega)}$, etc. However, neither $\mathring{V}_{[qn],n}$ nor $\mathring{J}_{[qn],n}$ is, for any q, an asymptotically optimal approximator of $\mathring{\mathscr{A}}_\alpha$. This is related to the fact that the bounds in (11.2) and (11.3) are not uniform in r, as $\mu_r q^r$ $(r = 1, 2, \cdots)$ is not bounded. We easily show

$$e^{n\alpha} \sup_{x\in\mathring{\mathscr{A}}_\alpha} E(x, \mathring{V}_{mn}x) \to \infty, \qquad n \to \infty, \tag{11.5}$$

if $m/n \leqq q < 1$. The function $x_n(t) = (\operatorname{sech} m\alpha)\cos mt$ is in $\mathring{\mathscr{A}}_\alpha$, and $x_n - \mathring{V}_{mn}x_n = x_n/(n-m)$. Therefore

$$\begin{aligned} E(x_n, \mathring{V}_{mn}x_n) &= \frac{1}{n-m}\operatorname{sech} m\alpha \\ e^{n\alpha}E(x_n, \mathring{V}_{mn}x_n) &> \frac{2}{n-m}e^{(n-m)\alpha} > \frac{2}{n}e^{n(1-q)\alpha} \end{aligned} \tag{11.6}$$

and this proves (11.5).

On the other hand, $\mathring{S}_{n-1}$ which is an asymptotically optimal approximator of each $\mathring{\mathscr{A}}_\alpha(\alpha > 0)$, is not an asymptotically optimal approximator of any $\mathring{\mathscr{S}}^{(r)}$, the error $\sup_{x\in\mathring{\mathscr{S}}^{(r)}} E(x, \mathring{S}_{n-1}x)$ being by a factor $\log n$ too large. Whether there is a linear transformation $L_n: \mathring{\mathscr{C}} \to \mathring{\mathscr{P}}_n$, which is an asymptotically optimal approximator of each $\mathring{\mathscr{S}}^{(r)}$, $\mathring{\mathscr{S}}^{(r,\omega)}$ $(r = 1, 2, \cdots)$ as well as of each $\mathring{\mathscr{A}}_\alpha$ $(\alpha > 0)$ remains an unsolved problem.

REFERENCES

1. M. Golomb, *Lectures on theory of approximation*, Argonne National Laboratory Applied Math. Division, 1962.

2. J. P. Natanson, *Konstruktive Funktionentheorie* (Transl. from Russian), Akademie Verlag, Berlin, 1955.

3. N. A. Sapogov, *Norms of linear polynomial operators*, Soviet Math. Dokl. **3** (1962), 602–604.

4. G. Freud, *Ueber gleichzeitige Approximation einer Funktion und ihrer Derivierten*, Internat. Math. Nachr. No. 47–48 (1957), 36–37.

5. A. L. Garkavi, *Simultaneous approximation of periodic functions and their derivatives by trigonometric polynomials*, Izv. Akad. Nauk SSSR Ser. Mat., **24** (1960), 103–128 (Russian).

6. A. Zygmund, *Trigonometric series*, Vol. II. second edition, Cambridge Univ. Press, Cambridge, 1959.

7. S. B. Stečkin, *The order of best approximation of continuous functions*, Izv. Akad. Nauk SSSR Ser. Mat. **15** (1951), 219–242 (Russian).

8. D. L. Berman, *Extremal problems in the theory of polynomial operators*, Soviet Math. Dokl. **2** (1961), 691–694.

———, *Linear polynomial operators*, Soviet Math. Dokl. **3** (1962), 460–463.

9. N. I. Akhiezer, *Theory of approximation* (Transl. from Russian), Ungar, New York, 1956.

10. A. F. Timan, *Theory of approximation of functions of a real variable* (Transl. from Russian), Pergamon Press, Oxford, 1963.

11. N. P. Korneĭčuk, *The best uniform approximation of some classes of continuous functions*, Soviet Math. Dokl. **2** (1961), 1254–1257.

———, *The existence of a linear polynomial operator affording the best approximation on a class of functions*, Soviet Math. Dokl. **3** (1962), 324–326.

———, *The exact constant in D. Jackson's theorem on best uniform approximation of continuous periodic functions*, Soviet Math. Dokl. **3** (1962), 1040–1041.

12. N. A. Pogodičeva and A. F. Timan, *A relation in the theory of the summation of interpolation polynomials and Fourier series*, Dokl. Akad. Nauk SSSR **111** (1956), 542–543 (Russian).

13. I. M. Ganzburg, *A method of approximating continuous functions by trigonometric polynomials*, Dokl. Akad. Nauk SSSR **64** (1949), 13–16 (Russian).

APPROXIMATION BY GENERALIZED RATIONAL FUNCTIONS[1]

E. W. CHENEY[2]
University of California, Los Angeles

1. **Introduction.** This paper may be regarded as a continuation of the study begun in [**1**] by H. L. Loeb and the author. In that paper we considered various problems of approximation in the space $C[a, b]$ by "generalized rational functions". The latter were taken to be functions of the form $r = p/q$ where p varies freely in a linear subspace P and q varies in a linear subspace Q but subject to the restriction $q(x) > 0$ on $[a, b]$. (We write $q > 0$ for brevity.) The subspaces P and Q are to be finite-dimensional and remain fixed during the discussion. It is only necessary to assume that Q contains at least one positive function. The class of such generalized rational functions is denoted by $R(P, Q)$ or simply by R, and this forms our approximating class. Given an element f of $C[a, b]$ we may inquire into the existence, uniqueness, characterization, etc., of best approximations in R to f. As examples of the type of results sought one may cite the well-known theorems given in Achieser's treatise [**2**] for "ordinary" rational approximation. We employ this term to distinguish the special case when P and Q are the subspaces of polynomials of degrees $\leqq n$ and $\leqq m$ respectively.

The existence question for best approximations in R has been recently studied by Boehm [**3**] and Shapiro [**4**]. It is touched upon briefly here in the final theorem. We are concerned mainly with uniqueness and characterization theorems and with the continuity properties of the best approximation operator. The characterization theorems given here differ from those of [**1**] in that these depend upon the oscillatory properties of the error functions, $f - r$. However, the more basic results of [**1**] appear prominently in the proofs here.

2. **Some definitions and lemmas.** The approximation problems considered here are all posed in the space $C[a, b]$ of continuous real-valued functions defined on the closed interval $[a, b]$ with norm $\|f\| = \max_{a \leqq x \leqq b} |f(x)|$. The norm could be redefined so as to include a fixed positive weight function, but this apparent additional generality is not real in the situations considered here. An n-dimensional subspace of $C[a, b]$ having a basis $\{f_1, \cdots, f_n\}$ is said to be a *Haar subspace* if for every n distinct points $x_1, \cdots, x_n$ in $[a, b]$ the $n \times n$ determinant, det $[f_i(x_j)]$, is

---

[1] Presented to the American Mathematical Society under abstract no. 64T-319. Notices of the Amer. Math. Soc. **11** (1964), 461.

[2] The author gratefully acknowledges support by the Air Force Office of Scientific Research through its grant AFOSR 77-63. Presently at the University of Texas, Austin, Texas.

non-zero. That this property is independent of the basis is a consequence of the following well-known fact. See, for example, Natanson's treatise [5].

LEMMA 1. *An n-dimensional subspace M in C[a, b] is a Haar subspace if and only if the zero function is the only element of M having more than n — 1 roots in [a, b].*

For some arguments, a refinement of this result is required. See for example Korovkin's book [6].

LEMMA 2. *If M is an n-dimensional Haar subspace of C[a, b] then a non-zero function in M can have at most n — 1 roots in [a, b], even if we count doubly all the roots in (a, b) where the function does not change sign.*

These results and others to be given later are conveniently described in terms of certain indices which may be defined for any finite dimensional subspace M in $C[a, b]$. We put

$\eta(M) =$ dimension of a maximal Haar subspace in M,
$\delta(M) =$ dimension of M,
$\nu(M) = 1 +$ maximum number of variations in sign possessed by elements of M,
$\zeta(M) = 1 +$ maximum number of roots possessed by non-zero elements of M,
$\zeta^*(M) = 1 +$ maximum number of roots possessed by non-zero elements of M, counting doubly all roots in (a, b) where the function does not change sign.

That these indices are in general different from each other may be demonstrated by taking M to be the subspace spanned by a single function $f(x) = (x - 1)(x - 2)^2$ on the interval $[0, 3]$. The indices are in this case respectively 0, 1, 2, 3, 4.

For an arbitrary subspace M it may happen that δ and η are finite while ν, ζ, and ζ^* are infinite. Generally, the following relationships must exist among these indices when M is finite-dimensional.

LEMMA 3. (i) $\zeta^* \geqq \zeta \geqq \nu \geqq \delta \geqq \eta$,
(ii) $\eta = \delta \Rightarrow \zeta^* = \zeta = \nu = \delta = \eta$,
(iii) $\zeta = \delta \Rightarrow \zeta^* = \zeta = \nu = \delta = \eta$.

PROOF. In order to establish the inequality $\nu \geqq \delta$, take a basis $\{f_1, \cdots, f_\delta\}$ for M. By the linear independence, there exist points $a \leqq x_1 < x_2 < \cdots < x_\delta \leqq b$ such that $\det [f_i(x_j)] \neq 0$. Hence the equations $\sum_i c_i f_i(x_j) = (-1)^j$ $(j = 1, \cdots, \delta)$ have a simultaneous solution. The function $g = \Sigma\, c_i f_i$ then has $\delta - 1$ variations in sign, and consequently $\nu \geqq \delta$. The remaining inequalities in (i) are obvious. Implications (ii) and (iii) follow from Lemmas 1 and 2.

Next we cite the basic characterization theorem of [1] for generalized rational approximations. Given $r \in R$, we form the linear space $P + rQ$ consisting of all functions of the form $p + rq$ in which $p \in P$ and $q \in Q$.

LEMMA 4. *In order that r be a best approximation to f out of class R it is necessary and sufficient that* 0 *lie in the convex hull of the set* $\{e(x)\hat{x}\colon |e(x)| = \|e\|\}$. *Here* $e = f - r$ *and* $\hat{x}$ *denotes the vector* $[\phi_1(x), \cdots, \phi_n(x)]$, *where* $\{\phi_1, \cdots, \phi_n\}$ *is any basis for* $P + rQ$.

Finally we cite a technical lemma from **[1]** which bridges the gap between the theory of convex sets and the alternation properties of best approximations.

LEMMA 5. *Let* $\{g_1, \cdots, g_n\}$ *be a basis for a Haar subspace in* $C[a, b]$. *Let* 0 *lie in the convex hull of* $\{\lambda_0\hat{x}_0, \cdots, \lambda_n\hat{x}_n\}$ *where* $\lambda_i \neq 0$, $\hat{x} = [g_1(x), \cdots, g_n(x)]$, *and* $a \leqq x_0 < \cdots < x_n \leqq b$. *Then the coefficients* λ_i *alternate in sign.*

3. **Characterization of best approximations.** The main result of this section is a theorem which provides two conditions, one *necessary* and the other *sufficient*, on a generalized rational function of best approximation. Given $r \in R$ we consider the subspace $P + rQ$. The indices $\eta(P + rQ)$ and $\nu(P + rQ)$ as defined in §2 are now functions of r. We say that a function f *alternates* k *times* if points x_i exist satisfying the conditions $a \leqq x_1 < x_2 < \cdots < x_k \leqq b$, $f(x_i) = (-1)^i\lambda$, and $|\lambda| = \|f\|$. The following result will be found to be reminiscent of Rice's theory of varisolvence **[7]**.

CHARACTERIZATION THEOREM. *If* $f - r$ *alternates* $1 + \nu(P + rQ)$ *times then r is a best approximation to f. If r is a best approximation to f then* $f - r$ *alternates* $1 + \eta(P + rQ)$ *times.*

PROOF. Suppose first that r is not a best approximation to f. We shall show that $e \equiv f - r$ cannot alternate $1 + \nu$ times. By Lemma 4, the origin is not in the convex hull of the point set $\{e(x)\hat{x}\colon |e(x)| = \|e\|\}$. By a standard separation theorem there exists a coefficient vector $c = [c_1, \cdots, c_n]$ such that $e(x)\langle c, \hat{x}\rangle > 0$ whenever $|e(x)| = \|e\|$. Now if $e(x)$ alternates $1 + \nu$ times then it has ν variations in sign, and the inequality just written shows that $\langle c, \hat{x}\rangle$ must also have ν variations in sign. But if we write $\psi(x) = \langle c, \hat{x}\rangle = \Sigma\, c_i\phi_i(x)$ it is clear that $\psi \in P + rQ$, and consequently ψ can have at most $\nu - 1$ variations in sign.

Now suppose that r is a best approximation to f. We shall show that e alternates $1 + \eta$ times. By Lemma 4, the origin lies in the convex hull of the set $\{e(x)\hat{x}\colon |e(x)| = \|e\|\}$. By the definition of $\eta(P + rQ)$ there exists a Haar subspace of dimension η in $P + rQ$. Let $\{\phi_1, \cdots, \phi_\eta\}$ be a basis for this Haar subspace, and let $\bar{x} = [\phi_1(x), \cdots, \phi_\eta(x)]$. Since the components of $\bar{x}$ are linearly related to those of $\hat{x}$, the origin lies in the convex hull of the set $\{e(x)\bar{x}\colon |e(x)| = \|e\|\}$. By Carathéodory's theorem about convex sets there exist points $x_0, \cdots, x_k$ such that $k \leqq \eta$, $|e(x_i)| = \|e\|$, and such that the origin lies in the convex hull of $\{e(x_i)\bar{x}_i\colon 0 \leqq i \leqq k\}$. By the characteristic property of a Haar subspace, every set of η points $\bar{x}$ is independent. Consequently $k \geqq \eta$. We may assume that $a \leqq x_0 < \cdots < x_\eta \leqq b$. Then by Lemma 5, $e(x_i)$ alternates in sign.

The case of ordinary rational approximations is easily handled by establishing first that $P + rQ$ is always a Haar subspace in this case. Thus the two indices $\nu(P + rQ)$ and $\eta(P + rQ)$ are equal, and the preceding theorem provides a single condition which is both necessary and sufficient. Then we may proceed to give a formula for $\nu(P + rQ)$: if $r = p/q$ with p and q relatively prime then $\nu(P + rQ) = \eta(P + rQ) = 1 + \max\{n + \partial q, m + \partial p\}$ where ∂ means "degree of". If $p = 0$ we interpret $\partial p = -\infty$ and relative primeness to imply $q = 1$.

LEMMA 6. *Let P and Q be the spaces of polynomials of degree $\leqq n$ and $\leqq m$ respectively. Let $r = p/q$ with $p \in P$, $q \in Q$, $q > 0$ on $[a, b]$ and r irreducible. Then $P + rQ$ is a Haar subspace of dimension* $1 + \max\{n + \partial q, m + \partial p\}$.

PROOF. Put $k = 1 + \max\{n + \partial q, m + \partial p\}$. By Lemma 3 it suffices to prove that $k \geqq \zeta$ and $\delta \geqq k$. In order to prove the first of these inequalities, suppose that $P + rQ$ contains an element $\phi = p_1 + pq_1/q \neq 0$ with k or more roots. Then $p_1q + pq_1$ has k roots. But this is not possible because this polynomial is of degree at most $\max\{n + \partial q, m + \partial p\} \equiv k - 1$. In order to prove that $\delta \geqq k$, observe first that this is trivial if $r = 0$ since k and δ are both $n + 1$. Assume therefore that $r \neq 0$, and consider the well-known equation

$$\delta(P + rQ) = \delta(P) + \delta(rQ) - \delta(P \cap rQ).$$

The dimensions of P and rQ are $n + 1$ and $m + 1$ respectively. As for $P \cap rQ$, observe that $rQ = \{pq_1/q : \partial q_1 \leqq m\}$. Now $pq_1/q \in P$ if and only if q divides q_1 leaving a quotient of degree $\leqq n - \partial p$. Hence q_1 must be of the form $q_1 = qq_2$ with $\partial q_2 \leqq n - \partial p$ and $\partial q_2 \leqq m - \partial q$. Thus the dimension of $P \cap rQ$ is $1 + \min\{n - \partial p, m - \partial q\} \equiv m + n + 2 - k$, and hence $\delta(P + rQ) = k$.

4. **Uniqueness theorems.** This section is devoted to two theorems giving conditions on best approximations in order that they be unique. The second of these theorems provides a quantitative form of uniqueness similar to one proved first in [**1**].

UNIQUENESS THEOREM. *Let r be a best approximation in R to f. If $\delta(P + rQ) = \eta(P + rQ)$, or equivalently, if $P + rQ$ is a Haar subspace, then r is unique.*

PROOF. Suppose that f possesses two distinct best approximations in R, $r = p/q$ and $r^* = p^*/q^*$. By the characterization theorem we may find points of alternation $x_1 < \cdots < x_k$ for the function $f - r$, with $k \geqq 1 + \eta(P + rQ)$. Let $\phi = p^* - q^*r$. From the equation

$$\phi(x_i) = [q^*(r^* - r)](x_i) = q^*(x_i)[(f - r)(x_i) - (f - r^*)(x_i)]$$

we see that the numbers $(-1)^i\phi(x_i)$ do not change sign. Let us say that $(-1)^i\phi(x_i) \geqq 0$. In the simplest case, the numbers $\phi(x_i)$ are all non-zero and hence alternate in sign. Then ϕ must have $k - 1$ variations, and consequently $\nu(P + rQ) \geqq k$. But then $\nu(P + rQ) > \eta(P + rQ)$, contradicting Lemma 3, Part (ii). In the general case we reach the same contradiction. Suppose, for example, that there is a string of j zeros among the numbers $\phi(x_i)$:

$$\phi(x_n) \neq 0,\ \phi(x_{n+1}) = \cdots = \phi(x_{n+j}) = 0,\ \phi(x_{n+j+1}) \neq 0.$$

In this case either one of the roots $x_{n+1}, \cdots, x_{n+j}$ is a *double* root of ϕ or else ϕ possesses a root different from any of these in the interval (x_n, x_{n+j+1}). Indeed, in the contrary case, ϕ retains the sign $(-1)^n$ in (x_n, x_{n+1}), the sign $(-1)^{n+1}$ in (x_{n+1}, x_{n+2}), etc., and the sign $(-1)^{n+j}$ in (x_{n+j}, x_{n+j+1}). But this is not possible because we have assumed that $(-1)^{n+j+1}\phi(x_{n+j+1}) \geqq 0$. The number of roots of ϕ in (x_n, x_{n+j+1}) is therefore at least $j + 1$ if we count doubly a zero where ϕ does not change sign. This argument shows that the total number of roots of ϕ (counted in this way) is at least $k - 1$, and that $\zeta^*(P + rQ) \geqq k$. Hence $\zeta^*(P + rQ) > \eta(P + rQ)$, again contradicting Lemma 3.

It might be conjectured that $P + rQ$ is always a Haar subspace when P and Q are Haar subspaces. A counterexample may be constructed on $[0, 3]$ by taking P to be the linear span of $\{1, x^2\}$ and Q to be the linear span of $\{1, x\}$. Then let $r = (1 + x^2)/(1 + x)$. The space $P + rQ$ is spanned by $\{1, x^2, (1 + x^2)/(1 + x), (x + x^3)/(1 + x)\}$. The dimension of $P + rQ$ is only 3 because

$$\frac{x + x^3}{1 + x} = 1 + x^2 - \frac{1 + x^2}{1 + x}.$$

Now if $P + rQ$ were a Haar subspace, its members could have at most two roots on $[0, 3]$. But the function

$$\phi(x) = 6 + x^2 - 6\,\frac{1 + x^2}{1 + x}$$

can be written as $\phi(x) = (1 + x)^{-1}x(x - 2)(x - 3)$ and therefore has three roots on $[0, 3]$.

STRONG UNIQUENESS THEOREM. *Let r^* be a best approximation in R to f. If $\eta(P + r^*Q) = \delta(P) + \delta(Q) - 1$ then there exists a constant $\gamma > 0$ such that for all $r \in R$, $\|f - r\| \geqq \|f - r^*\| + \gamma\,\|r^* - r\|$.*

PROOF. Put $e = f - r^*$. The case $e = 0$ is trivial since we may write $\|f - r\| = \|f - r^* + r^* - r\| = \|f - r^*\| + \|r^* - r\|$. Let us assume therefore that $e \neq 0$. Select a basis $\{g_1, \cdots, g_n\}$ for P and a basis $\{h_1, \cdots, h_m\}$ for Q. Let $r^* = \sum_{i=1}^n a_i g_i / \sum_{i=1}^m a_{n+i} h_i$, and let $|a| \equiv (\Sigma\, a_i^2)^{1/2} = 1$. For any $(n + m)$-tuple, b, define $r_b = \sum_{i=1}^n b_i g_i / \sum_{i=1}^m b_{n+i} h_i$. For any $x \in [a, b]$ put $\hat{x} = [-g_1(x), \cdots, -g_n(x), r_a(x)h_1(x), \cdots, r_a(x)h_m(x)]$. Let $c_1 = \inf_x \Sigma\, a_{n+i} h_i(x)$. Select $c_2 > 0$ so that

$$|a - b| \leqq c_2 \Rightarrow \inf_x \sum b_{n+i} h_i(x) \geqq \tfrac{1}{2} c_1.$$

Now define

$$\gamma_1 = \inf_{\substack{|b|=1 \\ |a-b|\leqq c_2}} \frac{\|f - r_b\| - \|f - r_a\|}{\|r_a - r_b\|}$$

and

$$\gamma_2 = \inf_{\substack{|b|=1 \\ |a-b|\geqq c_2 \\ r_b \in R}} \frac{\|f - r_b\| - \|f - r_a\|}{\|r_a - r_b\|}.$$

If we can show that the number $\gamma = \min \{\gamma_1, \gamma_2\}$ is positive then we shall be finished since

$$\|f - r_b\| \geqq \|f - r_a\| + \gamma \, \| r_a - r_b\|.$$

By Lemma 4, 0 lies in the convex hull of the set $\{e(x)\hat{x}\colon |e(x)| = \|e\|\}$. The points $\hat{x}$ lie in the $(n + m - 1)$-dimensional subspace $a^\perp$ since

$$\langle a, \hat{x}\rangle = -\sum_{i=1}^{n} a_i g_i(x) + r_a(x) \sum_{i=1}^{m} a_{n+i} h_i(x) = 0.$$

Hence by Carathéodory's theorem 0 lies in the convex hull of a set of $n + m$ of the points $e(x)\hat{x}$, with $|e(x)| = \|e\|$. By the hypothesis $\eta(P + r_a Q) = \delta(P) + \delta(Q) - 1 = n + m - 1$, every set of $n + m - 1$ points $\hat{x}$ is independent. Thus there exist points $x_i \in [a, b]$ and coefficients $\theta_i > 0$ such that

$$0 = \sum_{i=1}^{n+m} \theta_i \sigma_i \hat{x}_i$$

with $\sigma_i = \operatorname{sgn} e(x_i)$ and $|e(x_i)| = \|e\|$. If $b \perp a$ and $|b| = 1$ then $\langle b, \hat{x}_i\rangle \neq 0$ for at least one i, and from the equation $0 = \Sigma\, \theta_i \sigma_i \langle b, \hat{x}_i\rangle$ it follows that at least one of the numbers $\sigma_i\langle b, \hat{x}_i\rangle$ is *positive*. Hence the attained infimum

$$c_3 = \min_{\substack{b \perp a \\ |b|=1}} \max_i \sigma_i \langle b, \hat{x}_i\rangle$$

is positive. By homogeneity, we have for any $b \perp a$,

$$\max_i \sigma_i\langle b, \hat{x}_i\rangle \geqq c_3\, |b|.$$

Since $b - \langle b, a\rangle a$ is orthogonal to a, we have for arbitrary b,

$$\max_i \sigma_i\langle b - \langle b, a\rangle a, \hat{x}_i\rangle \geqq c_3\, |b - \langle b, a\rangle a|,$$

whence

$$\max_i \sigma_i\langle b, \hat{x}_i\rangle \geqq c_3\, |b - \langle b, a\rangle a|.$$

Now define

$$c_4 = \max_{a \leqq x \leqq b} 2\, |\hat{x}|/c_1$$

and consider any vector b satisfying $|b| = 1$ and $|b - a| \leqq c_2$. We have for it

$$\begin{aligned}\|r_a - r_b\| &= \max_x |(r_a - r_b)(x)| \\ &= \max_x \frac{|\langle b, \hat{x}\rangle|}{\sum b_{n+j}h_j(x)} \\ &\leqq \frac{2}{c_1} \max_x |\langle b - \langle b, a\rangle a, \hat{x}\rangle| \\ &\leqq c_4 \, |b - \langle b, a\rangle a|.\end{aligned}$$

Let

$$c_5 = \max_{|b|=1} \left\| \sum_{j=1}^{m} b_{n+j}h_j \right\|.$$

For some i we must have

$$\begin{aligned}\sigma_i(r_a - r_b)(x_i) &= \sigma_i \frac{\langle b, \hat{x}_i\rangle}{\sum_{j=1}^{m} b_{n+j}h_j(x_i)} \\ &\geqq \frac{c_3 \, |b - \langle b, a\rangle a|}{c_5} \\ &\geqq \frac{c_3}{c_5} \frac{\|r_a - r_b\|}{c_4}.\end{aligned}$$

Then we have for such a vector b,

$$\begin{aligned}\|f - r_b\| &\geqq \sigma_i[f(x_i) - r_b(x_i)] \\ &= \sigma_i[f(x_i) - r_a(x_i)] + \sigma_i[r_a(x_i) - r_b(x_i)] \\ &\geqq \|f - r_a\| + \frac{c_3}{c_4c_5} \|r_a - r_b\|.\end{aligned}$$

This proves that $\gamma_1 \geqq c_3/(c_4c_5)$. Now suppose that $\gamma_2 = 0$. Then there exists a sequence b^k such that $|b^k| = 1$, $r_{b^k} \in R$, $|b^k - a| \geqq c_2$, and such that the numbers

$$\varepsilon_k = \frac{\|f - r_{b^k}\| - \|f - r_a\|}{\|r_{b^k} - r_a\|}$$

converge to zero. We may suppose that $\varepsilon_k \leqq \frac{1}{2}$. From this there follows

$$\begin{aligned}\|r_a - r_{b^k}\| &\leqq \|r_a - f\| + \|f - r_{b^k}\| \\ &\leqq \|r_a - f\| + \|f - r_a\| + \tfrac{1}{2} \|r_{b^k} - r_a\|,\end{aligned}$$

and thus $\|r_a - r_{b^k}\| \leqq 4 \, \|r_a - f\|$. Now we write

$$\begin{aligned}\varepsilon_k \|r_{b^k} - r_a\| + \|f - r_a\| &= \|f - r_{b^k}\| \\ &\geqq \max_i \sigma_i[f(x_i) - r_{b^k}(x_i)] \\ &= \max_i \{\sigma_i[f(x_i) - r_a(x_i)] + \sigma_i[r_a(x_i) - r_{b^k}(x_i)]\} \\ &= \|f - r_a\| + \max \sigma_i[r_a(x_i) - r_{b^k}(x_i)],\end{aligned}$$

whence $\varepsilon_k \|r_{b^k} - r_a\| \geqq \max_i \sigma_i[r_a(x_i) - r_{b^k}(x_i)]$. Since the numbers $\|r_{b^k} - r_a\|$ are bounded as $k \to \infty$, we have

$$\overline{\lim_{k\to\infty}} \max_i \sigma_i[r_a(x_i) - r_{b^k}(x_i)] \leqq 0,$$

or

$$\overline{\lim_{k\to\infty}} \max_i \frac{\sigma_i\langle b^k, \hat{x}_i\rangle}{\sum_{j=1}^{m} b^k_{n+j} h_j(x_i)} \leqq 0.$$

Since the denominators are bounded above and positive, we conclude that

$$\overline{\lim_{k}} \max_i \sigma_i\langle b^k, \hat{x}_i\rangle \leqq 0.$$

By compactness we may assume that the vectors b^k converge say to a vector b. Then $|b| = 1$, $|b - a| \geqq c_2$, and

$$\max_i \sigma_i\langle b, \hat{x}_i\rangle \leqq 0.$$

But this is not possible, for if b is not a multiple of a, one of the numbers $\sigma_i\langle b, \hat{x}_i\rangle$ must be positive according to the earlier argument. Thus $\gamma_2 > 0$.

5. **Continuity theorem.** The setting of the previous sections is retained here. Thus two finite dimensional subspaces P and Q are prescribed in $C[a, b]$ and we consider approximations from the class $R = \{r = p/q : p \in P,\ q \in Q, \text{ and } q > 0\}$. It is now convenient to introduce a *best approximation operator* or *Tchebycheff operator* $\mathcal{T}$ in the space $C[a, b]$ by defining $\mathcal{T}f$ to be the (possibly empty) set of all optimal approximations to f in the class R. Formally, $\mathcal{T}f = \{r \in R : \|f - r\| = \min!\}$.

In the case of ordinary rational approximations, $\mathcal{T}f$ is non-empty and consists of a single element of R for all $f \in C[a, b]$. Nevertheless, even in this case $\mathcal{T}$ is discontinuous, as was observed first by Maehly and Witzgall [**8**]. They gave a sufficient condition on f that $\mathcal{T}$ should be continuous at f, and this condition was shown by Werner [**9**] to be necessary as well. The theorem of Maehly and Witzgall may be extended to generalized rational approximation in the following manner.

CONTINUITY THEOREM. *If $r \in \mathcal{T}f$ and if $\eta(P + rQ) = \delta(P) + \delta(Q) - 1$ then $\mathcal{T}g$ is non-empty for all g in a neighborhood of f, and $\mathcal{T}$ is continuous at f in the sense that there exists an $\alpha > 0$ such that $\|r - r_1\| \leqq \alpha \|f - g\|$ whenever $r_1 \in \mathcal{T}g$.*

PROOF. Let $\{g_1, \cdots, g_n\}$ be a basis for P and $\{h_1, \cdots, h_m\}$ a basis for Q. Let an element of R, $\sum c_i g_i / \sum c_{n+i} h_i$ with $|c| = 1$, be denoted by r_c. Let $r_a \in \mathcal{T}f$. In seeking a best approximation to g we may confine our search to those r_c which satisfy $\|r_c - g\| \leqq \|r_a - g\|$. For such an r_c the Strong Uniqueness Theorem implies

$$\begin{aligned}(1)\qquad \gamma \|r_a - r_c\| &\leqq \|f - r_c\| - \|f - r_a\| \\ &\leqq \|f - g\| + \|g - r_c\| - \|f - r_a\| \\ &\leqq \|f - g\| + \|g - r_a\| - \|f - r_a\| \\ &\leqq \|f - g\| + \|g - f\|.\end{aligned}$$

Thus we may confine our search to those r_c for which $\|r_c - r_a\| \leqq 2\gamma^{-1}\|f - g\|$. Now let $2\varepsilon_1 = \inf_{a \leqq x \leqq b} \sum_{j=1}^{m} a_{n+j}h_j(x)$. By continuity, there exists an $\varepsilon_2 > 0$ such that

$$|c - a| < \varepsilon_2 \Rightarrow \inf_{a \leqq x \leqq b} \sum_{j=1}^{m} c_{n+j}h_j(x) \geqq \varepsilon_1.$$

Next select $\varepsilon_3 > 0$ such that

$$\|r_c - r_a\| < \varepsilon_3 \Rightarrow |c - a| < \varepsilon_2 .$$

In order to verify that this is possible, suppose that it is not. Then we may find a sequence of functions $r_{c(k)} \in R$ such that $\lim_{k\to\infty} \|r_{c(k)} - r_a\| = 0$ and $|c(k) - a| \geqq \varepsilon_2$. By an argument familiar from the preceding theorem we may write

$$\|r_{c(k)} - r_a\| \geqq \max_{a \leqq x \leqq b} \frac{|\langle c(k), \hat{x}\rangle|}{\sum c(k)_j h_j(x)}$$

$$\geqq \frac{1}{M} \max_{a \leqq x \leqq b} |\langle c(k), \hat{x}\rangle|,$$

where $M = \max_{|c|=1} \|\sum_{j=1}^{m} c_{n+j}h_j(x)\|$. By compactness we may assume that $c(k) \to c$. Then $\langle c, \hat{x}\rangle = 0$ for all $x \in [a, b]$. This implies that c is a multiple of a. Since $|c| = |a| = 1$ and since the denominators of r_c and r_a are positive, it follows that $c = a$, a contradiction of the inequality $|c(k) - a| \geqq \varepsilon_2$.

Now to complete the proof, suppose that $\|f - g\| \leqq (\gamma\varepsilon_3)/2$. Then our search for a best approximation may be confined to those r_c such that $\|r_c - r_a\| \leqq \varepsilon_3$. From the above it follows that the denominators of such functions are bounded below by ε_1. In this restricted set of generalized rational functions, best approximations exist, by a routine compactness argument. Thus $\mathscr{T}g$ is non-empty when $\|f - g\| \leqq (\gamma\varepsilon_3)/2$. The continuity of $\mathscr{T}$ then follows from inequality (1), taking $r_c \in \mathscr{T}g$ and $\alpha = 2\gamma^{-1}$.

In conclusion we mention some typical questions (not necessarily deep) which remain to be answered. 1. If $\mathscr{T}f$ is non-void does it follow that $\mathscr{T}g$ is non-void for all g in a neighborhood of f? 2. In case $\nu(P + rQ) = +\infty$ what sufficient condition can be given that r be a best approximation to f? 3. Is each element of R a best approximation to some function not in R? 4. If $f \neq r \in \mathscr{T}f$ and $\eta(P + rQ) < \delta(P) + \delta(Q) - 1$ does it follow that $\mathscr{T}$ is discontinuous at f? 5. Can a similar theory be given for approximations of the form pq with $p \in P$ and $q \in Q$?

REFERENCES

1. E. W. Cheney and H. L. Loeb, *Generalized rational approximation*, Soc. Indust. Appl. Math., J. of Numerical Analysis **1** (1964), 11–25.

2. N. I. Achieser, *Theory of approximation*, Ungar Publ. Co., New York, 1956.

3. B. W. Boehm, *Existence of best rational Tchebycheff approximations*, Pacific J. of Math., to appear.

4. D. Newman and H. S. Shapiro, *Approximation by generalized rational functions*, to appear.

5. I. P. Natanson, *Constructive function theory*, Office of Technical Services, U.S. Dept. of Commerce, Washington, D.C. 1963.

6. P. P. Korovkin, *Linear operators and approximation theory*, Hindustan Publ. Co., New Delhi, 1960.

7. J. R. Rice, *Tschebyscheff approximations by functions unisolvent of variable degree*, Trans. Amer. Math. Soc. **99** (1961), 298–302.

8. H. Maehly and C. Witzgall, *Tschebyscheff-Approximationen in Kleinen Intervallen.* II, Numerische Math. **2** (1960), 293–307.

9. H. Werner, *On the local behavior of the rational Tchebycheff operator*, Bull. Amer. Math. Soc. **70** (1964), 554–555.

NONLINEAR APPROXIMATION

JOHN R. RICE
General Motors Research Laboratories, Warren, Michigan

1. **Introduction.** The purpose of this paper is to explore the possibility of placing non-linear approximation into a geometrical framework. Actually, there is no question that this can be done. The question is whether there is any profit in it, i.e., will we obtain any new insight into and information about the approximation problem.

This interpretation process is very well defined for linear problems in terms of "spheres" and "planes" [**20**, Chapter 1]. It is safe to say that most workers in approximation theory use this geometrical interpretation from time to time and that many of them consider it a valuable intuitive aid and guide to insight. We feel that this will be the case for non-linear approximation also. It is unlikely that this approach is developed in this particular paper either in its most polished or its most complete form, yet one can see the beginnings of a geometrical theory of non-linear approximation.

Rather than give a running resumé of the contents of the paper, we give below an informal table of contents:

§2. Approximation problems as projection problems.
§3. Unisolvent and locally unisolvent functions as manifolds.
§4. Projections on submanifolds of finite dimensional Banach spaces—with emphasis on uniqueness problems.
§5. Non-manifold problems or why manifold theory alone is inadequate for non-linear approximation.
§6. Projections on objects in finite dimensional Banach spaces.
§7. A topological property of the set of points of non-unique projection.
§§8, 9. The difficulties and opportunities in infinite dimensional spaces—as concerns existence (8.) and uniqueness (9.).

The bulk of the results are concerned with finite dimensional problems. One would naturally expect this, for not only are these problems the first ones that come to mind, but they are also the easiest. Even so, there are still many avenues of development to be explored, some of which are non-trivial. The difficulties in infinite dimensional spaces are formidable, and hence the opportunities for research (and frustration) are great. We are aware from functional analysis of the possible complications in such spaces. In order to visualize the new realm of complication, recall, for example, that finite dimensional subspaces of Hilbert space present little difficulty for analysis. Compare this with the fact that finite dimensional *submanifolds* are not the least bit tractable (at least at this time).

As a final comment, note the strong relationship between non-linear approximation and other non-linear extremal problems. Indeed, it is almost certain that the two areas will be indistinguishable when placed in a geometrical framework such as the one presented here. This has been recognized by many people, but, so far, has not been vigorously exploited. It is very likely that there are results and techniques developed in these other fields which are very pertinent to (and unknown to) non-linear approximation.

2. **Approximation problems as projection problems.** Let us first consider the typical situation for an approximation problem. We have a Hausdorf space X and a Banach space B of real functions $b(x)$ defined on X. Further we have an approximating function $F(A, x)$ depending on the parameter $A \in P$ where P is some domain set for the parameters. The statement of the approximation problem is:

APPROXIMATION PROBLEM. *Given $b \in B$ determine the parameters $A^* \in P$ such that*

$$\|F(A^*) - b\| \leqq \|F(A) - b\|$$

for all $A \in P$.

Here the norm of B is denoted by $\| \;\; \|$. A solution of this problem is called a *best approximation* to b.

Now let us define a projection problem. Consider an arbitrary Banach space B and a subset $\mathscr{F} \subset B$. Given $b \in B$, the point $f^* \in \mathscr{F}$ is said to be a *projection* of b onto $\mathscr{F}$ if

$$\|f^* - b\| = \inf_{f \in \mathscr{F}} \|f - b\|. \tag{2.1}$$

We now state the

PROJECTION PROBLEM. *Given $b \in B$ and $\mathscr{F}$, determine the projection f^* of b onto $\mathscr{F}$.*

The identification of these two problems is straight forward. Associated with the approximating function $F(A, x)$ we have in B the set

$$\mathscr{F} = \{F(A, x) \mid A \in P\}. \tag{2.2}$$

Thus the best approximations to $b(x)$ by $F(A, x)$ are identified as the projections of b onto $\mathscr{F}$. We shall use the identification in (2.2) throughout this paper and will, from time to time, use $\mathscr{F}$ and $F(A, x)$ interchangeably. Thus, for example, we may say that $\mathscr{F}$ is continuous or unisolvent (which means that $F(A, x)$ is continuous in A or unisolvent) or that $F(A, x)$ is connected or closed (which means that $\mathscr{F}$ is connected or closed). At times we may speak of the set $\mathscr{F}$ as an independent entity rather than a subset of B. However, we always have in the background that $\mathscr{F}$ is embedded in B(i.e., the topology of $\mathscr{F}$ is derived from B). Thus if we say $\mathscr{F}$ is a manifold, we mean that $\mathscr{F}$ is a submanifold of B unless explicitly stated otherwise.

A good portion of this paper is concerned with the case when X is finite; i.e., $X = \{x_i \mid i = 1, 2, \cdots, m\}$. In this case we identify B as the real vector space

$$B^m = \{(b(x_1), b(x_2), \cdots, b(x_m)) \mid |b(x_i)| < \infty\}.$$

The projection problem is, in a sense, more general than the usual approximation problems. For example, we may also consider the following

LINEAR CONSTRAINED APPROXIMATION PROBLEM. *Given* $b \in B$ *and a set*

$$\{\phi_i \mid i = 1, 2, \cdots, n\} \subset B$$

and a set $\mathscr{H} \subset E^n$ *determine coefficients* $\{a_i^*\} \in \mathscr{H}$ *so that*

$$\| \sum a_i^* \phi_i - b \| \leqq \| \sum a_i \phi_i - b \|$$

for all $\{a_i\} \in \mathscr{H}$.

For the special case of a convex set H, this problem is studied in [**16**] and an interpretation of it as a projection problem is given. However, in this case, one may also interpret it as a projection in E^n as well as in B. Consider a fixed b and set

$$\rho^* = \inf_{a_i \in E^n} \|\sum a_i \phi_i - b\|.$$

The sets

$$S(\rho) = \{\{a_i\} \in E^n \mid \|\sum a_i \phi_i - b\| \leqq \rho\}$$

are convex in E^n for $\rho \geqq \rho^*$ and define a "distance function" which measures the distance of points in E^n from $S(\rho^*)$. This distance function need not define a norm or metric for all of E^n.

It is proposed in [**16**] to replace this problem by "approximation in the parameter space norm". That is to say that the problem is replaced by two problems: 1) determine $S(\rho^*)$, 2) determine $\{a_i^*\} \in \mathscr{H}$ such that

$$\begin{aligned} &\inf \{\|\{b_i\} - \{a_i^*\}\|_{E^n} \mid \{b_i\} \in S(\rho^*)\} \\ &\qquad = \inf \{\inf \{\|\{a_i\} - \{b_i\}\|_{E^n} \mid \{b_i\} \in S(\rho^*)\} \mid \{a_i\} \in \mathscr{H}\}. \end{aligned}$$

where the norm $\| \ \|_{E^n}$ is a norm in E^n. Normally, $S(\rho^*)$ consists of a single point and the first of these two problems is a typical unconstrained linear problem. Furthermore, the second of these two problems is a standard projection problem in the finite dimensional vector space E^n.

One can, of course, make the same interpretation for a non-linear constrained problem *provided* the parameter domain P of $F(A, x)$ can be reasonably interpreted as a subset of E^n. We shall see later that this is not always possible. On the other hand, one may view the constraint as simply a restriction of the set $\mathscr{F}$ to some smaller set and the interpretation as a projection problem in B^m remains unaltered.

3. **Unisolvent and locally unisolvent functions as manifolds.** We begin with some established definitions for the case where $X = [0, 1]$ and the function $F(A, x)$ is continuous in x and A [**1, 13, 21**].

DEFINITION 1. *$F(A, x)$ has Property Z of degree n at A^* if $A^* \neq A$ implies that $F(A^*, x) - F(A, x)$ has at most $n - 1$ zeros in X.*

DEFINITION 2. *$F(A, x)$ is locally solvent of degree n at A^* if given*

$$\{x_i \in X \mid i = 1, 2, \cdots, n\},$$

$A^* \in P$ and $\varepsilon > 0$, then there is a $\delta(A^*, \varepsilon, x_i) > 0$ such that

$$|F(A^*, x_i) - y_i| < \delta \tag{3.1}$$

implies the existence of a solution $A \in P$ to

$$F(A, x_i) = y_i \tag{3.2}$$

with $\max_{x \in X} |F(A, x) - F(A^*, x)| < \varepsilon$.

DEFINITION 3. *$F(A, x)$ is locally unisolvent of degree n if $F(A, x)$ is locally solvent and has Property Z of degree n for every A. $F(A, x)$ is unisolvent of degree n if $F(A, x)$ has Property Z for every A and* (3.2) *has a solution for every set $\{y_i\}$.*

DEFINITION 4. *A set $\mathcal{M}$ is a manifold if there is an atlas (a collection) of charts $\{(W_\alpha, \eta_\alpha) \mid \alpha \in I\}$ where W_α is an open subset of E^n; $\eta_\alpha : W_\alpha \to \mathcal{M}$ is a homeomorphism of W_α onto an open subset U_α of $\mathcal{M}$ such that*[1]

(i) *if $f \in \mathcal{M}$, then there is an $\alpha \in I$ such that $f \in U_\alpha$.*

(ii) *if $U_\alpha \cap U_\beta = U$ is not empty, then $\eta_\beta^{-1}\eta_\alpha$ is a homeomorphism of $\eta_\alpha^{-1}(U)$ onto $\eta_\beta^{-1}(U)$.*

We depart from the usual convention in geometry and speak of $\mathcal{F}$ being a *submanifold* of B^m only if the *topology of $\mathcal{F}$ as a manifold is the topology induced on $\mathcal{F}$ from B^m*. This is the usual convention in differential topology.

The purpose of this section is to establish some properties of the set $\mathcal{F}$ associated with unisolvent and locally unisolvent functions. We have

THEOREM 1. *If $\mathcal{F}$ is locally unisolvent of degree n, then $\mathcal{F}$ is a manifold of dimension n.*

PROOF. Let us fix n distinct points x_i, $i = 1, 2, \cdots, n$ in X and define the mapping ϕ from $\mathcal{F}$ to E^n by

$$\phi : [f = F(A, x)] \in \mathcal{F} \to (F(A, x_1), F(A, x_2), \cdots, F(A, x_n)).$$

Set

$$W(f, \delta) = \{V \mid V \in E^n, \|V - \varphi(f)\|_{E^n} < \delta\}$$

and for $V \in W(f, \delta)$ define $\eta = \phi^{-1}$. It follows from Property Z that ϕ is one-to-one and hence $\eta = \phi^{-1}$ is well defined. It follows from local solvence that ϕ is continuous and it is known [**22, 20**—Lemma 3-4] that ϕ^{-1} is continuous. Hence the mapping $\eta : W(f, \delta) \to \mathcal{F}$ is a homeomorphism. It is clear that $f \in \eta[W(f, \delta)]$ for any $\delta > 0$. If

$$U = W(f_1, \delta_1) \cap W(f_2, \delta_2) \neq \text{empty set}$$

---

[1] A third condition is also to be satisfied, but if the atlas satisfies (i) and (ii) then it is known that there is another atlas, containing all the charts of this atlas, which satisfies this third condition.

then $\eta^{-1}\eta$ is the identity function on U. This concludes the proof that $\mathcal{F}$ is a manifold.

COROLLARY: *If $\mathcal{F}$ is unisolvent, then $\mathcal{F}$ is homeomorphic to E^n.*

The following examples illustrate two facts, namely that $\mathcal{F}$ may be homeomorphic to E^n without being unisolvent and that if $\mathcal{F}$ is locally unisolvent, $\mathcal{F}$ need not be homeomorphic to E^n.

EXAMPLES:

$$\mathcal{F} = \left\{\frac{a}{1 + ax} \,\middle|\, X = [-1, 1]; -1 < a < 1\right\},$$

$$\mathcal{F} = \left\{\frac{a}{1 + ax} \,\middle|\, X = [-1, 1]; -1 < a < -\tfrac{1}{2}, \tfrac{1}{2} < a < 1\right\}.$$

If X is a finite subset of [0, 1] then the manifold $\mathcal{F}$ may be identified with an n-dimensional submanifold of B^m. Thus the study of approximation of functions on a finite subset X of [0, 1] by locally unisolvent functions is subsumed by the study of projections of points of B^m onto a submanifold $\mathcal{F}$ of B^m.

We note, however, that every submanifold of B^m is not locally unisolvent. For example, in B^3, the one-dimensional linear manifold

$$\mathcal{M} = \{(x, y, z) \mid x = y, z = 1\}$$

does not have Property Z of degree 1 and hence is not locally unisolvent.

Thus, it is of interest to know just which submanifolds of B^m may be identified as unisolvent. We require

DEFINITION 5. *A set $\mathcal{M} \in B^m$ is said to be k-skewed if, for every pair $f_1, f_2 \in \mathcal{M}$ the point $(f_1 - f_2) \in B$ does not lie in an $m - k$ dimensional coordinate plane.*

The closed locally unisolvent submanifolds of B^m are characterized by the following

THEOREM 2. *The closed*[2] *manifold $\mathcal{M} \in B^m$ is locally unisolvent of degree n if and only if $\mathcal{M}$ is n-skewed.*

PROOF. We first note that if $\mathcal{M}$ has Property Z, then, by definition, $\mathcal{M}$ is n-skewed. It is likewise evident that if $\mathcal{M}$ is n-skewed, then $\mathcal{M}$ has Property Z.

To show that $\mathcal{M}$ is locally solvent, consider any n distinct points in X and the corresponding n coordinates in B^m. For simplicity, we assume these to be the first n coordinates, though the analysis clearly does not depend on this. Define the mapping ϕ of $\mathcal{M}$ into E^n by

$$\phi : f = (f_1, \cdots, f_{n-1}, f_n, f_{n+1}, \cdots f_m) \to (f_1, \cdots, f_{n-1}, f_n).$$

The mapping ϕ is one-to-one for if $\phi(f') = \phi(f^*)$, then $f' - f^*$ lies in an $m - n$

[2] We use the adjective closed to mean topologically closed rather than closed and bounded as is usual in the geometry literature.

dimensional coordinate plane of B^m. It is clear that ϕ is continuous. We now assert that $\phi(\mathcal{M})$ is an open set in E^n. Indeed, consider any $P = \phi(f)$, then there is a chart (W, η) associated with f such that η maps W into $\mathcal{M}$ and $f \in \eta(W)$. Thus $\phi\eta$ maps W from E^n into E^n such that $\phi\eta : \eta^{-1}\phi^{-1}(P) \rightarrow P$. Hence $\phi\eta(W)$ is contained in $\phi(\mathcal{M})$ and P is an interior point of $\phi(\mathcal{M})$. It is readily established that $\mathcal{M}$ is locally solvent if $\phi(\mathcal{M})$ is open for any choice of n coordinates. This concludes the proof.

The following example shows that stronger conditions are required to characterize unisolvent manifolds.

EXAMPLE: Let $X = \{-1, 0, +1\}$; $F(A, x) = a/(1 + ax)$, $-1 < a < 1$. The manifold $\mathcal{F}$ is shown in Figure 1.

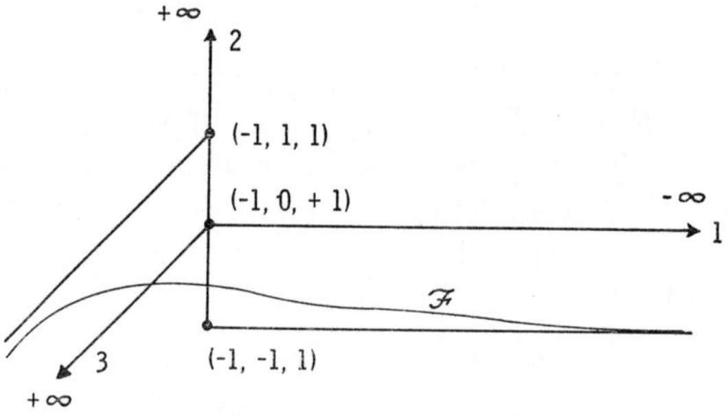

FIGURE 1. The manifold $\mathcal{F}$ for $a/(1 + ax)$, $-1 < a < 1$ and $X = \{-1, 0, +1\}$.

It may be verified that the following condition is sufficient to insure that $\mathcal{M}$ is a unisolvent manifold: Let $|f_1 - f_2|_n$ be the norm of the projection $f_1 - f_2$ onto a $m - n$ dimensional coordinate plane. If $|f_1 - f_2|_n \geqq \alpha \, \|f_1 - f_2\|$ where $\alpha > 0$ holds for any such coordinate plane and any pair $f_1, f_2 \in \mathcal{F}$, then $\mathcal{F}$ is a unisolvent manifold. It is not known if this condition is also necessary.

4. **Projections on submanifolds of finite dimensional Banach spaces.** In this section we attempt a general study of projections on submanifolds of B^m. In some areas we only scratch the surface, but more depth is possible in others. There are these principal questions to be considered:

(1) Does a point $b \in B^m$ have a projection on $\mathcal{F}$?
(2) How are projections characterized?
(3) Are projections uniquely determined?

We consider the questions in this sequence. The first question is easily resolved:

THEOREM 3. *Every point of B^m has a projection on $\mathcal{F}$ if and only if $\mathcal{F}$ is closed.*[3]

PROOF. This result is not of great depth and we merely remark if $\mathcal{F}$ is not closed, then it does not contain all of its limit points. These points clearly do not have

[3] We mean again that $\mathcal{F}$ is topologically closed rather than a "closed manifold".

projections on $\mathscr{F}$. If $\mathscr{F}$ is closed, then it follows directly from the finite dimensionality of B^m that every point has a projection on $\mathscr{F}$.

In order to discuss the characterization of projections we need to define the *ball*

$$\sigma(b^*, r) = \{b \in B^m \mid \|b - b^*\| \leqq r\}$$

with center b^* and radius r. The *ball* $\sigma(b^*, r)$ is said to be *tangent* to the manifold $\mathscr{F}$ at the point f if $f \in \sigma(b^*, r)$ and $\mathscr{F} \cap \operatorname{int} \sigma(b^*, r)$ is empty. The following resolves the second question.

THEOREM 4. *The* $f \in \mathscr{F}$ *is a projection of* b^* *onto* $\mathscr{F}$ *if and only if the ball* $\sigma(b^*, r^*)$ *is tangent to* $\mathscr{F}$ *at* f *where*

$$r^* = \inf_{f \in \mathscr{F}} \|b^* - f\|.$$

This result is little more than a restatement of the definition of a projection. However, if either $\mathscr{F}$ or the ball $\sigma(b^*, r^*)$ have additional properties, then stronger results may be established. For example, the ball $\sigma(b^*, r^*)$ is convex and if, in addition, $\mathscr{F}$ is convex, then a necessary and sufficient condition for tangency is that the ball σ and $\mathscr{F}$ have a common plane of support and have non-intersecting interiors. If $\mathscr{F}$ and the boundary of σ are differentiable manifolds, then even more exact results are possible.

More specifically, call B^m *differentiable* if the boundary

$$\partial\sigma(b^*, r) = \{b \in B^m \mid \|b^* - b\| = r\}$$

of σ is a differentiable manifold of dimension $m - 1$. We may now apply the tools of differential geometry, in particular the idea of *critical points*.[4] We have

COROLLARY 1. *Let* B^m *be differentiable and let* $\mathscr{F}$ *be a differential submanifold of* B^m. *A necessary condition that* $f^* \in \mathscr{F}$ *be a projection of* b *onto* $\mathscr{F}$ *is that* f^* *be a critical point of the function* $\|b - f\|$.

The point f^* is the absolute minimum of a real valued differentiable function of several variables and thus all partials with respect to the y_i must be zero.

COROLLARY 2. *Let* B^m *be differentiable and let* $\mathscr{F}$ *be a differentiable submanifold of* B^m. *A necessary and sufficient condition that* $f^* \in \mathscr{F}$ *be a critical point of* $\|b - f\|$ *is that the normal of* $\partial\sigma(b, \|b - f^*\|)$ *be normal to* $\mathscr{F}$ *at* f^*.

In order to carry out a proof of this, one has to introduce the notion of normals of submanifolds of B^m. How this is done is outlined as follows. At a point $b \in B^m$

---

[4] A point $f \in \mathscr{F}$ is a critical point of $\|b - f\|$ if

$$\frac{\partial \|b_i - f\|}{\partial y_i} = 0, \qquad i = 1, 2, \cdots, k,$$

where k is the dimension of $\mathscr{F}$ and $(y_1, y_2, \cdots, y_k)$ is a local coordinate system of $\mathscr{F}$ in a neighborhood containing f.

we have the tangent space $T(B^m)$ which is m-dimensional Hilbert space. Now at b the tangent space $T(\partial\sigma)$ is an m-1 dimensional subspace of $T(B^m)$. Let α be the unit normal of $T(\partial\sigma)$ in $T(B^m)$. Now α is an equivalence class of curves in B^m. Take that member α^1 of α which is linear and choose a point $b^1 \notin \sigma$ on α^1 at a distance 1 from b. Then $b^1 - b$ is the unit normal of $\partial\sigma$ at b. A similar construction applies to $T(\mathscr{F})$ and $T(B^m)$ to define the normals of $\mathscr{F}$ at $b \in \mathscr{F}$.

For more results in the special case of Euclidean space see **[12]**.

The results that we have obtained concerning existence and characterization are not unexpected. The uniqueness problem leads to a result which, while intuitively plausible, is usually unanticipated. This result says, in general terms, that no global uniqueness theorem is possible for non-linear approximation if the unit ball of B^m is smooth. This is made precise by the following development.

For the remainder of this section we *assume* that $\mathscr{F}$ is *closed* (topologically). This assumption implies by Theorem 3 that every point of B^m has a projection on $\mathscr{F}$. While problems without this assumption are of interest, the uniqueness problem becomes extremely complex without it.

The space B^m is said to be *smooth* if at each point $b \in \partial\sigma$ there is a unique plane of support to σ. If B^m is smooth, then σ has no corner points. The space B^m is said to be *strictly convex* if every ball $\sigma(b, r)$ is strictly convex.

The first result is due to Motzkin **[14]** and has been reestablished elsewhere.

THEOREM 5. *Let $\mathscr{F}$ be a closed subset of a smooth Banach space B^m. Then each point has a unique projection on $\mathscr{F}$ if and only if $\mathscr{F}$ is convex.*

It is convenient to introduce the following

DEFINITION 6. *A subset $\mathscr{M}$ of a Banach space B is said to be a Chebyshev set if every point $b \in B$ possesses a unique projection on $\mathscr{M}$.*

One must distinguish between this definition of Chebyshev set and the more common definition of a Chebyshev set of functions, though there is a clear relationship. There is a stronger form of Theorem 5 (which we do not require) which is stated in terms of Chebyshev sets: *The Banach space B^m, $m \geqq 3$, is smooth and strictly convex if and only if every Chebyshev set in B^m is convex.*

By the use of Theorem 5 we obtain the following

THEOREM 6. *Let $\mathscr{F}$ be a closed submanifold of a smooth Banach space B^m. Then $\mathscr{F}$ is a Chebyshev set if and only if $\mathscr{F}$ is a linear manifold.*

PROOF. It follows from Theorem 5 that $\mathscr{F}$ is convex. The proof is completed by showing that every closed convex manifold is a linear manifold.

Consider a point $f_0 \in \mathscr{F}$ and a neighborhood U in $\mathscr{F}$ of f_0. Let n be the dimension of $\mathscr{F}$, then there is a system $(y_1, y_2, \cdots, y_n)$ of linearly independent coordinates in U. Choose n points $f_i \in \mathscr{F}$, $f_i \neq f_0$, one on each coordinate curve. Set $\varepsilon = \min \|f_i - f_0\|$ for all i and denote by U' the convex hull of the points f_i. By definition U' is a subset of a linear manifold $\mathscr{L}$. Assume that $U_0 = \sigma(f_0, \varepsilon) \cap U$

contains a point f_{n+1} not in $\mathscr{L}$. The convex hull of U' and f_{n+1} is in U and it follows that the dimension of U is at least $n + 1$. This is a contradiction and we have established that every point $f_0 \in \mathscr{F}$ has a neighborhood which is the intersection of a ball and an n-dimensional linear manifold.

Consider any two distinct points $f_1, f_2 \in \mathscr{F}$ and the line

$$l = \{b \mid b = f_1 + \alpha(f_2 - f_1), -\infty < \alpha < \infty\}.$$

The set $l \cap \mathscr{F}$ is closed. Assume, if possible, that $l \cap \mathscr{F}$ has a boundary point f_0 in the relative topology of l. Then f_0 has a neighborhood U which is a subset of an n-dimensional linear manifold $\mathscr{L}$. If $U \cap l = f_0$, then the convex hull of U and f_1 is $n + 1$ dimensional, which is impossible. Hence $U' \cap l$ contains a segment of l and $l \subset \mathscr{L}$. This contradicts the assumption that f_0 is a boundary point of $l \cap \mathscr{F}$. It immediately follows that $\mathscr{F} \supset \mathscr{L}$, where $\mathscr{L}$ is the linear manifold defining a neighborhood of f_1. If $\mathscr{F}$ contains a point not in $\mathscr{L}$, then the dimension of $\mathscr{F}$ is at least $n + 1$, which is impossible. This concludes the proof.

COROLLARY. *Let $F(A, x)$ be a non-linear unisolvent approximating function, X be finite, and $\| \ \|_p$ denote the L_p norm, $1 < p < \infty$. Then there exists a function $f(x)$ defined on X such that*

$$\|f - F(A_1)\|_p = \|f - F(A_2)\|_p = \inf_A \|f - F(A)\|_p,$$

where $A_1 \neq A_2$.

Thus for L_p, $1 < p < \infty$, and non-linear unisolvent approximation, there is no global uniqueness theorem possible.[5] This corollary may be compared with the fact [13] that for the L_∞ (Chebyshev) norm, best approximations are uniquely determined. We have the curious situation that, for linear approximation, there is a trivial global uniqueness theorem for L_p, $1 < p < \infty$, while the uniqueness question for L_1 and L_∞ is delicate and not resolved a priori in either direction. On the other hand, for non-linear approximation (at least by unisolvent functions), there is no possible global uniqueness theorem for L_p, $1 < p < \infty$, and the L_1 and L_∞ cases are again undetermined a priori. Thus, as concerns uniqueness, there is a complete change in polarity in going from linear approximation to non-linear approximation.

For non-linear approximation, there is still hope for and interest in a "local" uniqueness theorem. We establish such a result in the case that B^m is a Hilbert space and $\mathscr{F}$ is sufficiently smooth.

THEOREM 7. *Let $\mathscr{F}$ be a closed submanifold of E^m which has its curvature bounded at each point. Then there exists a neighborhood $\mathscr{F}_u$ of $\mathscr{F}$ such that each point in $\mathscr{F}_u$ has a unique projection onto $\mathscr{F}$.*

---

[5] This remark holds equally well for locally unisolvent approximating functions if every function on X possesses a best approximation.

In order to establish this result, we must consider the "folding" of $\mathscr{F}$ at a point. We say that $f_0, f_1 \in \mathscr{F}$ are separated by the ball $\sigma(f_0, \rho)$ if there is no path in int $\sigma(f_0, \rho) \cap \mathscr{F}$ joining f_0 and f_1. Set

$$(4.1)\quad \rho^*(f_0) = \inf \{\rho \mid \text{there exists } f_1 \in \mathscr{F} \text{ such that } f_1 \text{ is separated from } f_0 \text{ by } \sigma(f_0, \rho)\}.$$

DEFINITION 7. *The folding* $\eta = \eta(f_0)$ *of* $\mathscr{F}$ *at* f_0 *is* $1/\rho^*(f_0)$.

LEMMA 1. *Let* $\mathscr{F}$ *be a closed submanifold of* E^m. *Then* $\eta < \infty$ *at every point of* $\mathscr{F}$ *and, if* $\eta(f_0) > 0$, *there exists* $f_1 \in \mathscr{F}$ *such that the* inf *is assumed in* (4.1).

PROOF. We first show $\eta(f) < \infty$ or, equivalently, $\rho^*(f) > 0$. Assume that there is a sequence $\{f_i\}$ such that $f_i \to f$ and f_i is separated from f by $\sigma(f, 1/i)$. Thus every neighborhood N of B^m containing f also contains some point f_i. Thus $N \cap \mathscr{F}$ is not connected and since the topology of $\mathscr{F}$ is induced from B^m, it follows that $\mathscr{F}$ does not have a neighborhood containing f which is homeomorphic to a Euclidean neighborhood. This shows $\eta(f) < \infty$.

Assume that $\rho^*(f) < \infty$. Then for $\varepsilon > 0$ there is an f_ε such that f_ε is separated from f by $\sigma(f, \rho^* + \varepsilon)$. Since closed and bounded subsets of B^m are compact, there is an $f_1 \in \mathscr{F}$ such that a subsequence of $\{f_\varepsilon\}$ converges to f_1 as ε tends to zero. Clearly $f_1 \in \sigma(f, \rho^*)$. If f_1 is connected to f in $\sigma(f, \rho^*)$ than every neighborhood $\sigma(f_1, \varepsilon)$ of f_1 in B^m is connected to f in $\sigma(f, \rho^* + \varepsilon)$, since $\sigma(f_1, \varepsilon)$ is connected. For some $\varepsilon_0 > 0$, $\sigma(f_1, \varepsilon_0) \cap \mathscr{F}$ is connected and hence f_{ε_0} is connected to f in $\sigma(f_1, \varepsilon_0)$. This contradicts the definition of f_{ε_0} and concludes the proof.

LEMMA 2. *Let* $\mathscr{F}$ *be a submanifold of* E^m *with curvature bounded at each point. Let* $f_0 \in \mathscr{F}$ *and* N *a unit normal to* $\mathscr{F}$ *at* f_0. *Then there is an* $\varepsilon > 0$ *such that the projection of* $f_t = f_0 + tN$ *onto* $\mathscr{F}$ *is* f_0 *for* $|t| < \varepsilon$.

PROOF. If $|t| < \frac{1}{2}\eta(f_0) = \eta_0$, then all projections of f_t onto $\mathscr{F}$ lie in a neighborhood U of $\mathscr{F}$ containing f_0. Consider coordinates $\boldsymbol{u} = (u_1, u_2, \cdots, u_n)$ in U. Set $k = m - n$ and consider sets $\{T_\alpha(\boldsymbol{u}), \mid \alpha = 1, 2, \cdots, n\}$, $\{N_\beta(\boldsymbol{u}) \mid \beta = 1, 2, \cdots, k\}$ of orthonormal basis vectors for the tangent space of $\mathscr{F}$ at $\boldsymbol{u}$ and the normal space of $\mathscr{F}$ at $\boldsymbol{u}$, respectively. Consider any point $b \in E^m$

$$(4.2)\qquad b = b(\boldsymbol{r}, \boldsymbol{u}) = \boldsymbol{u} + \sum_{\beta=1}^{k} r_\beta N_\beta(\boldsymbol{u})$$

where $\boldsymbol{r} = (r_1, r_2, \cdots, r_k)$ and $\sum_{\beta=1}^{k} r_\beta^2 \leqq \eta_0^2$. It is known that (4.2) defines a manifold provided the vectors

$$b_\alpha = \frac{\partial b}{\partial u_\alpha}$$

are linearly independent and (4.2) is one-to-one between b and $(\boldsymbol{r}, \boldsymbol{u})$. We may compute

$$b_\alpha = T_\alpha(\boldsymbol{u}) + \sum_{\beta=1}^{k} r_\beta \frac{\partial N_\beta(\boldsymbol{u})}{\partial u_\alpha}.$$

Since the curvature is bounded, the vectors $\partial N_\beta(\boldsymbol{u})/\partial u_\alpha$ are uniformly bounded in U. Thus, there is an $\varepsilon_0 > 0$, such that if $\sum_{\beta=1}^{k} r_\beta^2 \leqq \varepsilon_0^2$, then the n vectors b_α are linearly independent. Thus, if $\sum_{\beta=1}^{k} r_\beta^2 \leqq \varepsilon = \min [\eta_0, \varepsilon_0]$, (4.2) defines a manifold $\mathcal{M}_u$. Any point $m \in \mathcal{M}_u$ lies on exactly one normal of $\mathcal{F}$ in U. Since projections in E^m are along normals, it follows that the projection of each point of $\mathcal{M}_u$, in particular the point f_t, is uniquely determined. This concludes the proof.

We have actually established the following stronger result.

COROLLARY 1. *Let $\mathcal{F}$ be a submanifold of E^m with curvature bounded at each point. Given $f_0 \in \mathcal{F}$ there is a neighborhood $U(f_0)$ in $\mathcal{F}$ of f_0 and a second neighborhood $\mathcal{M}_u$ in E^m of U such that every point of $\mathcal{M}_u$ has a unique projection onto $\mathcal{F}$ and that projection lies in U.*

We may complete the proof of Theorem 7 by noting that

$$\mathcal{F}_u = \bigcup_{f \in \mathcal{F}} U(f)$$

is the required neighborhood of $\mathcal{F}$.

It is reasonable to conjecture that Theorem 7 is not peculiar to E^m for the fact that E^m is a Hilbert space rather than a general Banach space appears in the technique of the proof rather than the philosophy of the proof. On the other hand, we do not have a well developed concept of curvature in B^m. If we define the curvature of objects in B^m as their Euclidean curvature, then the following is plausible.

COROLLARY 2. *Let the unit ball of B^m have curvature bounded from zero and infinity. Then Theorem 7 is valid with E^m replaced by B^m.*

We shall not pause here to develop the geometrical machinery required to establish this result. We do note that the method used in this corollary to define curvature in B^m is completely unreasonable.

In order to illustrate that Theorem 7 does not extend without limit, we consider L_p space, $1 < p < \infty, p \neq 2$.

EXAMPLE. $X = [-1, +1]$, $F(A, x) = \{a + bx \mid a^2 + b^2 = 1\}$

$$b_1(x) = \begin{cases} 1, & x = \pm 1 \\ 1 - 3\varepsilon + 4\varepsilon^2, & x = 0 \\ \text{linear fill elsewhere,} & \end{cases}$$

$$b_2(x) = 1 - 4\varepsilon.$$

The following facts are easily established.

(i) $F(A^+, x) = (1 - 4\varepsilon^2) + 2\varepsilon x$ and $F(A^-, x) = (1 - 4\varepsilon^2) - 2\varepsilon x$ are better L_∞ approximations to $b_1(x)$ than $F(A^0, x) = 1$.

(ii) $F(A^+, x)$ and $F(A^-, x)$ are better L_1 approximations to $b_2(x)$ than $F(A^0, x)$.

(iii) As $\varepsilon \to 0$ we have $\|b_1 - F(A^0)\|_p \to 0$, $\|b_2 - F(A^0)\|_p \to 0$.

Thus for some $p < \infty$, $F(A^+)$ and $F(A^-)$ are better L_p approximations to b_1 than $F(A^0)$ and for some $p > 1$, they are better L_p approximations to b_2 than $F(A^0)$.

In the above example, the Banach space is not finite dimensional. It is simpler to construct similar examples in B^m. We would like to propose that the difficulty of extending Theorem 7 to cover this example lies not with L_p space, $p \neq 2$, but rather with the definition of curvature in L_p space. That is to say that the manifold defined in this example would have infinite curvature at some points with a more intrinsic definition of curvature.

We close this section with a simple interpretation of Theorems 6 and 7 for the Constrained Linear Approximation Problem.

COROLLARY 3. *If $\mathscr{H}$ is a closed manifold and B^m is strictly convex, then best constrained linear approximations in the parameter space norm are unique for every function if and only if $\mathscr{H}$ is a linear manifold.*

COROLLARY 4. *Let $\mathscr{H}$ be a closed manifold with curvature bounded at each point and choose the Euclidean norm in the parameter space. Then there is a neighborhood $\mathscr{H}_u$ of $\mathscr{H}$ such that each function whose unconstrained best approximation lies in $\mathscr{H}_u$ has a unique best constrained approximation in the parameter space norm.*

5. **Non-manifold approximation problems.** The study of projections on manifolds is a natural and essential first step toward understanding non-linear approximation; however, it is immediately apparent that this study will not apply to many of the most interesting approximating functions. This section is devoted to showing why this is the case. The requirements for a connected set $\mathscr{F} \subset B^m$ to be a manifold are quite restrictive. In particular, $\mathscr{F}$ must be of constant dimension and have no "boundary" points.[6] We consider two common approximating functions in some detail to illustrate the mechanisms by which $\mathscr{F}$ fails to be a manifold.

EXAMPLE.

$$X = \{x_1 < x_2 < x_3 < x_4, x_i \in [0, 1]\},$$

$$F(A, x) = \frac{a + bx}{c + dx} \quad \text{for}$$

$$A \in P = \{(a, b, c, d) \mid c^2 + d^2 = 1, c + dx > 0 \quad \text{for} \quad x \in [x_1, x_4]\}.$$

Then

$$\mathscr{F} = \{(F(A, x_1), F(A, x_2), F(A, x_3), F(A, x_4)) \mid A \in P\}$$

is a subset of the space B^4 of real functions defined on X. It is readily verified that $\mathscr{F}$ is homeomorphic to the interior of a double wedge plus the line of intersection of the planes defining the wedge. A two-dimensional cross-section is shown in Figure 2 below. This set is not closed and, as is well known, best approximations

[6] $\mathscr{F}$ also cannot have "branch" points, but approximating functions for which $\mathscr{F}$ has such points are unusual.

do not exist for all functions defined on X. The set $\mathscr{F}$ may be closed by adjoining the pseudo-rational functions which are constant on $[x_1, x_4]$ except for a jump discontinuity at x_1 or x_4. The appropriate functions are shown in the figure. The line of intersection of the two planes corresponds to the constant functions. A general treatment of the process of adjoining pseudo-rational functions has been

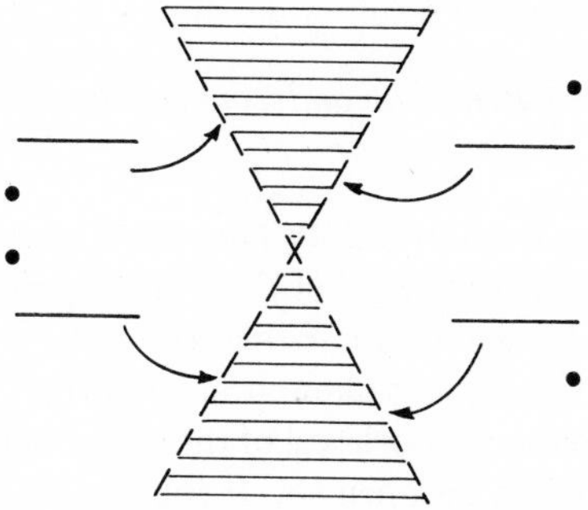

FIGURE 2. A cross-section of the set $\mathscr{F}$ for the approximating function $(a + bx)/(c + dx)$.

made in [7] with the concept of stabilized approximations. Further developments are given in the paper by Goldstein of these proceedings (p. 57).

Although the homeomorphic image of $\mathscr{F}$ in E^3 is open (except at the line of intersection), every point of $\mathscr{F}$ is a boundary point in the topology of B^4.

If we choose to consider the closure $\overline{\mathscr{F}}$ of $\mathscr{F}$ in B^4, we still do not obtain a manifold. We conclude with the observation that if we consider only $\mathscr{F}$ then best approximations are always unique, but do not always exist and that if we consider $\overline{\mathscr{F}}$, then they always exist, but are not always unique.

EXAMPLE. $F(A, x) = ab^x + c$, X as above. The set P is defined so as to include the straight lines. It is readily shown that $\mathscr{F}$ for this example is homeomorphic to that of the preceding example. Furthermore, the pseudo-exponential functions required to close $\mathscr{F}$ are the same functions as in the preceding example. This example is considered in detail in **[15, 18]**. The concluding observation of the preceding example applies here.

The properties exhibited by these two examples are shared in some extent by all varisolvent approximating functions. We proceed to establish this. The following definition is given in **[17]**.

DEFINITION 8. *The approximating function $F(A, x)$ is said to be varisolvent if there is a non-constant bounded function $n(A)$ such that $F(A, x)$ is locally solvent and has Property Z of degree $n(A)$ at each point $A \in P$.*

Note that a locally unisolvent function is *not* varisolvent since $n(A)$ is constant for such a function. That varisolvent functions have certain topological properties is known. Define

$$\mathscr{F}_k = \{f \in \mathscr{F} \mid f = F(A, x) \quad \text{with} \quad n(A) \geqq k\}$$

and set $n_0 = \max \{n(A) \mid A \in P\}$. Then we have

THEOREM 8. *i) The set* $\mathscr{F}_k$ *is open in* $\mathscr{F}$. *ii) The set* $\mathscr{F}_{n_0}$ *is a manifold.*

The result i) is known **[21]** and the result ii) is established by a repetition of the argument of Theorem 1.

We have the following general result concerning varisolvent functions.

THEOREM 9. *Let* $\mathscr{F}$ *be varisolvent and connected, X finite. Then* $\mathscr{F}$ *is not a manifold.*

PROOF. Assume that $\mathscr{F}$ is a manifold. By Theorem 8 and connectedness it follows that $\mathscr{F}$ is a manifold of dimension n_0. Let $f \in \mathscr{F}$ be a point where $n(A) = p < n_0$. Such a point must exist. By definition $\mathscr{F}$ has Property Z of degree p at f or, by Theorem 2, the manifold $\mathscr{F} - f$ is p-skewed at the origin.

Now every n_0-dimensional neighborhood of the origin intersects every $m - n_0 + 1$ dimensional subspace of B^m in an open set. It follows that $\mathscr{F} - f$ is not $(n_0 - 1)$-skewed at the origin and hence not p-skewed for $p < n_0$. This is a contradiction and the original assumption is untenable.

It is rather remarkable that approximation by $(a + bx)/(c + dx)$ and $ab^x + c$ should turn out to be such similar problems when interpreted as projection problems. Of course, the mechanics of the projection are distinct, but the intrinsic nature of the problems must be the same. Indeed, it immediately raises the interesting (and probably quite difficult) question of what features of the projection (approximation) are invariant under a homeomorphism of $\mathscr{F}$. There are some such features.

Although the two examples above lead to sets $\mathscr{F}$ which are homeomorphic, one cannot conclude that every pair of varisolvent functions with similar behavior of $n(A)$ lead to sets $\mathscr{F}$ which are homeomorphic. Consider the varisolvent function

$$F(A, x) = \{a + bx + cx^2 \mid |a| < \infty ; b > 0 \quad \text{if} \quad c \neq 0; |b| < \infty \quad \text{if} \quad c = 0; \\ b + 2c > 0 \quad \text{if} \quad c \neq 0\}$$

with $X \subset [0, 1]$. This is the constrained linear approximating function for straight lines plus parabolas strictly increasing on [0, 1]. One can also consider the set of parabolas strictly monotonic on [0, 1] plus all straight lines. In this latter case the set $\mathscr{F}$ is homeomorphic to the $\mathscr{F}$ for $ab^x + c$.

6. **Projections on objects in B^m.** The preceding discussion leads to the conclusion that we must consider projections onto more general objects than manifolds. In this section we consider to what extent the results of §4 may be extended to more general objects. We have immediately:

THEOREM 3A. *Let* $\mathscr{F}$ *be an object in* B^m. *Then every point of* B^m *has a projection on* $\mathscr{F}$ *if and only if* $\mathscr{F}$ *is closed.*

THEOREM 4A. *The point $f \in \mathscr{F}$ is a projection of b onto $\mathscr{F}$ if and only if the ball $\sigma(b, r^*)$ is tangent to $\mathscr{F}$ at f where*

$$r^* = \inf_{f \in \mathscr{F}} \|b - f\|.$$

Note that Theorem 5 applies directly to the projection onto general objects. There is, of course, no extension possible of Theorem 6. Concerning uniqueness, however, we have the following result.

THEOREM 10. *Let $\mathscr{F}$ be varisolvent in B^m. Then $\mathscr{F}$ is not convex.*

PROOF. Assume that $\mathscr{F}$ is convex and set $n_0 = \max\{n(A) \mid A \in P\}$. The argument contained in the proof of Theorem 6 shows that $\mathscr{F}$ lies in some n_0-dimensional linear manifold $\mathscr{L}$ in B^m. In the remainder of the proof we restrict our attention to $\mathscr{F}$ as a subset of $\mathscr{L}$.

The set $\mathscr{F}_{n_0}$ (see Theorem 8) is of dimension n_0 and convex. Furthermore, the closure $\overline{\mathscr{F}}_{n_0} \supset \mathscr{F}$ if $\mathscr{F}$ is convex. Consider a point $f \in \mathscr{F}$ of degree $p < n_0$. Such a point must exist, and it lies on the boundary of $\mathscr{F}$. There is a plane P of support to $\mathscr{F}$ at f_0 (P is a plane in $\mathscr{L}$). Consider the coordinate system of B^m translated to f_0. There is at least one coordinate semi-axis which is separated from $\mathscr{F}$ by P. For concreteness assume that it is the lth negative semi-axis. Then it is not possible to solve the equation (with $f = F(A_0, x)$)

$$F(A, x_l) = F(A_0, x_l) - \varepsilon$$

for any $\varepsilon > 0$. Thus $F(A_0, x)$ is not locally solvent of any degree at A_0. This is a contradiction and concludes the proof.

We have the following conjecture concerning the topological nature of a varisolvent $\mathscr{F}$.

CONJECTURE. *Let X be finite and $\mathscr{F}$ varisolvent. Then $\mathscr{F}$ is not closed.*

This conjecture is not correct if X is an interval.

If this conjecture is correct, then the nature of the examples of rational and exponential functions is typical of general varisolvent functions. We would obtain as immediate consequences of Theorem 10 and this conjecture the following results concerning varisolvent functions and approximation on finite point sets.

(1) Best approximations do not always exist.

(2) If B^m is smooth then best approximations are not always unique (whether one considers $\mathscr{F}$ or its closure).

Note that for the Chebyshev norm, best approximations are uniquely determined.

We briefly consider the possibility of extending Theorem 7 to more general objects. It is clear that a neighborhood of unique projection does exist for many "smooth" objects which are not manifolds. Consider, for example, a "solid" torus in E^3 or the set $\mathscr{F} = \{f = (f_1, f_2, \cdots, f_m) \mid \sum_{i=2}^m f_i^2 \leqq f_1^4 \text{ if } f_1 > 0, \sum_{i=2}^m f_i^2 = 0 \text{ if } f_1 < 0\}$ in E^m. On the other hand, the set $\mathscr{F}$ cannot become too complex and yet retain a smooth boundary. For example, in E^2, if $\mathscr{F}$ is one-dimensional and connected, then $\mathscr{F}$ has a neighborhood of unique projection only if $\mathscr{F}$ is homeomorphic to a line or a circle (i.e., no figure 8, etc., is allowed). We will not pursue this question further here, but it is likely that the characterization of those objects with a neighborhood of unique projection involves some deep topological results.

7. **A topological property.** Let us assume that $\mathscr{F}$ is closed and then consider the set

$$N(\mathscr{F}) = \{b \mid b \text{ does not have a unique projection on } \mathscr{F}\}$$

which we call the set of *nup* (non-unique projection) points. We denote by P the *projection operator* which associates with $b \in B^m$ its projections $P(b)$ onto $\mathscr{F}$. The operator P is multivalued at the *nup* points. We have the following easily established result.

LEMMA 3. *Let $\mathscr{F} \subset B^m$ be closed, then $P(b)$ is continuous at b if and only if b is not a nup point.*

The continuity of the projection operator P implies quite a restriction on $\mathscr{F}$; indeed we have

COROLLARY. *Let B^m be smooth. $P(b)$ is continuous for all $b \in B^m$, if and only if $\mathscr{F}$ is convex.*

We require the following

DEFINITION 9. *Let B_1, B_2 be subsets of B^m with $B_1 \subset B_2$ and let $I = [0, 1]$. The set B_1 is said to be a deformation retract of B_2 if there exists a continuous function $\phi(t, b)$ defined on $I \times B_2$ such that $\phi(0, B_2) = B_2$ and $\phi(1, B_2) = B_1$.*

An equivalent definition is to require that B_2 be homotopic to B_1. We are now able to establish an interesting topological property of $\bar{N}(\mathscr{F})$. We perform the usual one-point compactification of B^m to obtain the sphere S^m. We assume that the new point is *not* contained in $\mathscr{F}$ and is contained in $N(\mathscr{F})$.

THEOREM 11. *Let B^m be strictly convex. The set $\bar{N}(\mathscr{F})$[7] is a deformation retract of $S^m - \mathscr{F}$.*

PROOF. Consider $b_0 \notin \bar{N}(\mathscr{F})$, $b_0 \in S^m - \mathscr{F}$. Set

$$L(b_0) = \{b \mid b = P(b_0) + \alpha(b_0 - P(b_0)),\, 0 < \alpha \leqq \infty\}$$

and $\alpha'(b_0) = \min\{\|P(b_0) - b\| \mid b \in L(b_0) \cap \bar{N}(\mathscr{F})\}$ and $\alpha(b_0) = \alpha'(b_0)/\|P(b_0) - b_0\|$. We define the function $\phi(t, b)$ on $I \times (S^m - \mathscr{F})$ by

$$\phi(t, b) = P(b) + \frac{1}{1 - t\left[1 - \dfrac{1}{\alpha(b)}\right]}(b - P(b)), \qquad b \notin \bar{N}(\mathscr{F}),$$

$$\phi(t, b) = b, \qquad b \in \bar{N}(\mathscr{F}).$$

[7] The set $\bar{N}$ is the closure of N.

It is clear that $\phi(0, b) = b$ and $\phi(1, b) \in \bar{N}(\mathscr{F})$. Further $\phi(t, b)$ is a continuous function of t and $\alpha(b)$ in the topology of S^m. Thus $\phi(t, b)$ will be continuous if we show that $\alpha(b)$ is a continuous function of b.

Suppose $b \notin \bar{N}(\mathscr{F})$. Then there is a neighborhood of b such that each point in the neighborhood has a unique projection on $\mathscr{F}$. By Lemma 3, the projection operator P is continuous in this neighborhood. Thus the lines $L(b)$ depend continuously on b (in the obvious sense of continuity).

Assume then, if possible, that a sequence $\{b_n\}$ converges to b and $|\alpha(b_n) - \alpha(b)| \geqq \eta > 0$. There are three cases; we first consider $\alpha(b_n) < \alpha(b)$. Let z_n be the point $\phi(1, b_n)$. Since $\bar{N}(\mathscr{F})$ is closed and $\{z_n\}$ is bounded, this sequence has a limit point $z_0 \in \bar{N}(\mathscr{F})$. Clearly z_0 lies in $L(b_0)$ and $\|z_0 - P(b_0)\| < \alpha'(b_0)$. This contradicts the definition of $\alpha'(b_0)$.

Consider $\infty > \alpha(b_n) > \alpha(b)$ and the corresponding points z_n, z_0. We assert that $P(b_0)$ is a projection of z_0 onto $\mathscr{F}$. Indeed $\|P(b_0) - z_0\| \leqq \|P(b_0) - P(b_n)\| + \|P(b_n) - z_n\| + \|z_n - z_0\|$. It is easily shown that $P(b_n)$ is a projection of z_n on $\mathscr{F}$ and that distance from $\mathscr{F}$ is a continuous function in the whole space. Thus $\lim_{n\to\infty} \|P(b_n) - z_n\| \to \min\{\|z_0 - f\| \mid f \in \mathscr{F}\}$ and $P(b_0)$ is a projection of z_0 onto $\mathscr{F}$. Let z^* be the point for which $\alpha'(b_0)$ is assumed. The following assertion is easily established:

ASSERTION: *Let b_1 be an interior point of the line segment $[b, P(b)]$. Then b_1 has a unique projection on $\mathscr{F}$ which is $P(b)$.*

Since z^* is an interior point of the segment $[z_0, P(z_0)]$, z^* does not lie in $\bar{N}(\mathscr{F})$, which is a contradiction.

Finally, consider the case when $\alpha(b_n) - \alpha(b)$ is unbounded. We show that this is not possible in a strictly convex space. The proof is based on the following assertion which is readily established.

ASSERTION. *Let S_1 and S_2 be two spheres in a strictly convex space B^m such that they have a common plane of support at a common point which is colinear with the centers of the spheres. Then either $S_1 = S_2$ or $S_1 \cap S_2$ consists of a single point.*

With the above notation, let $f^* \in \mathscr{F}$ be a projection of z^* on $\mathscr{F}$ which is distinct from $P(b_0)$. Then the sphere S_0 with center on line $L(b_0)$ with plane on support at $P(b_0)$ and center further from b_0 than z^* contains the point f^* in its interior. Furthermore, for n sufficiently large, the sphere S_n similarly situated on $L(b_n)$ is arbitrarily close to S_0 and hence also contains f^* in its interior. Thus $P(b_n)$ is not a projection of the center of S_n which is a contradiction. This concludes the proof.

It may not be necessary to assume that B^m is strictly convex in order to prove this result. Examples show, however, that the projection operator cannot always be used to define the function $\phi(t, b)$ in this case.

With the aid of Theorem 11 and the Alexander duality theorem we are able to characterize the topological nature of $\bar{N}(\mathscr{F})$ in terms of that of $\mathscr{F}$. Let $R_\pi^p(\mathscr{X})$ denote the pth Betti number of $\mathscr{X}$ for chains mod π **[10]**. Then we have

COROLLARY. *The following relation exists between the Betti numbers of $\mathscr{F}$ and $\bar{N}(\mathscr{F})$ in a strictly convex Banach space B^m, where δ_{ij} is the Kronecker delta:*

$$R_\pi^p(\mathscr{F}) = R_\pi^p(\bar{N}(\mathscr{F})) + \delta_{p,m-1} - \delta_{p,0}.$$

Note that $\mathscr{F}$ must satisfy some mild conditions in order that the Alexander duality theorem may be applied.

8. **Projection in infinite dimensional Banach spaces—existence problems.** It is well known from our experiences with functional analysis that there are fundamental differences between finite and infinite dimensional Banach spaces. On the other hand, linear problems with a finite number of parameters (i.e., projections on finite dimensional linear manifolds) can be treated in infinite dimensional Banach spaces without much added difficulty. We shall see that this is no longer the case for finite dimensional nonlinear manifolds.

We were able to resolve the basic existence problem in B^m with Theorems 3, 3A. Only half of this result extends to the present situation.

THEOREM 3B. *Let $\mathscr{F}$ be an object in B. Then every point of B has a projection on $\mathscr{F}$ only if $\mathscr{F}$ is closed.*

In B^m all closed $\mathscr{F}$ are *boundedly compact* (i.e., bounded subsets of $\mathscr{F}$ are compact). This is no longer true for B in general and it is not quite clear what the exact property is that is necessary and sufficient for existence of a projection for every point in B. It is easy to show that bounded compactness is sufficient for the existence of projections. In case $\mathscr{F}$ is finite dimensional, we have the following result which bears on the existence problem. We say that $\mathscr{F} \subset B$ may be *boundedly embedded in E^r* if there is a homeomorphism of $\mathscr{F}$ into a subset of E^r which carries bounded sets in $\mathscr{F}$ into bounded sets of E^r.

THEOREM 12. *Let $\mathscr{F} \subset B$ be closed and boundedly embeddable in E^r for some r. Then $\mathscr{F}$ is boundedly compact.*

PROOF. The proof is a straight forward exercise, the outline of which is as follows. Let ϕ denote the homeomorphism, if $\{f_i\}$ is bounded in $\mathscr{F}$, then $\{\phi(f_i)\}$ is bounded in E^r and has a limit point $\phi(f_0) \in \phi(\mathscr{F})$. Then f_0 is a limit point of $\{f_i\}$ in $\mathscr{F}$.

COROLLARY. *If $\mathscr{F}$ is closed and boundedly embeddable in E^r, then every point of B has a projection on $\mathscr{F}$.*

Let us consider two examples of nonlinear approximation which lead to an infinite dimensional Banach space.

EXAMPLE.

$$F(A, x) = \frac{a_1 + a_2x + a_3x^2}{a_4 + a_5x + a_6x^2}, \qquad X = [0, 1],$$

$$P = \left\{\{a_i\} \,\middle|\, \sum_{i=4}^{6} a_i^2 = 1;\ a_4 + a_5x + a_6x^2 > 0 \text{ for } x \in X\right\}.$$

One may readily verify that there is a sequence $\{F(A_k, x\}$ such that in the space $L_p[0, 1]$, $1 \leqq p < \infty$, we have

$$\|F(A_k)\|_p \leqq K < \infty,$$

$$\|F(A_k) - F(A_j)\|_p \geqq 1, \qquad j \neq k.$$

That is to say that the associated set $\mathscr{F}$ is not boundedly compact.

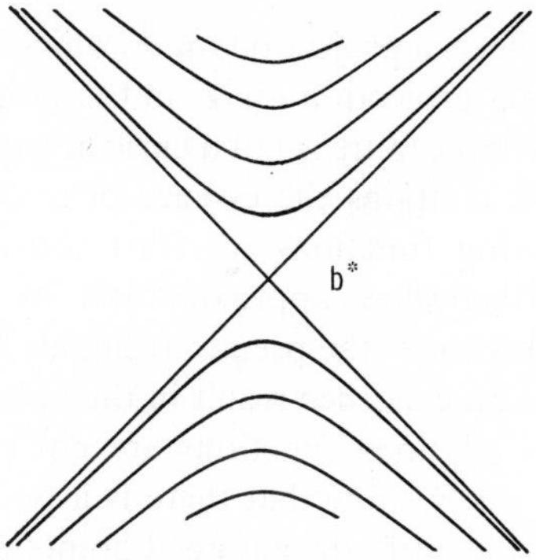

FIGURE 3. A cross-section of $\mathscr{F}$ showing lines equidistant from a constant function b^* in $L_p[0, 1]$.

EXAMPLE.

$$F(A, x) = \frac{a + bx}{c + dx}, \qquad X = [0, 1],$$

$$P = \{(a, b, c, d) \mid c^2 + d^2 = 1;\ c + dx > 0,\ x \in X\}.$$

Let us consider a "cross-section" of the set $\mathscr{F}$ for this example. Figure 3 also shows several loci of points of $\mathscr{F}$ which are equidistant from b^*. Note that this cross-section does not correspond to a bounded embedding of $\mathscr{F}$ into E^3 and thus the "double wedge" visualization made in §5 is no longer entirely accurate.

In the finite dimensional case, we closed $\mathscr{F}$ by adjoining the appropriate pseudo-rational functions. While these functions are not rational, they do lie in B^m and one can very legitimately consider projection on $\overline{\mathscr{F}}$. However, we find that $\mathscr{F}$ is already closed in the present case and that it cannot be made boundedly compact by adjoining any elements of $L_p[0, 1]$. Nevertheless, it is true that every element of $L_p[0, 1]$, $p < \infty$ possesses a projection on $\mathscr{F}$.[8]

[8] Indeed $\mathscr{F}$ is "approximately compact" as defined in [4]. This is not true for $p = \infty$.

One can show this by a direct classical analysis approach. We shall do this in another, apparently more roundabout, way. We shall make $\mathscr{F}$ boundedly compact not by adjoining elements of $L_p[0, 1]$ to $\mathscr{F}$, but rather by adjoining new elements to $L_p[0, 1]$ itself to obtain a new space, M. These new elements are then in turn adjoined to $\mathscr{F}$ in M. Without going into details, we assert that the appropriate new elements are the distributions (δ-functions) $e + f\,\delta(x)$ and $e + f\,\delta(x - 1)$ where e and f are real numbers. One may extend the L_p norm and topology to M and show that $\overline{\mathscr{F}} \subset M$ is boundedly embeddable in E^3. Thus, by Theorem 12, every point of M has a projection onto $\overline{\mathscr{F}}$.

The following assertion is readily established.

ASSERTION. *No point of $L_p[0, 1] \subset M$ has as projection on $\overline{\mathscr{F}} \subset M$, one of the distributions adjoined to $L_p[0, 1]$, $p < \infty$.*

Thus every point in $L_p[0, 1]$ has a projection on $\overline{\mathscr{F}}$ which lies in $\mathscr{F}$ or, equivalently, every point of $L_p[0, 1]$ has a projection on $\mathscr{F}$ in the original setting.

I would propose that this procedure is not a curiosity applicable to this particular example, but rather that it contains the essence of a variety of existence proofs for non-linear approximating functions (at least those which are non-trivial). Consider, for example, Chebyshev approximation by rationals to continuous functions. There one adjoins to $\mathscr{F}$ the pseudo-rationals with isolated singularities. One then easily establishes an existence result in the enlarged context. In this case one cannot show that the adjoined functions are not projections—as was done above. However, one can easily show that there is a point in $\mathscr{F}$ which is equally good. One then proceeds to identify the adjoined points with points in $\mathscr{F}$ and then forget them.

Although these pseudo-rationals with isolated singularities have been "forgotten" (or, at least, identified into oblivion), their presence is still felt in the theory. Consider the results [**3**, **11**, **24** and the paper of Cheney in these proceedings (p. 101)] on the continuity of the "Chebyshev approximation" operator T which associates with a function its best Chebyshev approximation by rational functions of specified degree. This operator is not continuous at certain "non-normal" points.

Assume that every point in B has a projection on $\mathscr{F}$ and consider the set $\bar{N}(\mathscr{F})$, the closure of the *nup* points. We have the following easily established result concerning the projection operator P.

LEMMA 4. *Let $\mathscr{F}$ be boundedly compact, then $P(b)$ is continuous at b if and only if b is not a nup point.*[9]

Consider the space M consisting of $C[0, 1]$ and $\alpha\delta_0(x) + \beta\delta_1(x) + \gamma$ where α, β, γ are real and

$$\delta_0(x) = \begin{cases} 1, & x = 0, \\ 0, & x > 0; \end{cases} \qquad \delta_1(x) = \begin{cases} 0, & x < 1, \\ 1, & x = 1. \end{cases}$$

[9] One may replace boundedly compact by "approximately compact" [**4**].

The Chebyshev norm may be extended to M and the subspace spanned by 1, $\delta_0(x)$ and $\delta_1(x)$ may be added to $\mathscr{F}$. Then the set $\mathscr{F}$ associated with $(a + bx)/(c + dx)$ is approximately compact. Those functions in $C[0, 1]$ whose best approximations do not alternate as often as possible now have several best approximations. Thus the projection operator P is not continuous at those points. In order to conclude the argument, one must show that its restriction to $C[0, 1]$ is also not continuous. This is not done here.

A similar procedure is carried out for Chebyshev approximation by exponentials in **[19]**.

With L_p approximation, $p < \infty$, we will not encounter this phenomena because there, as in the simple example above, the adjoined elements will not be projections of any points of the original space.

There may be certain difficulties encountered in carrying out this procedure in a rigorous fashion. For example, in order to include $\delta(x)$, $\delta(x - 1)$ we can enlarge $L_1[0, 1]$ to the measure space M on $[0, 1]$. Since M is a Banach space, there is little difficulty in carrying out the details for approximation by $(a + bx)/(c + dx)$. However, for rational functions of higher degree, it appears that one must include other distributions, such as the "dipole" distribution, which are not in measure space. There may be difficulties in defining the topology in the enlarged space in an appropriate manner. On the other hand, the new adjoined elements are usually a finite dimensional subset of the enlarged space, and this may allow one to readily define the appropriate topology.

9. **Projection in infinite dimensional Banach space—uniqueness problems.** The uniqueness problem also becomes more difficult when we leave finite dimensionality The keystone of the theory is an analog of Theorem 5. A fair number of partially successful efforts have been made to extend this result. The basic hypotheses of Theorem 5 are smoothness and strict convexity for B. With these hypotheses alone, no one has been able to extend the result, though it is not known whether this is due to lack of ingenuity on the part of mathematicians or to the fact that the result is false.

The first effort is **[8]** where an extension was made using an additional hypothesis that the projection is continuous (both strongly and weakly). This appears to be a strong hypothesis, though the result is not a consequence of any more recent result. Then in **[5]** it was shown that a compact Chebyshev set is necessarily convex in a smooth Banach space with "uniformly small curvature". This awkward hypothesis was removed in **[6]** where it was shown that a boundedly compact Chebyshev set is necessarily convex in a smooth and uniformly convex Banach space. Later **[4]**, it was announced that "boundedly compact" may be replaced by "approximately compact". This latter result apparently includes the result **[9]** that a weakly closed Chebyshev set is necessarily convex in a uniformly smooth and uniformly convex Banach space. In the same year Vlasov **[23]** was able to remove the hypothesis of uniform convexity from the earlier result **[4]**.

Thus we can consider this problem to be one of the leading open problems in this field. Several talented mathematicians have attacked it without complete success. This particular problem is, however, only the most obvious of the open questions in this area. Once one attempts to extend the finite dimensional results to infinite dimensional spaces, one encounters a host of open questions, many of which may call for new concepts of geometry in Banach spaces.

Once we settle the question of what Chebyshev sets are convex, we can then generate a variety of results similar to Theorem 6 and its Corollary. That is to say that we will be able to conclude that in most (if not all) smooth Banach spaces, non-linear approximation implies no possibility of a global uniqueness theorem.

There are also certain obstacles to the extension of the local uniqueness result Theorem 7 and its Corollaries. It is very likely that some interesting extensions are possible without doing more than giving a rational definition of "bounded curvature" in Hilbert space and developing a little machinery for analyzing such questions. How difficult the final extension to a general Banach space will be is quite unknown. Indeed, we are not yet sure of the results in finite dimensional Banach spaces.

References

1. L. Auslander and R. E. Mackensie, *Introduction to differentiable manifolds*, McGraw-Hill, New York, 1960.

2. H. Buseman, *Note on a theorem of convex sets*, Mat. Tidsskr. B. (1947), 32–34.

3. E. W. Cheney and H. L. Loeb, *Generalized rational approximations*. I, Aerospace Corp. Report (1963).

4. N. V. Efimov and S. S. Steckin, *Approximative compactness and Chebyshev sets*, Dokl. Akad. Nauk SSSR **140** (1961), 522–524.

5. ———, *Chebyshev sets in Banach spaces*, Dokl. Akad. Nauk SSSR **121** (1958), 582–585.

6. ———, *Some supporting properties of sets in Banach spaces as related to Chebyshev sets*, Dokl. Akad. Nauk SSSR **127** (1959), 254–257.

7. A. A. Goldstein, *On the stability of rational approximation*, Numer. Math. **5** (1963), 431–438.

8. V. L. Klee, *Convex bodies and periodic homeomorphisms in Hilbert space*, Trans. Amer. Math. Soc. **74** (1953), 10–43.

9. ———, *Convexity of Chebyshev sets*, Math. Ann., **142** (1961), 292–304.

10. S. Lefschetz, *Introduction to topology*, Princeton Univ. Press, Princeton, N.J., 1949.

11. H. Maehly and C. Witzgall, *Tschebyscheff-Approximationen in kleinen Intervallen II, Stetigkeitssätze für gebrochene Rationale Approximationen*, Numer. Math. **2** (1960), 293–307.

12. J. W. Milnor, *Morse Theory*, Princeton Univ. Press, Princeton, N.J., 1963.

13. T. S. Motzkin, *Approximation by curves of a unisolvent family*, Bull. Amer. Math. Soc. **55** (1949), 789–793.

14. ———, *Sur quelques propriétés caractéristiques des ensembles convexes*, Atti. R. Acad. Lincei, Rend. VI **21** (1935), 562–567.

15. J. R. Rice, *Algorithms for Chebyshev approximation by* $ab^x + c$, J. Soc. Indust. Appl. Math. **9** (1961), 571–583.

16. ———, *Approximation with convex constraints*, J. Soc. Indust. Appl. Math. **11** (1963), 15–32.

17. ———, *Best approximations and interpolating functions*, Trans. Amer. Math. Soc. **101** (1961), 477–498.

18. ———, *Chebyshev approximation by* $ab^x + c$, J. Soc. Indust. Appl. Math. **8** (1960), 691–702.

19. ———, *Chebyshev approximation by exponentials*, J. Soc. Indust. Appl. Math. **10** (1962) 149–161.

20. ———, *The approximation of functions, Vol. I—Linear theory*, Addison-Wesley, Reading, Mass., 1964.

21. ———, *The characterization of best nonlinear Tchebycheff approximations*, Trans. Amer. Math. Soc. **96** (1960), 322–340.

22. L. Tornheim, *On n-parameter families of functions and associated convex functions*, Trans. Amer. Math. Soc. **69** (1950), 457–467.

23. L. P. Vlasov, *Chebyshev sets in Banach spaces*, Dokl. Akad. Nauk SSSR **141** (1961), 19–20.

24. H. Werner, *On the local behavior of the rational Tschebyscheff operator*, Bull. Amer. Math. Soc. **70** (1964), 554–555.

NONLINEAR SEQUENCE TRANSFORMATIONS

F. L. BAUER
Technische Hochschule, München, Germany

Sequence-to-sequence transformations is an important subject of pure mathematics. Useful transformations are regular, which means convergence-preserving and limit-preserving. Regular transformations may serve to relate to a convergent sequence a new sequence having certainly the same limit and thus defining the same number. They may also be applied to give a meaning to a divergent sequence, provided the transformed sequence is convergent. These techniques are used particularly in connection with series, a series being the sequence of its partial sums; summation of divergent series has been a most fascinating subject since Euler.

Regular sequence-to-sequence transformations are also highly interesting under practical aspects. The transform of a convergent sequence may be more rapidly convergent, which means $|r'_n|/|r_n| \to 0$, where $\{r_n\}$, $\{r'_n\}$ are the sequences of remainders of the original and the transformed sequence, respectively. In fact, it seems to be somehow natural that a transformation which can transform at least one divergent sequence into a convergent one, should also improve convergence quite generally. This, however, is not true without exceptions: The Euler transformation of a series

$$a_0 - a_1 + a_2 - a_3 + \cdots,$$

namely the series $a'_0 + a'_1 + a'_2 + a'_3 + \cdots$ with $a'_n = \Delta^n a_0/2^{n+1}$, may be less rapid in its convergence, since

$$a_i = q^i \quad \text{implies} \quad a'_i = 2^{-i-1}(1-q)^i \quad \text{and} \quad |q| < |1-q|/2 \quad \text{for} \quad -1 < q < 1/3.$$

Nevertheless, the Euler transformation is a useful tool for convergence acceleration in suitable cases: It does indeed strictly improve convergence, if

(i) the original series is alternating, $a_i \geqq 0$,
(ii) the a_i is a totally monotone sequence,
(iii) $a_{i+1}/a_i > a \geqq 1/2$.

In particular, under these conditions we have $|r'_n|/|r_n| \leqq 2^{-n}a^{-n-1}$. This means that those alternating series with totally monotone coefficients, which in the sense of (iii) are not very rapidly convergent, will be improved. Especially those intolerably slowly convergent series, which have $a_{i+1}/a_i \to 1$ and thus $a = 1$, will be considerably improved, their transforms now being convergent as well as or better than the geometric series $\Sigma\, 2^{-n}$.

Even limitation and summation of divergent sequences and series may be of some practical importance, say in the stage of more intuitive and heuristic exploration of a situation. In this connection, the existence of Tauberian theorems should be kept in mind, namely the fact that a summation method fails inevitably if the series does not diverge rapidly enough; and that a violent summation method summing some rapidly divergent series, which a certain other method can not handle, may fail to sum a slowly divergent series which that other method can handle.

Linear sequence transformations. Usual limitation and summation methods based on sequence-to-sequence transformations[1] are linear, the elements of the transformed sequence being linear functions of the elements of the original sequence. Regularity of the transformation is expressed by the Toeplitz-Schur conditions upon the transformation matrix T, $a_i' = Ta_i$.

Methods of some profundity devised for convergence acceleration of sequences and series are frequently related to limitation and summation methods. This is true, for example, for the Romberg quadrature method **[1]**: It is a linear sequence-to-sequence transformation with a lower triangular Toeplitz matrix T, to be applied to the sequence of trapezoidal sums for a subdivision in 2^n intervals. Here, however, the transformation is especially adapted to the kind of sequences which undergo it. It is derived under the hypothesis that for trapezoidal sums $J(h)$ with intervals of length h, $J(h) \sim J_0 + h^2J_2 + h^4J_4 + \cdots$ asymptotically for $h \to 0$. Since for the given subdivision $h_i = 2^{-i}h_0$, the sequence is $s_i = J(h_i) = J_0 + 4^{-i}J_2^* + 16^{-i}J_4^* + \cdots$. Thus, the method is a specific one to accelerate convergence of a sequence

$$s_i = \alpha_0 + \alpha_1\lambda_1^i + \alpha_2\lambda_2^i + \alpha_3\lambda_3^i + \cdots \tag{1}$$

where $\lambda_1, \lambda_2, \lambda_3, \cdots$ are known. Other transformations have to be used if another asymptotic law or another kind of subdivision is present. In fact, Bulirsch and Stoer **[2]** most recently have successfully discussed a very general case. In our example, the Toeplitz matrix T of the Bulirsch transformation is such[2] that

(a) the sequence $\{1, 1, 1, \cdots\}$ is left invariant,

(b) the sequence $\{1, \lambda_1, \lambda_1^2, \lambda_1^3, \cdots\}$ is transformed into the sequence

$$\{1, 0, 0, 0, \cdots\},$$

(c) the sequence $\{1, \lambda_k, \lambda_k^2, \lambda_k^3, \cdots\}$ is transformed into a sequence with zeros following the kth element;

and, of course, the λ_k are ordered according to their absolute value. If applied to appropriate sequences, the Bulirsch sequence transformation produces excellent convergence acceleration, convergence of the transformed sequence now being supergeometric, that is, better than that of any geometric series. However, just

[1] Others, in the system of Perron, are based on sequence-to-function transformations, the function argument from the interval $(0, \infty)$ replacing the sequence subscript. They are also usually linear.

[2] Bulirsch gives a recursive algorithm, including the special case of Romberg; the actual matrix T is never formed.

because of this preference for a special class of sequence, it is not an interesting general limitation method.

On the other hand, these linear sequence-to-sequence transformations require exact knowledge about the power bases $\lambda_1, \lambda_2, \lambda_3, \cdots$ in (1). However, in case that such information is not available, a certain nonlinear sequence-to-sequence transformation method can be applied. It can be looked upon as a method which tries to approximate the power bases[1] and at the same time extrapolates the sequence. It should be expected, therefore, that its performance is not better than that of a Bulirsch transformation; experience has shown in a number of cases where the power bases were known and the Bulirsch transformation could be applied, that it is to be preferred, compared with the unspecific nonlinear transformation.

Heuristic approach to Stieltjes summation and limitation. The nonlinear sequence-to-sequence transformation method we are going to discuss has, among other variants, a variant dealing directly with sequences, and another dealing directly with series. It is this variant we are aiming at for the moment in a heuristic way, which is somehow related to Shanks' [**8**, **9**] approach.

Consider a series $\sum_0^\infty a_i$ with coefficients

$$a_i = \sum_1^n c_\mu \lambda_\mu^i, \tag{2}$$

that is, a sum of a finite number of terms of a geometric series, with n different λ_i, and $c_i \neq 0$. Assume, n is known to us; the c_i and λ_i, however, are not. Assume also, the elements a_i are made known to us one after another. As soon as we are given the first $2n$ elements $a_0, \cdots, a_{2n-1}$, and not earlier, we can determine the c_i and λ_i uniquely and completely. In fact, there is a polynomial of degree n,

$$P(\lambda) = \lambda^n - b_1\lambda^{n-1} - b_2\lambda^{n-2} - \cdots - b_n,$$

such that $P(\lambda_i) = 0$, and the elements a_i therefore obey the difference equation

$$a_{i+n} = a_{i+n-1}b_1 + a_{i+n-2}b_2 + \cdots + a_i b_n; \tag{3}$$

the polynomial coefficients can be determined uniquely from the matrix equation with non-singular matrix

$$\begin{Vmatrix} a_0 & a_1 & a_2 & \cdots a_{n-1} \\ a_1 & a_2 & a_3 & \cdots a_n \\ \cdot & \cdot & \cdot & \cdot \\ \cdot & \cdot & \cdot & \cdot \\ \cdot & \cdot & \cdot & \cdot \\ a_{n-1} & a_n & a_{n+1} & \cdots a_{2n-2} \end{Vmatrix} \begin{Vmatrix} b_n \\ b_{n-1} \\ \cdot \\ \cdot \\ \cdot \\ b_1 \end{Vmatrix} = \begin{Vmatrix} a_n \\ a_{n+1} \\ \cdot \\ \cdot \\ \cdot \\ a_{2n-1} \end{Vmatrix}.$$

[1] If the s_i are moments of a finite matrix, then the power bases are the eigenvalues of that matrix and the method may serve to approximate these eigenvalues. For this particular application, a variant of the method is known as a progressive *qd*-algorithm [**3**].

Since we can now even compute by means of (3) the next elements $a_{2n}, a_{2n+1}, \cdots$, we do not need to wait until we are given them one by one. We do not even need to compute them, since after computing the λ_i from $P(\lambda) = 0$ and then the c_i from a system of equations, we can get a sum of the series in the form

$$s'_{2n-1} = \sum_{\mu=1}^{n} \frac{c_\mu}{1 - \lambda_\mu} = \sum_{0}^{\infty} a_i,$$

if the series $\sum_0^\infty a_i$ converges. Thus we have a regular summation method working at least for some divergent series of the kind we have considered. And, no doubt, convergence has been greatly accelerated.

If we do not know n, the best we can do is to calculate s'_{2k-1} at each step. As soon as we have reached n, s'_{2n-1} will be the correct sum, and will equal $s'_{2n+1} = s'_{2n+3} = \cdots$. If, however, the elements a_i do not belong to the class considered, and say that there exists no finite n or no representation (2) at all, then we can still operate in the way described—but we can only hope that convergence is accelerated. Now we do not even know whether the series-to-sequence transformation is convergence-preserving.

Leaving practical aspects not completely out of consideration, we may observe that s'_{2n-1} can be expressed rationally in $a_0, a_1, \cdots, a_{2n-1}$. To this end, we form the formal power series

$$\frac{a_0}{z} + \frac{a_1}{z^2} + \frac{a_2}{z^3} + \cdots, \tag{4}$$

which is the term-by-term sum of n series

$$\frac{c_\mu}{z} \sum_{i=0}^{\infty} \left(\frac{\lambda_\mu}{z}\right)^i = \frac{c_\mu}{z - \lambda_\mu}$$

and converges to the rational function $r(z) \equiv \sum_{\mu=1}^n c_\mu(z - \lambda_\mu)^{-1}$ for $|z| > \max_\mu |\lambda_\mu|$. This rational function has a numerator of degree $n - 1$, if $a_0 = \Sigma\, c_\mu \neq 0$ (if $a_0 = 0$, we could have disregarded this element), and, expanded formally in powers of $1/z$, gives the coefficients of the series (4).

Thus, all we need is a rational function $r_{2k-1}(z)$ of exact degrees $(k - 1, k)$, which coincides in the first $2k$ coefficients of its expansion in descending powers[1] with the given $2k$ series elements $a_0 \cdots a_{2k-1}$, and, provided $r_{2k-1}(z)$ is uniquely determined, $s'_{2k-1} = r_{2k-1}(1)$ is our series-to-sequence transformation. In order not to lose every second term, we may also use rational functions $r_{2k}(z)$, which coincide in the first $2k + 1$ coefficients of their expansions in descending powers with $2k + 1$ given elements $a_0, \cdots, a_{2k}$. It is easily seen that the $r_{2k}(z)$ should be of exact degree $(k, k + 1)$; however, the constant term is zero in the denominator

[1] Otherwise speaking, we are led to osculatory approximation at $z = \infty$ or $1/z = 0$. This shows clearly the relation to the approximation problem discussed by Walsh in his lecture.

polynomial. We then put $s'_{2k} = r_{2k}(1)$ and have with $a'_\mu = s'_\mu - s'_{\mu-1}$ a series-to-series transformation.

We have found that our problem is closely related to the following definition of *Stieltjes summation* for a formal power series: *Given a formal power series* (4), *its Stieltjes sum is defined by the limit function, where it exists, of a sequence of rational functions $r_\mu(z)$ of the kind described above, $r_\mu(z)$ coinciding in the first $\mu + 1$ terms of its expansion in descending powers with the series* (4), *provided these functions are uniquely determined.* In fact, we consider the numerical side of a Stieltjes summation and therefore call our transformation a *Stieltjes series-to-series transformation.*

The moment problem. Stieltjes summation is a very "violent" method, as Hardy would say. It may sum in a certain region a formal power series which is divergent for every finite z, say an asymptotic expansion like

$$\frac{1}{z} - \frac{1!}{z^2} + \frac{2!}{z^3} - \frac{3!}{z^4} + \cdots$$

of $-e^z \operatorname{Ei}(-z)$. This formal power series, however, being an asymptotic expansion, does not determine this function uniquely. This itself sheds some light on the character of the transformation.

Stieltjes has introduced a representation of a function in the form

$$F(z) = \int_{-\infty}^{\infty} \frac{d\psi(t)}{z - t}, \tag{5}$$

with a real function $\psi(t)$, from which a formal series

$$\frac{a_0}{z} + \frac{a_1}{z^2} + \cdots, \qquad a_i = \int_{-\infty}^{\infty} t^i \, d\psi(t), \tag{6}$$

can be derived. The moment problem (for given a_i, to determine a function $\psi(t)$ subject to certain restrictions such that (6) holds) has become a major tool in studying the problems centering around Stieltjes summation. One famous result of Stieltjes asserts: If the moment problem has a solution with bounded, non-decreasing $\psi(u)$, $\psi(u) = \text{const.}$ for $u < 0$—one says such a series (4) is a *Stieltjes series*—then the rational functions as defined above exist; they converge in the complex plane except possibly on a cut along the positive real axis from ∞ to 0, and define there an analytic function coinciding with (5), if $\psi(u)$ is uniquely determined. Other conditions of an algebraic nature, involving Hankel determinants of the a_i, guarantee the existence of the sequence of rational functions, and known convergence theorems for continued fractions may be applied. More elaborate conditions, in which the quantities g_μ (to be introduced later) appear, guarantee that the moment problem has a bounded, non-decreasing solution with $\psi(u) = \text{const.}$ for $u < 0$ and for $u > 1$. We shall see that the conditions imposed on the quantities g_μ can be checked during the transformation process, in the sense that it will be found out when they are violated. These conditions are equivalent to the conditions that the sequence $a_0, a_1, a_2, \cdots$ is a totally monotone sequence.

We mention these results only to indicate that many theoretical questions about Stieltjes summation have been solved; however, frequently under restrictions and not always giving a clear picture. Other results are rather discouraging. Perron [**4**] gives an example of a series (4) which is convergent for $z = 1$, but the sequence of rational functions does not converge for $z = 1$. Thus, the domain where the Stieltjes sum of a power series (4) converges, does not necessarily include the domain where the power series converges in the usual sense. We have to conclude from this that the Stieltjes series-to-series transformation is not regular. It is a "violent" method, since it sums the series $1 - 1! + 2! - 3! + 4! - \cdots$, which is not summed by the usual linear summation methods. That it is not regular is the price we are paying for this.

Continued fractions. So far we have avoided speaking about continued fractions, although a sequence of rational functions $r_{2k-1}(z)$, $r_{2k}(z)$ of degrees $(k-1, k)$, $(k, k+1)$ is just what an S-fraction

$$\frac{a_0|}{|z} - \frac{q_1|}{|1} - \frac{e_1|}{|z} - \frac{q_2|}{|1} - \frac{e_2|}{|z} - \cdots \tag{7}$$

produces as the sequence of its approximants. On the other hand, such a sequence can always be converted into a continued fraction.

The theoretical apparatus of continued fractions we are using is given in full detail in the Appendix. We list here only the major steps. In now deriving algorithms for the Stieltjes summation, we assume first that an S-fraction (7) exists which is related to the coefficients a_i in the way described in the definition of Stieltjes summation.

Let $p_\mu(z)$ be the denominator of the approximant $r_\mu(z)$. For an arbitrary c such that $p_\mu(c) \neq 0$ for all μ, define

$$g_{2k}(c) = \frac{p_{2k}(c)}{c \cdot p_{2k-1}(c)}, \qquad g_{2k+1}(c) = \frac{c \cdot p_{2k+1}(c)}{p_{2k}(c)}.$$

Then identically in c

$$g_0(c) = 1,$$

$$q_k = g_{2k-2}(c) \cdot (c - g_{2k-1}(c)), \qquad e_k = g_{2k-1}(c) \cdot (1 - g_{2k}(c));$$

see Appendix, §1. Consequently, the approximant $r_n(z)$ of the S-fraction (7) reads

$$r_n(z) = \frac{a_0|}{|z} - \frac{g_0(c-g_1)|}{|1} - \frac{g_1(1-g_2)|}{|z} - \frac{g_2(c-g_3)|}{|1} - \frac{g_3(1-g_4)|}{|z} - \cdots - \begin{cases} \dfrac{g_{n-1}(c-g_n)|}{|1} \\ \dfrac{g_{n-1}(1-g_n)|}{|z} \end{cases} \tag{8}$$

where we have dropped the argument c of the quantities g_μ. This is the Garabedian-Wall [7] g-decomposition. Its importance for our problem is immediately seen. By an equivalence transformation, $r_n(z)$ can be brought to the form ($c \neq 0$)

$$r_n(z) = \frac{\frac{a_0}{c}\Big|}{\Big|\frac{z}{c}} - \frac{\frac{c-g_1}{g_1}\Big|}{\Big|1+\frac{c-g_1}{g_1}} - \frac{\frac{1-g_2}{g_2}\Big|}{\Big|\frac{z}{c}\left(1+\frac{1-g_2}{g_2}\right)} - \frac{\frac{c-g_3}{g_3}\Big|}{\Big|1+\frac{c-g_3}{g_3}} - \cdots.$$

This is, however, a segment of an Euler continued fraction, if $z = c$, and thus $r_n(c)$ can be given in the form of a sum

$$(9)\quad r_n(c) = \frac{a_0}{c}\left[1 + \frac{c-g_1}{g_1} + \frac{c-g_1}{g_1}\frac{1-g_2}{g_2} + \frac{c-g_1}{g_1}\frac{1-g_2}{g_2}\frac{c-g_3}{g_3} + \cdots + \frac{c-g_1}{g_1}\cdots\begin{Bmatrix}\dfrac{c-g_n}{g_n}\\[2mm] \dfrac{1-g_n}{g_n}\end{Bmatrix}\right].$$

The particular choice of $c = 1$ in the g-decomposition gives the sequence $r_n(1)$ and thus the transformed series term by term.

Rhombus algorithms. We still have to find the S-fraction corresponding to the initially given coefficients $a_0, a_1, \cdots$; that is, we have to expand $r_\mu(z)$ in ascending powers of z and to relate the expansion with the given power series. In order to do this, we have to relate each segment $r_\mu^{(i)}(z)$ with each segment $r_\mu^{(i+1)}$ of two S-fractions such that

$$r_\mu^{(i)}(z) = \frac{a_i}{z} + \frac{1}{z}\, r_\mu^{(i+1)}(z).$$

Assuming for both $r_\mu^{(i)}(z)$ and $r_\mu^{(i+1)}(z)$ the g-decomposition (for the same c) is given, it then follows (see Appendix, §2) that the sets $g_1^{(i)} \cdots g_\mu^{(i)}$ and $g_1^{(i+1)} \cdots g_{\mu-1}^{(i+1)}$ are related by the *g-rhombus rules* [5][1]

$$(10)\quad g_{2k-1}^{(i)} g_{2k}^{(i)} = g_{2k-2}^{(i+1)} g_{2k-1}^{(i+1)}, \qquad (1 - g_{2k}^{(i)})(c - g_{2k+1}^{(i)}) = (c - g_{2k-1}^{(i+1)})(1 - g_{2k}^{(i+1)}).$$

Moreover,

$$(11)\qquad a_{i+1} = a_i \cdot (c - g_1^{(i)}).$$

[1] In [5], these rules are called second g-rhombus rules.

The quantities $g_\mu^{(i)}$ may be written in a two-dimensional scheme

$$(12)\qquad \begin{array}{cccccc}
g_0^{(0)}=1 & & & & & \\
 & g_1^{(0)} & & & & \\
g_0^{(1)}=1 & & g_2^{(0)} & & & \\
 & g_1^{(1)} & & g_3^{(0)} & & \\
g_0^{(2)}=1 & & g_2^{(1)} & & g_4^{(0)} & \\
 & g_1^{(2)} & & g_3^{(1)} & & \cdot \\
g_0^{(3)}=1 & & g_2^{(2)} & & g_4^{(1)} & \cdot \\
\cdot & g_1^{(3)} & & g_3^{(2)} & & \cdot \\
\cdot & \cdot & g_2^{(3)} & & g_4^{(2)} & \cdot \\
\cdot & \cdot & \cdot & g_3^{(3)} & & \cdot \\
 & \cdot & \cdot & \cdot & g_4^{(3)} & \cdot \\
 & & \cdot & \cdot & \cdot & \cdot \\
 & & & \cdot & \cdot & \cdot \\
 & & & & \cdot &
\end{array}$$

The rhombus rules connect any four quantities forming a rhombus in the scheme above. It follows now, with $r_n(z) = r_n^{(0)}(z)$ and $g_\mu = g_\mu^{(0)}$, that

$$r_n(z) = \frac{a_0}{z} + \frac{a_1}{z^2} + \cdots + \frac{a_\mu}{z^{\mu+1}} + \frac{1}{z^{\mu+1}} r_n^{(\mu+1)}(z)$$

gives the desired expansion.

Using first (11) and then the rhombus rules (10), we can calculate recursively (provided no division by zero occurs) from μ series elements $a_0, \cdots, a_\mu$ just $g_1, \cdots, g_\mu$ and therefore just $r_\mu(z)$. Presumably, we choose $c = 1$ and apply the Euler series (9). This is the forward g-algorithm for Stieltjes summation.

There are a number of variants; historically first the qd-algorithm [3] of Rutishauser. It connects the quantities $q_k^{(i)}$, $e_k^{(i)}$ of the segment $r_n^{(i)}(z)$ by rhombus rules (see Appendix, §3). Its disadvantage for the Stieltjes summation problem is that the approximants are not so immediately evaluated for $z = 1$. Another variant (see Appendix, §4) works with quantities $\pi_\mu^{(i)}$, defined as suggested by (9) to be

$$\pi_{2k}^{(i)} = \frac{1 - g_{2k}^{(i)}}{g_{2k}^{(i)}}, \qquad \pi_{2k+1}^{(i)} = \frac{c - g_{2k+1}^{(i)}}{g_{2k+1}^{(i)}}.$$

Series transformation by the η-algorithm. Most interesting, however, is the direct use of the single terms in the sum (9). Thus, we define

$$(13)\qquad \eta_\mu^{(i)} = \frac{a_i}{c^{i+1}} \prod_{\nu=1}^{\mu} \pi_\nu^{(i)}$$

such that $\eta_0^{(i)} = a_i/c^{i+1}$; from (9) it follows that

$$(14)\qquad r_\mu(c) = \eta_0^{(0)} + \eta_1^{(0)} + \eta_2^{(0)} + \cdots + \eta_\mu^{(0)}.$$

It turns out (see Appendix, §5) that the quantities $\eta_\mu^{(i)}$, purposefully arranged in a scheme

$$
\begin{array}{cccccccc}
\eta_0^{(0)} & & & & & & & \\
& \eta_1^{(0)} & & & & & & \\
\eta_0^{(1)} & & \eta_2^{(0)} & & & & & \\
& \eta_1^{(1)} & & \eta_3^{(0)} & & & & \\
\eta_0^{(2)} & & \eta_2^{(1)} & & \eta_4^{(0)} & \cdot & & \\
& \eta_1^{(2)} & & \eta_3^{(1)} & & & \cdot & \\
\eta_0^{(3)} & & \eta_2^{(2)} & & \eta_4^{(1)} & \cdot & & \\
\cdot & \eta_1^{(3)} & & \eta_3^{(2)} & & & \cdot & \\
\cdot & \cdot & \eta_2^{(3)} & & \eta_4^{(2)} & \cdot & & \\
\cdot & \cdot & \cdot & \eta_3^{(3)} & & & \cdot & \\
& \cdot & \cdot & \cdot & \eta_4^{(3)} & \cdot & & \\
& & \cdot & \cdot & \cdot & & \cdot & \cdot, \\
& & & \cdot & \cdot & & & \\
& & & & \cdot & & &
\end{array}
$$

again obey rhombus rules, the *η-rhombus rules*

$$\eta_{2k-1}^{(i)} + \eta_{2k}^{(i)} = \eta_{2k-2}^{(i+1)} + \eta_{2k-1}^{(i+1)},$$

$$\frac{1}{\eta_{2k}^{(i)}} + \frac{1}{\eta_{2k+1}^{(i)}} = \frac{1}{\eta_{2k-1}^{(i+1)}} + \frac{1}{\eta_{2k}^{(i+1)}},$$

where, for notational convenience $1/\eta_{-1}^{(i)} = 0$.

The forward η-algorithm for $c = 1$ calculates recursively by means of the rhombus rules, from $\mu + 1$ series elements $\eta_0^{(i)} = a_i$, $\mu + 1$ terms $\eta_\nu^{(0)} = a'_\nu$ of the Euler series (9).

The η-algorithm is a direct nonlinear algorithm for the Stieltjes summation of a series. Since computation may be arranged to proceed along diagonals $\eta_0^{(0)}$; $\eta_0^{(1)}, \eta_1^{(0)}$; $\eta_0^{(2)}, \eta_1^{(1)}, \eta_2^{(0)}$; $\eta_0^{(3)}, \eta_1^{(2)}, \eta_2^{(1)}, \eta_3^{(0)}; \cdots$, the η-algorithm in this arrangement defines a (nonlinear) series transformation.

Examples of the series transformation by the η-algorithm.

(a) We begin with the divergent series

$$1 - 1! + 2! - 3! + 4! - \cdots.$$

The η-scheme is the following:

$$
\begin{array}{cccccc}
1 & & & & & \\
& -\frac{1}{2} & & & & \\
-1 & & \frac{1}{6} & & & \\
& \frac{2}{3} & & -\frac{2}{21} & & \\
2 & & -\frac{2}{12} & & \frac{4}{91} & \\
& -\frac{6}{4} & & \frac{6}{52} & & -\frac{6}{221} \\
-6 & & \frac{6}{20} & & -\frac{4}{91} & \\
& \frac{24}{5} & & -\frac{24}{105} & & \\
24 & & -\frac{24}{30} & & & \\
& -\frac{120}{6} & & & & \\
-120 & & & & &
\end{array}
$$

and the transformed series is

$$1 - \tfrac{1}{2} + \tfrac{1}{6} - \tfrac{2}{21} + \tfrac{4}{91} - \tfrac{6}{221} + \cdots .$$

It is indeed convergent, since the S-fraction corresponding to $\sum_0^\infty (-1)^i\, i! \cdot z^{-i-1}$ converges (to the function $\int_0^\infty e^{-u}(z+u)^{-1}\,du$) for z outside the cut along the real axis from $-\infty$ to 0, the limiting value being

$$\int_0^\infty \frac{e^{-u}\,du}{1+u} = 0.596\,3473 \cdots .$$

Thus, we have summed a rapidly divergent series, and the transformed series converges quite well. The sum of the first six terms given above is $10/17 = 0.588\,2352 \cdots$.

(b) Next, we consider the slowly convergent series

$$1 - \tfrac{1}{2} + \tfrac{1}{3} - \tfrac{1}{4} + \tfrac{1}{5} - \tfrac{1}{6} + \cdots .$$

We obtain the η-scheme

$$\begin{array}{cccccc}
1 & & & & & \\
 & -\frac{1}{3} & & & & \\
-\frac{1}{2} & & \frac{1}{30} & & & \\
 & \frac{1}{5} & & -\frac{1}{130} & & \\
\frac{1}{3} & & -\frac{1}{105} & & \frac{1}{975} & \\
 & -\frac{1}{7} & & \frac{1}{350} & & -\frac{1}{4725} \\
-\frac{1}{4} & & \frac{1}{252} & & -\frac{1}{4100} & \\
 & \frac{1}{9} & & -\frac{1}{738} & & \\
\frac{1}{5} & & -\frac{1}{495} & & & \\
 & -\frac{1}{11} & & & & \\
-\frac{1}{6} & & & & &
\end{array}$$

and the transformed series

$$1 - \tfrac{1}{3} + \tfrac{1}{30} - \tfrac{1}{130} + \tfrac{1}{975} - \tfrac{1}{4725} + \cdots$$

converges rapidly to $\ln 2 = 0.69\,314 \cdots$. While the first six terms of the original series give only $0.61\,666 \cdots$, the corresponding six terms of the transformed series give $0.69\,312 \cdots$. The S-fraction corresponding to

$$\sum_0^\infty (-1)^i \frac{1}{i+1}\frac{1}{z^{i+1}}$$

converges (to the function $\int_0^1 (z+u)^{-1}\,du$) for z outside the cut along the real axis from -1 to 0.

Note that the Euler transformation gives only

$$\frac{1}{1\cdot 2^1} + \frac{1}{2\cdot 2^2} + \frac{1}{3\cdot 2^3} + \frac{1}{4\cdot 2^4} + \frac{1}{5\cdot 2^5} + \frac{1}{6\cdot 2^6},$$

which is less rapidly convergent; the first six terms give $0.69\,145 \cdots$.

(c) The series

$$\frac{1}{2\cdot 3} + \frac{1}{3\cdot 4} + \frac{1}{4\cdot 5} + \frac{1}{5\cdot 6} + \frac{1}{6\cdot 7} + \frac{1}{7\cdot 8} + \cdots$$

converges to 1/2. The η-scheme is

$$\begin{array}{cccccc}
\frac{1}{6} & & & & & \\
 & \frac{1}{6} & & & & \\
\frac{1}{12} & & \frac{1}{24} & & & \\
 & \frac{1}{8} & & \frac{1}{16} & & \\
\frac{1}{20} & & \frac{1}{40} & & \frac{1}{80} & \\
 & \frac{1}{10} & & \frac{1}{20} & & \frac{1}{40} \\
\frac{1}{30} & & \frac{1}{60} & & \frac{1}{120} & \\
 & \frac{1}{12} & & \frac{1}{24} & & \\
\frac{1}{42} & & \frac{1}{84} & & & \\
 & \frac{1}{14} & & & & \\
\frac{1}{56}\,. & & & & &
\end{array}$$

The transformed series

$$\tfrac{1}{6} + \tfrac{1}{6} + \tfrac{1}{24} + \tfrac{1}{16} + \tfrac{1}{80} + \tfrac{1}{40} + \cdots$$

converges more rapidly.

In this example, the η-scheme is positive, and correspondingly the g_μ (for $c = 1$) fulfill the conditions $0 < g_\mu < 1$. Indeed, $a_i = \int_0^1 u^i u(1 - u)\, du$, and the corresponding S-fraction converges to $\int_0^1 u(1 - u)(z - u)^{-1}\, du$ outside the cut from 0 to 1 along the real axis.

(d) The series

$$1 - \frac{1}{3} + \frac{1}{3 \cdot 15} - \frac{1}{3 \cdot 15 \cdot 63} + \frac{1}{3 \cdot 15 \cdot 63 \cdot 255} - \frac{1}{3 \cdot 15 \cdot 63 \cdot 255 \cdot 1023} + \cdots$$

converges rapidly to the limit $0.688\,537\,5368 \cdots$. The η-scheme

$$\begin{array}{cccccc}
1 & & & & & \\
 & -\frac{1}{4} & & & & \\
-\frac{1}{3} & & -\frac{1}{16} & & & \\
 & \frac{1}{3 \cdot 16} & & \frac{1}{16 \cdot 64} & & \\
\frac{1}{3 \cdot 15} & & \frac{1}{15 \cdot 64} & & \frac{1}{64 \cdot 256} & \\
 & -\frac{1}{3 \cdot 15 \cdot 64} & & -\frac{1}{15 \cdot 64 \cdot 256} & & -\frac{1}{64 \cdot 256 \cdot 1024} \\
-\frac{1}{3 \cdot 15 \cdot 63} & & -\frac{1}{15 \cdot 63 \cdot 256} & & -\frac{1}{63 \cdot 256 \cdot 1024} & \\
 & \frac{1}{3 \cdot 15 \cdot 63 \cdot 256} & & \frac{1}{15 \cdot 63 \cdot 256 \cdot 1024} & & \\
\frac{1}{3 \cdot 15 \cdot 63 \cdot 255} & & \frac{1}{15 \cdot 63 \cdot 255 \cdot 1024} & & & \\
 & -\frac{1}{3 \cdot 15 \cdot 63 \cdot 255 \cdot 1024} & & & & \\
-\frac{1}{3 \cdot 15 \cdot 63 \cdot 255 \cdot 1023} & & & & &
\end{array}$$

gives the transformed series

$$1-\frac{1}{2^2}-\frac{1}{2^4}+\frac{1}{2^{10}}+\frac{1}{2^{14}}-\frac{1}{2^{24}}+\cdots$$

which is even slightly less rapidly convergent.

Sequence transformation by the ε-algorithm. Going from a sequence to a series and back, a sequence transformation can be effected by means of the η-algorithm. There is, however, a variant of our Stieltjes summation method which deals with sequences directly, the ε-algorithm of Wynn [**6**].

In order to obtain the quantities ε, we sum up the η-scheme. Thus, we define

$$\varepsilon_0^{(0)}=0, \qquad \varepsilon_{2k}^{(i)}=\sum_{\nu=0}^{i-1}\eta_0^{(\nu)}+\sum_{\lambda=0}^{2k-1}\eta_\lambda^{(i)}.$$

Then

$$\varepsilon_0^{(i)}=\sum_{\nu=0}^{i-1}\eta_0^{(\nu)}=\sum_{\nu=0}^{i-1}\frac{a_\nu}{c^{\nu+1}},$$

the partial sum of the original series; and

$$\varepsilon_{2k}^{(0)}=\sum_{\lambda=0}^{2k-1}\eta_\lambda^{(0)},$$

the partial sum $r_{2k}(c)$ of the transformed series (14) with an even number of terms. From the η-rhombus rules, it is seen easily that in fact the sum is independent of the path of summation in the η-scheme. Moreover, we observe that the partial sum with an odd number of terms is given by (see Appendix, §6)

$$\varepsilon_{2k}^{(1)}=\sum_{\lambda=0}^{2k}\eta_\lambda^{(0)}.$$

Introducing now in an obviously symmetric way also the quantities

$$\varepsilon_{2k+1}^{(i)}=\sum_{\lambda=0}^{2k}\frac{1}{\eta_\lambda^{(i)}},$$

and putting $\varepsilon_{-1}^{(i)}=0$ for notational convenience, it can be shown that the following ε-rhombus rules hold (see Appendix, §6):

$$(\varepsilon_\mu^{(i+1)}-\varepsilon_\mu^{(i)})(\varepsilon_{\mu+1}^{(i)}-\varepsilon_{\mu-1}^{(i+1)})=1,$$

connecting again any four quantities forming a rhombus in the ε-scheme

$$
\begin{array}{ccccccc}
\varepsilon_0^{(0)} & & & & & & \\
 & \varepsilon_1^{(0)} & & & & & \\
\varepsilon_0^{(1)} & & \varepsilon_2^{(0)} & & & & \\
 & \varepsilon_1^{(1)} & & \varepsilon_3^{(0)} & & & \\
\varepsilon_0^{(2)} & & \varepsilon_2^{(1)} & & \varepsilon_4^{(0)} & & \\
 & \varepsilon_1^{(2)} & & \varepsilon_3^{(1)} & & \cdot & \\
\varepsilon_0^{(3)} & & \varepsilon_2^{(2)} & & \varepsilon_4^{(1)} & & \cdot \\
 & \varepsilon_1^{(3)} & & \varepsilon_3^{(2)} & & \cdot & \\
\varepsilon_0^{(4)} & & \varepsilon_2^{(3)} & & \varepsilon_4^{(2)} & & \cdot \\
 & \varepsilon_1^{(4)} & & \varepsilon_3^{(3)} & & \cdot & \\
\cdot & & \varepsilon_2^{(4)} & & \varepsilon_4^{(3)} & & \cdot \\
\cdot & \cdot & & \varepsilon_3^{(4)} & & \cdot & \\
 & \cdot & \cdot & & \varepsilon_4^{(4)} & & \cdot \\
 & \cdot & \cdot & \cdot & & \cdot & \cdot \quad \cdot \\
 & & \cdot & \cdot & & & \\
 & & & \cdot & & &
\end{array}
$$

By the forward recursive use of the rhombus rules, the sequence

$$\varepsilon_0^{(1)}, \varepsilon_0^{(2)}, \varepsilon_0^{(3)}, \cdots, \varepsilon_0^{(2k)}, \varepsilon_0^{(2k+1)}, \cdots$$

is transformed into the sequence

$$\varepsilon_0^{(1)}, \varepsilon_2^{(0)}, \varepsilon_2^{(1)}, \varepsilon_4^{(0)}, \cdots, \varepsilon_{2k}^{(0)}, \varepsilon_{2k}^{(1)}, \cdots.$$

A convenience with the ε-algorithm is that only one form of rules is to be used. We give an example. The sequence

$$\tfrac{1}{6}, \tfrac{2}{8}, \tfrac{3}{10}, \tfrac{4}{12}, \cdots$$

is to be extrapolated. The ε-scheme is developed as follows:

$$
\begin{array}{ccccccc}
\frac{1}{6} & & & & & & \\
 & 12 & & & & & \\
\frac{2}{8} & & \frac{3}{8} & & & & \\
 & 20 & & 60 & & & \\
\frac{3}{10} & & \frac{4}{10} & & \frac{13}{30} & & \\
 & 30 & & 90 & & 180 & \\
\frac{4}{12} & & \frac{5}{12} & & \frac{16}{36} & & \frac{33}{72} \\
 & 42 & & 126 & & 252 & \\
\frac{5}{14} & & \frac{6}{14} & & \frac{19}{42} & & \\
 & 56 & & 168 & & & \\
\frac{6}{16} & & \frac{7}{16} & & & & \\
 & 72 & & & & & \\
\frac{7}{18}\,. & & & & & &
\end{array}
$$

The extrapolated value $33/72 = 0.45\ 833 \cdots$ is much closer to the limit $1/2$ than the last original value $7/18 = 0.38\ 888 \cdots$. Note that $\varepsilon_2^{(1)}$ is just the result of Aitken's δ^2-process applied to $\varepsilon_0^{(1)}$, $\varepsilon_0^{(2)}$, and $\varepsilon_0^{(3)}$.

Concluding remarks. The concept of the transformations discussed here has been approached historically from the two algorithms at the boundary of the spectrum of variants: the *qd*-algorithm of Rutishauser and the ε-algorithm of Wynn, related to Shanks' sequence transformation. The g-decomposition of Garabedian and Wall links these algorithms together. The relationship can be seen of course from the Hankel determinants involved in the q_μ, e_k, on the one hand, and the ε_μ on the other hand.

The rhombus rules formulated allow not only the forward process discussed. There exist limit theorems, based on a theory of Hadamard, about the columns of the sundry schemes. For terminating S-fractions, the limits are determined by the poles of the rational function which the S-fraction represents; thus a so-called progressive application of the rhombus rules from top to bottom of the scheme, with a boundary condition to the right, is an important instrument for the numerical computation of eigenvalues of a tridiagonal matrix.

Quite generally, in numerical computation with rhombus rules, the process may break down, caused by division by zero. Elaborate means have been devised by Rutishauser and Wynn to circumvent locations where this happens. The freedom in the choice of the number c in the g-decomposition may present a more elegant solution.

Infinitesimal analogs of some of the rhombus algorithms have been given by Rutishauser [3] and Wynn. These nonlinear differential and partial differential equations may deserve further studies of possible use in function transformation.

Finally, it should be noted that repeated application of the Stieltjes summation and limitation processes described has been tried experimentally quite often. Since there is, at least for the moment, no indication what this should mean theoretically, some caution is pertinent.

Nonlinear series and sequence transformations, such as the η-algorithm and the ε-algorithm, deserve further theoretical studies. Their practical usefulness seems to be already well established.

Appendix

1. **The g-decomposition of Garabedian-Wall [7].** The S-fraction (7):

$$\frac{a_0|}{|z} - \frac{q_1|}{|1} - \frac{e_1|}{|z} - \frac{q_2|}{|1} - \frac{e_2|}{|z} - \cdots$$

has the approximants $r_0(z) = a_0/z$, $r_1(z) = a_0/(z - q_1), \cdots$. Let $p_\mu(z)$ be the denominator of the approximant $r_\mu(z)$. These polynomials obey the three-term recurrence relations ($k = 1, 2, \cdots$)

$$p_{2k-1}(z) = p_{2k-2}(z) - q_k p_{2k-3}(z), \tag{A1}$$

$$p_{2k}(z) = z p_{2k-1}(z) - e_k p_{2k-2}(z), \tag{A2}$$

with the initial conditions

$$p_{-1}(z) = 1, \tag{A3}$$

$$p_0(z) = z. \tag{A4}$$

Thus, there holds identically in z

$$q_k = \frac{p_{2k-2}(z)}{p_{2k-3}(z)}\left(1 - \frac{p_{2k-1}(z)}{p_{2k-2}(z)}\right), \tag{A5}$$

$$e_k = \frac{p_{2k-1}(z)}{p_{2k-2}(z)}\left(z - \frac{p_{2k}(z)}{p_{2k-1}(z)}\right). \tag{A6}$$

Introducing now for an arbitrary c (in fact, c may be considered for a while as an indeterminate) the quantities ($k = 0, 1, 2, \cdots$)

$$g_{2k}(c) = \frac{p_{2k}(c)}{c \cdot p_{2k-1}(c)}, \tag{A7}$$

$$g_{2k+1}(c) = \frac{c \cdot p_{2k+1}(c)}{p_{2k}(c)}, \tag{A8}$$

we obtain

$$q_k = g_{2k-2}(c - g_{2k-1}), \tag{A9}$$

$$e_k = g_{2k-1}(1 - g_{2k}). \tag{A10}$$

For notational convenience, we have dropped the argument c in the quantities $g_\mu = g_\mu(c)$. Note that $g_0(c) = 1$ identically.

2. **Expansion in powers of $1/z$ for a g-decomposed S-fraction.** The even part of an S-fraction (8) is the J-fraction

$$r_n(z) = \frac{a_0|}{|z - g_0(c - g_1)} - \frac{g_0(c - g_1)g_1(1 - g_2)|}{|z - g_1(1 - g_2) - g_2(c - g_3)} - \frac{g_2(c - g_3)g_3(1 - g_4)|}{|z - g_3(1 - g_4) - g_4(c - g_5)} - \cdots - \frac{g_{2k-4}(c - g_{2k-3})g_{2k-3}(1 - g_{2k-2})|}{|z - g_{2k-3}(1 - g_{2k-2}) - g_{2k-2}(c - g_{2k-1})} \tag{A11}$$

for $n = 2k$; for $n = 2k - 1$ the term $g_{2k-2}(c - g_{2k-1})$ in the denominator of the last part is to be cancelled. We obtain this effect by putting g_{2k-1} equal to c. This can be rewritten in the form of a J-fraction in $z - c$:

$$r_n(z) = \frac{a_0|}{|(z - c) + g_0g_1} + \frac{g_0g_1(c - g_1)(1 - g_2)|}{|(z - c) + (c - g_1)(1 - g_2) + g_2g_3} + \cdots + \frac{g_{2k-4}g_{2k-3}(c - g_{2k-3})(1 - g_{2k-2})|}{|(z - c) + (c - g_{2k-3})(1 - g_{2k-2}) + g_{2k-2}g_{2k-1}}. \tag{A12}$$

The odd part of the S-fraction above is

$$\text{(A13)}\quad r_n(z) = \frac{a_0}{z} + \frac{1}{z}\cdot\frac{a_0(c-g_1)}{|z - g_0(c-g_1) - g_1(1-g_2)} - \frac{g_1(1-g_2)g_2(c-g_3)}{|z - g_2(c-g_3) - g_3(1-g_4)} - \cdots - \frac{g_{2k-3}(1-g_{2k-2})g_{2k-2}(c-g_{2k-1})|}{|z - g_{2k-2}(c-g_{2k-1})}$$

for $n = 2k$; for $n = 2k - 1$ the last part is to be cancelled altogether. This can again be effected by putting g_{2k-1} equal to c. This can be rewritten again

(A14)

$$r_n(z) = \frac{a_0}{z} + \frac{1}{z}\frac{a_0(c-g_1)}{|(z-c)+g_1g_2} + \frac{g_1g_2(1-g_2)(c-g_3)}{|(z-c)+(1-g_2)(c-g_3)+g_3g_4} + \cdots + \frac{g_{2k-3}g_{2k-2}(1-g_{2k-2})(c-g_{2k-1})}{|(z-c)+(1-g_{2k-2})(c-g_{2k-1})+g_{2k-1}}.$$

If now we put $r_n(z) = a_0/z + r_n^{(1)}(z)/z$, where $r_n^{(1)}(z)$ is of the form (A12) with quantities a_1 and $g_\mu^{(1)}$ instead of a_0 and $g_\mu = g_\mu^{(0)}$ we obtain by direct comparison the g-rhombus rules (10) and (11), replacing now in general 0 by i, 1 by $i + 1$.

3. ***qd*-rhombus rules.** If in (A11) and (A13) we replace the g_μ by the original q_k, e_k, we have for $n = 2k$ (and again, with $q_k = 0$ formally, for $n = 2k - 1$)

$$\text{(A15)}\quad r_n(z) = \frac{a_0}{|z-q_1} - \frac{q_1e_1}{|z-e_1-q_2} - \cdots - \frac{q_{k-1}e_{k-1}}{|z-e_{k-1}-q_k},$$

$$\text{(A16)}\quad r_n(z) = \frac{a_0}{z} + \frac{1}{z}\frac{a_0q_1}{|z-q_1-e_1} - \frac{e_1q_2}{|z-q_2-e_2} - \cdots - \frac{e_{k-1}q_k|}{|z-q_k}.$$

We get by comparison, similar to §2, the qd-rhombus rules

$$\text{(A17)}\quad q_k^{(i)} + e_k^{(i)} = e_{k-1}^{(i+1)} + q_k^{(i+1)}, \qquad e_k^{(i)}q_{k+1}^{(i)} = q_k^{(i)}e_k^{(i+1)},$$

$$\text{(A18)}\quad a_{i+1} = a_iq_1^{(i)}.$$

The $q_k^{(i)}$, $e_k^{(i)}$, and the $g_\mu^{(i)}$ are connected by

$$\text{(A19)}\quad q_k^{(i)} = g_{2k-2}^{(i)}(c - g_{2k-1}^{(i)}), \qquad e_k^{(i)} = g_{2k-1}^{(i)}(1 - g_{2k}^{(i)}).$$

The qd-rhombus rules can be verified also directly.

4. **π-rhombus rules.** The quantities $\pi_\mu^{(i)}$, as defined, obey the rhombus rules (with $\pi_0^{(i)} = 0$)

$$\text{(A20)}\quad \begin{aligned}(1+\pi_{2k-1}^{(i)})(1+\pi_{2k}^{(i)}) &= (1+\pi_{2k-2}^{(i+1)})(1+\pi_{2k-1}^{(i+1)}),\\ (1+1/\pi_{2k}^{(i)})(1+1/\pi_{2k+1}^{(i)}) &= (1+1/\pi_{2k-1}^{(i+1)})(1+1/\pi_{2k}^{(i+1)}),\end{aligned}$$

$$\text{(A21)}\quad \pi_1^{(i)} = \frac{a_{i+1}}{c\cdot a_i - a_{i+1}}.$$

This can be verified directly. Note that

$$\text{(A22)}\quad \begin{aligned} 1+\pi_{2k-1}^{(i)} &= \frac{c}{g_{2k-1}^{(i)}}, &\quad 1+\pi_{2k}^{(i)} &= \frac{1}{g_{2k}^{(i)}},\\ 1+1/\pi_{2k}^{(i)} &= \frac{1}{1-g_{2k}^{(i)}}, &\quad 1+1/\pi_{2k+1}^{(i)} &= \frac{c}{c-g_{2k+1}^{(i)}}.\end{aligned}$$

5. **Verification of the η-rhombus rules.** Verification of the η-rhombus rules is a little more complicated. In order to show $\eta_{2k-1}^{(i)} + \eta_{2k}^{(i)} = \eta_{2k-2}^{(i+1)} + \eta_{2k-1}^{(i+1)}$, we express both sides as follows:

$$\text{(A23)}\quad \eta_{2k-1}^{(i)} + \eta_{2k}^{(i)} = \frac{ca_i}{c^{i+2}}\pi_1^{(i)}\pi_2^{(i)}\cdots\pi_{2k-1}^{(i)}(1+\pi_{2k}^{(i)}),$$

$$\text{(A24)}\quad \eta_{2k-2}^{(i+1)} + \eta_{2k-1}^{(i+1)} = \frac{a_{i+1}}{c^{i+2}}\pi_1^{(i+1)}\pi_2^{(i+1)}\cdots\pi_{2k-2}^{(i+1)}(1+\pi_{2k-1}^{(i+1)}).$$

From (A21) we obtain

$$ca_i = a_{i+1}\left(1+\frac{1}{\pi_1^{(i)}}\right).$$

We decompose now

$$\pi_{2\rho}^{(\sigma)} = (1+\pi_{2\rho}^{(\sigma)})\frac{1}{1+\dfrac{1}{\pi_{2\rho}^{(\sigma)}}},$$

$$\pi_{2\rho+1}^{(\sigma)} = \frac{1}{1+\dfrac{1}{\pi_{2\rho+1}^{(\sigma)}}}\cdot(1+\pi_{2\rho+1}^{(\sigma)}).$$

After inserting this, the π-rhombus rules may be applied term by term.

6. **Verification of the ε-rhombus rules.** From the definition,

$$\begin{aligned}\varepsilon_{2k}^{(i+1)} - \varepsilon_{2k}^{(i)} &= \eta_0^{(i)} + \sum_{\lambda=0}^{2k-1}\eta_\lambda^{(i+1)} - \sum_{\lambda=0}^{2k-1}\eta_\lambda^{(i)}\\ &= \eta_{2k}^{(i)} + \sum_{\lambda=0}^{2k-1}\eta_\lambda^{(i+1)} - \sum_{\lambda=1}^{2k}\eta_\lambda^{(i)}\\ &= \eta_{2k}^{(i)} + \sum_{\rho=0}^{k-1}(\eta_{2\rho}^{(i+1)} + \eta_{2\rho+1}^{(i+1)} - \eta_{2\rho+1}^{(i)} - \eta_{2\rho+2}^{(i)}),\end{aligned}$$

$$\text{(A25)}\quad \varepsilon_{2k}^{(i+1)} - \varepsilon_{2k}^{(i)} = \eta_{2k}^{(i)}.$$

This shows that the $\varepsilon_{2k}^{(i)}$ can be summed up independently of the path of summation.

Similarly, one can show that

$$\varepsilon_{2k+1}^{(i+1)} - \varepsilon_{2k+1}^{(i)} = \frac{1}{\eta_{2k+1}^{(i)}}, \tag{A26}$$

$$\varepsilon_{2k+1}^{(i)} - \varepsilon_{2k-1}^{(i+1)} = \frac{1}{\eta_{2k}^{(i)}}, \tag{A27}$$

$$\varepsilon_{2k+2}^{(i)} - \varepsilon_{2k}^{(i+1)} = \eta_{2k+1}^{(i)}, \tag{A28}$$

can be shown the same way.

From multiplying (A25) and (A27), (A26) and (A28), the ε-rhombus rules follow for even and odd subscripts.

References

1. F. L. Bauer, H. Rutishauser, and E. Stiefel, *New aspects in numerical quadrature*, Proc. Symp. Appl. Math., Amer. Math. Soc. **15** (1963).

2. R. Bulirsch and J. Stoer, *Fehlerabschätzung und Extrapolation mit rationalen Funktionen bei Verfahren vom Richardson-Typus*, Numer. Math. **6** (1964), 413–427.

3. H. Rutishauser, *Der Quotienten-Differenzen-Algorithmus*, Mitt. Inst. angew. Math. ETH 7, Birkhäuser, Basel, 1957.

4. O. Perron, *Die Lehre von den Kettenbrüchen*, Teubner, Stuttgart, 1957.

5. F. L. Bauer, *The quotient-difference and epsilon algorithms*. On numerical approximation, Univ. of Wisc. Press, Madison, Wisc., 1959.

6. P. Wynn, *On a device for computing the* $e_m(S_m)$*-transformation*, Math. Tables Aids Comput. **10** (1956), 91–96.

7. H. L. Garabedian and H. S. Wall, *Hausdorff methods of summation and continued fractions*, Trans. Amer. Math. Soc. **48** (1940), 185–207.

8. D. Shanks, *An analogy between transients and mathematical sequences...*, Naval Ord. Lab. Memo. 9994, White Oak, Md., 1951.

9. ———, *Nonlinear transformations of divergent and slowly convergent sequences*, J. Math. and Phys. **34** (1955), 1–42.

APPROXIMATION THEORY IN THE FIRST TWO DECADES OF ELECTRONIC COMPUTERS

PHILIP J. DAVIS
Brown University, Providence, Rhode Island

"All exact science is dominated by the idea of approximation"—Bertrand Russell.

One of the minor results of the Republican National Convention a month ago was a discussion of who was and who was not in the main stream of Republicanism. The above quotation from Bertrand Russell should comfort us by the assurance that *all* approximators are in the main stream of science. The only thing left for us to decide—as in the case of social and political equality—which of us is more in the main stream than the others.

The theory of the approximation of functions has a venerable history. One might point to the approximation of the circle by regular polygons, done in the period of Greek Mathematics, as the first major accomplishment of the theory. Several hundred years later we find Claudius Ptolemy performing a kind of harmonic analysis by approximating the path of the planets by means of epicycles. To round out this particular story we should mention Kepler's fitting of ellipses to orbits. The pi story, judging from recent work at the Model Basin, is still an active one.

Kepler led to Newton who, in turn, led to such things as satellites and moonshots. Approximation theory clearly has had some very fine hours during its history. And after twenty five hundred years of it, it appears to be going as strong as ever. This fine conference is testimony to the fact that what is good for approximation theory is good for the country. Within the past several years—harking back to ancient history—we have had important papers on the approximation of curves by line segments and on approximation of data by ellipses. All experimental scientists are approximators and all dream of Kepler. Some dream of Newton.

It is the object of this paper to make some historical and philosophical remarks on approximation theory in the light of practical numerical analysis as carried out today on electronic computers. This paper cannot be a survey paper in the conventional sense because the subject is too broad, and my experience with it is too limited.

As part of my preparation for this paper, I did two things:

1. I looked through the Mathematical Reviews of the last two years for papers in approximation theory that seemed relevant to practical numerical analysis. I found over 120 papers and a dozen books. These have been listed in an appendix

to this paper for your convenience. This work together with the fact that there now have been four major conferences on approximation theory here and in Europe since 1958 is sure testimony of the vitality of the subject. And much good approximation theory lies hidden in other topics, pure and applied, promulgated by people with other main interests. All this has escaped my casual glance.

2. I visited a good friend of mine, a numerical analyst in charge of a computation laboratory which does a large and diverse computing business, and asked him how important approximation theory was in his business. His answer was unequivocal: "It is relatively *unimportant* to us." I asked him why this was so and his answer was: "Ignorance on the part of numerical analysts; unwillingness on the part of those who know how to concern themselves with numerical and machine matters; inertia; indifference due to marginal advantage competition with other methods; and, finally, novices can get into trouble with approximation theory."

I, in turn, was visited by a colleague from our engineering department who presented me with a practical problem of approximation in several variables which came from thermodynamics. After a few minutes I had to confess that whatever my acquaintance with the 2500 year backlog of approximation theory might be, it still wasn't sufficient to help him.

And so it goes. There is much to make us proud and much to make us modest. There is much that is known. Of what is known there is much that is relevant and far, far more that is irrelevant. There is much that is untried or unknown. There is much opportunity for developing the simple as well as the sophisticated idea. No one will have a monopoly on approximation theory.

The principal impact of computers on approximation theory is that they have simultaneously created the need for approximations and provided the means for fulfilling this need. Least square approximation, Tschebyscheff approximation have become commonplace. While the theoretical knowledge of these things is today—as it was a generation ago—largely in the hands of specialists, the time is not far off when all of the commonly employed mathematical and physical functions will be readily available in catalogs or in machine codes for their production. In a certain way, then, this problem is a closed book.

A second impact of computers is that their tremendous numerical power has raised our horizons. We are no longer afraid of doing things where the theory is known and the practice difficult, but we are also spurred on to tackle problems where the theory is unknown, but the practice may be possible. Mathematicians like to do things that are either pretty or useful, with a strong preference for the former. Since much that is pretty is not useful and much that is useful is not pretty, computing machines, by suppressing much detail, have contributed their backing to a movement toward the useful.

A third impact of computers—and who knows but that in the long run it may turn out to be the most important one—is that the computer research effort has been a great spur to the theoretical aspects of approximation theory. In blunt language, an awful lot of money has been spent on approximation theory in the name of "computation". We have also seen a restimulation of the theory of rational functions and of continued fractions. We have seen the blossoming of functional analysis within approximation theory and numerical analysis. Scores of special theoretical topics have been developed, though it must be expected that only a few of them will return dividends to computation itself.

There has also been some negative impact due to the computing machines. This is inevitable. There has been a decrease in the importance of an older type of numerical analysis which was centered around the symbolic difference calculus. Difference tables were convenient in the days of hand calculation, but are less so with automatic computers, and inevitably, the Lagrangian outlook has replaced the Newtonian.

There has been a decrease in the importance of computed tables of special functions. As hand computations have been automated out, systematic table look-ups seem to be going the way of peacock feathers and silent movies. On the other hand, given computers with very large internal memories, the insertion of whole tables once again becomes an attractive possibility. The whole rôle of tables is currently ambiguous and unresolved, and it will be interesting to watch the developments of the next ten years.

On the whole, approximation theory, following the rest of mathematics, has become during the first two decades of the computer age, more complex. As a reaction, my late associate at the Bureau of Standards, Milton Abramowitz, used to say in jest that all numerical analysis could be carried out using only Simpson's rule and linear interpolation. There is a kernel of truth in this. If we cannot make a simple computation without invoking a Banach space or two, surely there is a loss involved, if only a loss of innocence.

The production of literature in the last several years seems to fall into sixteen main categories. They are as follows, but the reader should take notice that these categories are neither exclusive nor exhaustive. 1. Books, 2. Application of approximation to other portions of numerical analysis, 3. Exponential fitting, 4. Functional analysis, 5. Least maximum deviation, 6. Minimization in general, 7. New computer applications of approximations, 8. Nonlinear estimation and approximation, 9. P and other norms, 10. Polygonal approximation, 11. Rational function approximation, 12. Several variables, 13. Approximation under side conditions, 14. Approximation to special functions, 15. Spline interpolation, 16. Tschebyscheff series.

I will now say a few words about several of these categories.

Functional analysis. One of the developments of approximation theory in the computer decade is that functional analysis has become firmly established. Those of us who were present at the Madison Approximation Conference a few years ago can recall with amusement how the participants in that conference were split into two groups: the "Earth Men" and the "Space Men". The earth men clamored that concepts of abstract spaces were confusing and unnecessary. I think there is no doubt but that the space men have had their way. The concepts of normed linear spaces are too valuable to be put off by "mere" computation.

I don't think that electronic computers have had much to do with the vitality of the functional analysis movement. As a matter of fact, one can trace its appearance in approximation theory back to the very beginnings of functional analysis. On the other hand, the possibility of effectively carrying out numerical approximations in a variety of norms has lent a concrete punch to the movement.

Functional analysis has provided a unifying point of view and language and a geometric intuition which is of considerable beauty. I do not think that it has provided as yet much in the practical domain that was not formerly available, but it is such a pretty child that everyone follows its career with interest.

"Production" approximation. As matters stand now it is possible with the flip of the wrist to turn out yards of polynomial and rational approximations. In the Fall of 1962, Frank W. J. Olver and I called an informal conference on approximations at the National Bureau of Standards. It was thought over that by bringing together the principal producers of approximation, we might arrive at a plan for a handbook of approximations of international scope and of unified approach. This handbook might then be produced at one of the larger computer centers for the benefit of the whole scientific community. Between ten and twenty people participated in these discussions.

I have rarely been so sanguine or so naive. It became apparent within the first ten minutes of our discussion that a common basis for action did not exist. We found no agreement on what kind of approximations to present or on the format of presentation. Some people were not even convinced that there was any reason to put them out in a book.

Over the next few years we shall therefore have available a wide variety of approximations of all types and of varying utility. Having failed at this ecumenical effort, I consoled myself with the following thought. How does nature grow the great oak trees? She has the trees drop acorns by the thousands. Only a few sprout. It is crucial that many ideas be tried out and perhaps it was just as well that our effort failed.

Spline approximation. One of the striking developments in numerical analysis in the past 5 years has been the use of spline curves for interpolation and approximation. A spline curve is one which is a piecewise polynomial and which has an appropriate amount of continuity where the pieces join. Splines have recently found substantial applications ranging from the approximation of mortality curves to automatic milling machines in the automotive industry. Backed up by a beautiful theory and the possibility of simple computation, it promises much, and a considerable following has jumped on its band wagon. Spline approximation contains the delicious paradox of Prokofieff's Classical Symphony: it seems as though it might have been written several centuries ago, but of course it could not have been.

Novel applications. Novel application of approximation and interpolation appear everyday, and go all the way from computer reruns of Kepler's original data to the computer production of terrain models in cartography One very practical development that appears to be of great importance is numerical control of machine contouring. If we now have the Chevy II and the Corvair, there is no reason why in a few years we should not have the *Walsh* 3 or the *Birkhoff* 4! This puts approximaters *squarely* among those who have fostered automation and invites us all to consider seriously Norbert Wiener's question "What is the human use of human beings?"

Another novel use of interpolation—probably a simple-minded one—has occurred in the computer production of animated cartoons. We may soon be led to the problem of what is the best norm for Mickey Mouse.

What of the future? The historian Arnold Toynbee once wrote that if a man had been given a political map of the North American Continent in 1730 and asked to predict the dominant language there in the 1900's, he would not have predicted English. The flag of Louis XV's France flying in Detroit across the street from our hotel reminds us of the reliability of historical predictions.

Over the next five years, I personally would like to see (a) the "automatic French curve", (b) Numerical approximation in the complex plane, (c) Accessible approximation in several variables, (d) Numerical experimentation in approximation theory on the computer, utilizing primitive methods, and possibly visual displays, (e) Approximation under side conditions, particularly convexity conditions. Whether these topics will flower, and what their impact will be on numerical and computer mathematics I leave unanswered. Approximation theory is capable of surprising us, and at a meeting five years hence, we may find ourselves waving altogether a different flag.

Appendix

SELECTED PAPERS ON APPROXIMATION THEORY AND ITS APPLICATION TO NUMERICAL ANALYSIS THAT HAVE APPEARED WITHIN THE LAST FEW YEARS[1]

BOOKS

N. I. Achieser, *Theory of approximation*, Ungar, New York, 1956.

Juan Horvath, *Approximacion y funciones casi-analiticas*, Madrid, 1956.

J. C. Burkill, *Lectures on approximation by polynomials*, Tata Institute, Bombay, 1959.

P. P. Korovkin, *Linear operations and approximation theory*, Hindustan Publ. Corp., Delhi, 1960.

A. F. Tiemann, *The theory of the approximation of functions of a real variable*, GIF-ML, Moscow, 1960.

National Physical Laboratory, *Modern computing methods*, Notes on Applied Science, No. 16, Her Majesty's Stationery Office, London, 1961.

[1] Compiled: Summer, 1964.

J. P. Kahane, *Teoria constructiva de funciones*, Universidad de Buenos Aires, 1961.

C. W. Clenshaw, *Chebyshev series for mathematical functions*, NPL Math. Tables, Vol. 5, Her Majesty's Stationery Office, London, 1962.

E. W. Cheney, *Approximation theory*, UCLA, to be published.

P. J. Davis, *Interpolation and approximation*, Blaisdell Publ. Co., New York, 1963.

Michael Golomb, *Lectures on theory of approximation*, Argonne National Lab., Appl. Math, Div., to be published.

A. N. Kovanskii, *The application of continued fractions and their generalization to problems in approximation theory*, translated by Peter Wynn, P. Noordhoff N. V., Groningen, 1963.

Proceedings of the conference on approximation theory, held at Oberwolfach, Germany, August, 1963, Birkhauser, Basel, 1964.

Proceedings of the conference on approximation theory, held at Gatlinburg, Tennessee, October, 1963, J. Soc. Indust. Appl. Math. Ser. B, Numerical Analysis, **1** (1964).

Arthur Sard, *Linear approximation*, Amer. Math. Soc., Providence, R.I., 1963.

John Todd, *Constructive theory of functions*, Academic Press, New York, 1963.

Lothar Collatz, *Funktionalanalysis und numerische Mathematik*, Springer, Berlin, 1964.

Handbook of Mathematical Functions, U.S. Dept. of Commerce, National Bureau of Standards, Applied Mathematics Series No. 55, U.S. Government Printing Office, Washington, D.C., 1964.

Gunter Meinardus, *Approximation von Funktionen und ihre numerische Behandlung*, Springer, Berlin, 1964.

John R. Rice, *The approximation of functions*, Addison-Wesley, Reading, Mass., 1964.

APPLICATION OF APPROXIMATION TO OTHER PORTIONS OF NUMERICAL ANALYSIS

L. Fox, *Chebyshev methods for ordinary differential equations*, Comput. J. **4** (1962), 318.

B. Gluss, *A line segment curve-fitting algorithm related to the encoding of information*, Information and Control **5**, 3 (1962), 261–267.

D. A. Bell, *Approximations in Fourier transforms*, Comput. J. **6** (1963), 244–247.

C. W. Clenshaw and H. J. Norton, *The solution of nonlinear ordinary differential equations in Chebyshev series*, Comput. J. **6** (1963), 88–92.

David Elliott, *A Chebyshev series method for the numerical solution of Fredholm integral equations*, Comput. J. **6** (1963), 102–110.

G. J. Tee, *Eigenvectors of the successive over-relaxation process, and its combination with Chebyshev semi-iteration*, Comput. J. **6** (1963), 250–262.

Boris Podolsky, *Curve fitting with allowance for errors in given data*, Flight Propulsion Lab Report R59FPD442, General Electric Co., Cincinnati, Ohio (1959).

R. Amer and H. R. Schwartz, *Contributions to the approximation problem of electrical filters*, Mitt. Inst. Angew. Math. Zurich (1964).

A. R. Curtis, NPL Mathematical Tables, Vol. 7, *Tables of Jacobian elliptic functions whose arguments are rational fractions of the quarter period*, London Dept. Scientific and Industrial Research (1964).

H. H. Denman and J. E. Howard, *Application of ultraspherical polynomials to nonlinear oscillations*. I, *Free oscillation of the pendulum*, Quart. Appl. Math. **21** (1964), 323–330.

H. H. Denman and Y. K. Liu, *Application of ultraspherical polynomials to nonlinear oscillations*. II, *Free oscillations*, Quart. Appl. Math., to appear.

H. J. Norton, *The iterative solution of nonlinear ordinary differential equations*, Comput. J. **7** (1964), 76–85.

K. Wright, *Chebyshev collocation methods for ordinary differential equations*, Comput. J. **6** (1963).

EXPONENTIAL FITTING

D. G. Gardner, J. C. Gardner, G. Lausch, and W. W. Meinke, *Method of the analysis of multi-component exponential decay curves*, J. Chem. Phys. **31,** 4 (1959), 978.

W. Perl, *A method for curve-fitting by exponential functions*, Int. J. Appl. Radiat. Isotop. **8,** 4 (1960), 211.

O. Jaroch, *Approximation by exponential functions*, Appl. Math. **7** (1962), 249–264.

H. J. Maehly, *Numerical solution of a certain transcendental equation involving exponentials* (a remark on a paper of J. R. Rice), J. Soc. Indust. Appl. Math. **10** (1962), 30–34.

P. Wynn, *A note on the fitting of certain types of experimental data*, Statistica Neerlandica **16** (1962), 143–150.

J. W. Layman, *A finite difference exponential approximation method*, Math. Comp. **18** (1964), 113–118.

Beatrice H. Worsley, *Analysis of decay-type data*, Comm. ACM **7** (1964), 39–44.

FUNCTIONAL ANALYSIS

T. J. Rivlin and H. S. Shapiro, *A unified approach to certain problems of approximation and minimization*, J. Soc. Indust. Appl. Math. **9** (1961), 670–699.

H. F. Weinberger, *Optimal approximation for functions prescribed at equally spaced points*, J. Res. Nat. Bur. Standards **65B** (1961), 99–104.

S. I. Zuhovickii, *On best approximation of functions in normed linear spaces and in normed rings* (Russian). Funkcional'nyi Analiz i ego Primenenie (Trudy 5 Konf. po Funkcional'nomu Analizu i ego Primeneniju), Izdat. Akad. Nauk Azerbaidzan SSR, Baku (1961), 86–88.

E. W. Woronowskaja, *Die Methode der Funktionale bei klassische Aufgaben der Approximationstheorie*. Wiss. Z. Humboldt-Univ. Berlin Math.-Nat. Reihe **11** (1962/63), 243–247.

LEAST MAXIMUM DEVIATION

L. Collatz, *Tschebyscheffsche Annäherung mit rationalen Funktionen*, Abh. Math. Sem. Univ. Hamburg **24** (1960), 70–78.

L. Veidinger, *On the numerical determination of the best approximation in the Chebyshev sense*, Numer. Math. **2** (1960), 99–105.

G. Meinardus and H. D. Strauer, *Über die Approximation von Funktionen bei der Aufstellung von Unterprogrammen*. Elektron. Datenverarbeitung **12** (1961), 180–187.

Johannes C. C. Nitsche, *Über die Abhängigheit der Tschebyscheffschen Approximierenden einer differenzierbaren Funktion von Intervall*, Numer. Math. **4** (1962), 262–276.

E. Y. Remez, *General computational methods of Chebyshev approximation, The problem with linear and real parameters* (Eng. translation). U.S. Atomic Energy Comm., Washington, D.C. (1962).

T. J. Rivlin, *Polynomials of best uniform approximation to certain rational fractions*, Numer. Math. **4** (1962), 345–349.

E. Y. Remez, *On the construction of Chebyshev approximations of linear functional and certain related types*, Ukrain. Mat. Z. **15** (1963), 400–411.

A. S. Steinberg, *On the effective construction of best trigonometric approximations*, Ukrain. Mat. Z. **15** (1963), 173–184.

C. W. Valentine and C. Peter Van Dine, *An algorithm for minimax polynomial curve-fitting of data*, J. Assoc. Comput. Mach. **10** (1963), 283–290.

R. Zurmühl, *Zur angenäherten ganzrationalen Tschebysheffapproximation mit hilfe trigonometrischer Interpolation*, Numer. Math. **6** (1964), 1–5.

MINIMIZATION IN GENERAL

H. H. Rosenbrock, *An automatic method for finding the greatest or least value of a function*, Comput. J. **3** (1960), 175–184.

P. Hooke and T. A. Jeeves, *Direct search solution of numerical and statistical problems*, J. Assoc. Comput. Mach. **8** (1961), 212–229.

C. F. Wood, *Recent development in direct search technique*, Res. Report 62-159-522-R1, Westinghouse Res. Labs. Pittsburgh, Pa.

R. Fletcher and M. J. D. Powell, *A rapidly convergent descent method for minimization*, Comput. J. **6** (1963), 163–168.

P. Krolak and L. Cooper, *An extension of fibonaccian search to several variables*, Comm. Assoc. Comput. Mach. **6** (1963), 639–640.

D. W. Marquardt, *An algorithm for least squares estimation of nonlinear parameters*, J. Soc. Indust. Appl. Math. **11** (1963), 431–441.

A. A. Goldstein and B. R. Kripke, *Mathematical programming by minimizing differentiable functions*, Numer. Math. **6** (1964), 47–48.

NEW COMPUTER APPLICATIONS OF APPROXIMATIONS

D. D. Morrison, *Methods for nonlinear least squares problems and convergence proofs, tracking programs and orbit determination*, Proc. Jet Propulsion Lab. Seminar (1960), 1–9.

M. E. Stiefel, *Le problème d'approximation dans la théorie des filtres électriques*, Colloque sur l'analyse numérique, Libraire Gauthier-Villars, Paris (1961), 81–87.

F. Theilheimer and W. Starkweather, *The fairing of shiplines on a high-speed computer*, Math. Comp. **15**, 76 (1961), 338–355.

O. J. Wilde, *Optimization methods*, Advances in chemical engrg. **3,** 277–292.

F. Landis and E. N. Nilson, *The determination of thermodynamic properties by direct differentiation techniques* (presented at 1962 Second Symposium on Thermophysical Properties, January 24–26, 1962, Princeton University). Progress in International Research on Thermodynamic and Transport Properties by the American Society of Mechanical Engineers, United Engineering Center, 345 East 47th Street, New York 17, New York, pp. 218–227.

J. R. Rice, *Computer approximations for physical tables*, General Motors Research Report, GMR 387, 1962.

Anon.—*Computer production of terrain models*, Comm. Assoc. Comput. Mach. **6** (1963), 190–191.

E. F. Carlberg and J. J. Childs, *Boeing expands numerical control contouring capability*, Machine and Tool Blue Book, 58, 1 (1963).

J. R. Killian, Jr., *Old engineers and new technologies*, Think **29** (1963), 7–10.

G. Turner Wilson, Jr., *Short range forecasting of gasoline sales*, Data Processing for Science/Engineering, Vol. 1, No. 2 (1963), 35–40.

Owen Gingerich, *The computer versus Kepler*, American Scientist **52** (1964), 218–226.

Arthur Wouk, *Approximation and allocation*, J. Math. Anal. Appl. **8** (1964), 135–143.

E. E. Zajac, *Computer-made perspective movies as a scientific and communication tool*, Comm. Assoc. Comput. Mach. **7** (1964), 169–170.

NONLINEAR ESTIMATION AND APPROXIMATION

G. W. Booth, G. E. P. Box, M. E. Muller and T. I. Peterson, *Forecasting by generalized regression methods, nonlinear estimation*, Princeton-IBM, IBM Corp. Mimeo. (IBM share program No. 687, WL NL 1) (1959).

R. W. Preisendorfer and B. W. Roos, *On the best fit to experimental data curves using homogeneous two-parameter functions*, Math. Comp. **17** (1963), 231–236.

J. R. Rice, *On the existence and characterization of best nonlinear Tschebyscheff approximations*, Trans. Amer. Math. Soc. **110** (1964), 88–97.

P AND OTHER NORMS

T. J. Rivlin and B. R. Kripke, *Approximation in the metric of $L^1(X, \mu)$*. IBM Research Paper RC 524 (1961).

P. Althammer, *Eine Erweiterung des Orthogonalitätsbegriffes bei Polynomen und deren Anwendung auf die beste Approximation*, J. Reine Angew. Math. **211** (1962), 192–204.

J. L. Walsh and T. S. Motzkin, *Polynomials of best approximation on an interval*, Proc. Nat. Acad. Sci. U.S.A. **48** (1962), 1533–1537.

J. Descloux, *Approximations in L^p and Chebyshev approximants*, J. Soc. Indust. Appl. Math. **11** (1963), 1017–1026.

D. G. Moursund, *Chebyshev approximation of a function and its derivatives*, Math. Comp. **18** (1964), 382–389.

Boris Podolsky and Harry H. Denman, *Conditions on minimization criteria for smoothing*, Math. Comp. **18** (1964), 441–448.

J. R. Rice, *On the computation of L_1 approximations by exponentials, rationals and other functions*, Math. Comp. **18** (1964), 390–396.

B. R. Kripke, *Best approximation with respect to nearby norms*, to appear.

POLYGONAL APPROXIMATIONS

Hans Schwerdtfeger, *Interpolation and curve fitting by sectionally linear functions*, Canad. Math. Bull. **3** (1960), 41–57.

R. Bellman, *On the approximation of curves by line segments using dynamic programming*, Comm. Assoc. Comput. Mach. **4** (1961), 284.

Hans Schwerdtfeger, *Notes on numerical analysis*. III, *Further remarks on sectionally linear functions*, Canad. Math. Bull. **4** (1961).

H. Stone, *Approximation of curves by line segments*, Math. Comp. **15** (1961), 40–47.

B. Gluss, *Further remarks on line segment curve-fitting using dynamic programming*, Comm. Assoc. Comput. Mach. **5** (1962), 441–443.

R. Bellman, R. Kalaba, B. Kotkin, *Polynomial approximation—a new computational technique in dynamic programming: allocation process*, Math. Comp. **17** (1963), 155–161.

Miroslav Manas, *Application of linear programming methods to the approximation of linear functions*, Apl. Mat. **8** (1963), 206–215.

Hans Schwerdtfeger, *Théorie des fonctions—fonctions polygonales et relations récurrentes*, CR Acad. Sc., t. 256, p. 4350–4353, Séance du 20 Mai 1963, Groupe 1.

RATIONAL FUNCTION APPROXIMATION

G. Hornecker, *Méthodes pratiques pour le détermination approchée de la meilleure approximation polynomiale ou rationelle*, Chiffres **3** (1960), 143–228.

H. J. Maehly, *Methods for fitting rational approximations, Part I: Telescoping procedures for continued fractions*, J. Assoc. Comput. Mach. **7** (1960).

P. Wynn, *The rational approximation of functions which are formally defined by a power series expansion*, Math. Comp. **14** (1960), 147–186.

E. W. Cheney and H. L. Loeb, *Two new algorithms for rational approximation*, Numer. Math. **3** (1961), 72–75.

W. Fraser and J. F. Hart, *On the computation of rational approximations to continuous functions*, Comm. Assoc. Comput. Mach. **5** (1962), 401–403.

H. Werner, *Tschebyscheff-approximationen im Bereich der rationalen Funktionen bei Vorliegen einer guten Ausgangsnäherung*, Arch. Rational Mech. Anal. **10** (1962), 205–219.

H. Werner, *Ein Satz über diskrete Tschebyscheff-Approximation bei gebrochen linearen Funktionen*, Numer. Math. **4** (1962), 154–157.

H. Werner, *Die konstruktive Ermittlung der Tschebyscheff-Approximierenden im Bereich der rationalen Funktionen*, Arch. Rational Mech. Anal. **11** (1962), 368–384.

P. Wynn, *The epsilon algorithm and operational formulas of numerical analysis*, Math. Comp. **15** (1962), 151–158.

P. Wynn, *The numerical efficiency of certain continued fraction expansions*, Nederl. Akad. Wetensch. Proc. Ser. A **65** (1962), 127–148.

P. Wynn, *Upon a second confluent form of the ε-algorithm*, Proc. Glasgow Math. Assoc. **5** (1962), 160–165.

P. Wynn, *Una Nota su un Analogo Infinitesimale del q-d Algorithmo*, Rend. di Math. di Roma **21** (1962), 77–85.

E. W. Cheney and T. H. Southard, *A survey of methods for rational approximation, with particular reference to a new method based on a formula of Darboux*, SIAM Rev. **5** (1963), 219–231.

C. de Boor and John R. Rice, *Chebyscheff approximation by* $\prod_{i=1}^{n}[(x - r_i)/(x + s_i)]$ *and application to ADI Iteration*, J. Soc. Indust. Appl. Math. **11** (1963), 159.

A. A. Goldstein, *On the stability of rational approximation*, Numer. Math. **5** (1963), 431–438.

C. L. Lawson, *Segmented rational minimax approximation, characteristic properties and computational methods*, Jet Propulsion Lab., T.R. No. 32-579 (1963).

H. J. Maehly, *Methods for fitting rational approximations*. Pts. II and III, J. Assoc. Comput. Mach. **10** (1963), 257–277.

Anthony Ralston, *Economization of rational functions*, J. Assoc. Comput. Mach. **10** (1963), 278–282.

R. Sankar and V. Malini, *A note on the relative merits of Padé and Maehly's diagonal convergents*, Math. Comp. **17** (1963), 414–418.

H. Werner, *Rationale Tschebyscheff-Approximation, Eigenwerttheorie, und Differenzenrechnung*, Arch. Rational Mech. Anal. **13** (1963), 330–347.

P. Wynn, *On a connection between the first and second confluent forms of the ε-algorithm*, Nieuw Arch. Wisk. **11** (1963), 19–21.

Josef Stoer, *A direct method for Chebyshev approximation by rational functions*, J. Assoc. Comput. Mach. **11** (1964), 59–69.

SEVERAL VARIABLES

G. Birkhoff and H. L. Garabedian, *Smooth surface interpolation*, J. Math. and Phys. **39** (1960), 258–268.

M. B. A. Babaev, *On the best degree of approximation of functions of two variables by functions of the type* $\phi(x) \cdot \psi(y)$, Izv. Akad. Nauk Azerbaidjan, SSR Ser. Fiz. Mat. Tehn. Nauk (1962), 25–40.

N. V. McEachern, *A polynomial surface-fitting program for the Bendix G-15 digital computer*, NRC, LR-347, Nat. Res. Council, Nat. Aero. Establ, Ottawa, Canada (1962).

B. Gluss, *Least squares fitting of planes to surfaces using dynamic programming*, Comm. Assoc. Comput. Mach. **6** (1963), 172–175.

D. J. Newman and H. S. Shapiro, *Some theorems on Chebysev approximation*, Duke Math. J. **30** (1963), 673–681.

J. R. Rice, *Tchebyscheff approximation in several variables*, Trans. Amer. Math. Soc. **109** (1963), 444–466.

James Ferguson, *Multivariable curve interpolation*, J. Assoc. Comput. Mach. **11** (1964), 221–228.

SIDE CONDITIONS

G. G. Lorentz, *The degree of approximation by polynomials with positive coefficients*, Math. Ann. **151** (1963), 239–251.

J. R. Rice, *Approximation with convex constraints*, J. Soc. Indust. Appl. Math. **11** (1963), 15–32.

S. I. Zuhovickii, R. A. Poljak and M. E. Primak, *An algorithm for solving the convex Chebyshev approximation problem* (Russian), Dokl. Akad. Nauk. SSSR **151** (1963), 27–30.

SPECIAL FUNCTIONS

Kurt Spielberg, *Efficient continued fraction approximations to elementary functions*, Math. Comp. **15** (1961), 409–417.

C. W. Clenshaw, G. F. Miller and M. Woodger, *Algorithms for special functions*. I, Handbook series special functions, Numer. Math. **4** (1962/63), 403–419.

Kurt Spielberg, *Polynomial and continued-fraction approximation for logarithmic functions*, Math. Comp. **16** (1962), 205–217.

Renata Babushkova, *Eine Bemerkung zur Tschebyscheffschen Approximation der Funktion* sin x/x, Wiss. Z. Techn. Univ. Dresden **12** (1963), 111–112.

F. D. Burgoyne, *Approximations to Kelvin functions*, Math. Comp. **17** (1963), 295–298.

R. F. Gloden, *Recherche de la meilleure approximation pour l'évaluation d'une fonction donnée*, Euratom, CETIS, Brussels (1963).

W. D. Ray and A. E. N. T. Pitman, *Chebyshev polynomials and other new approximations to Mill's ratio*, Ann. Math. Statist. **34** (1963), 892–902.

H. Werner and G. Raymann, *An approximation to the Fermi integral* $F_{1/2}(x)$, Math. Comp. **17** (1963), 193–194.

R. Gloden, *Approximation des fonctions de Bessel*, Euratom, CETIS, Brussels (1964).

SPLINE INTERPOLATION

C. de Boor, *Bicubic spline interpolation*, J. Math. and Phys. **41** (1962), 212–218.

J. L. Walsh, J. H. Ahlberg and E. N. Nilson, *Best approximation properties of the spline fit*, J. Math. Mech. **11** (1962), 225–234.

C. de Boor, *Best approximation properties of spline functions of odd degree*, J. Math. Mech. **12** (1963), 747–749.

E. N. Nilson and J. H. Ahlberg, *Convergence properties of the spline fit*, J. Soc. Indust. Appl. Math. **11** (1963), 95–104.

T. N. E. Greville, *Numerical procedures for interpolation by spline functions*, Math. Res. Center Technical Summary Report #450, U. S. Army, The University of Wisconsin, Madison, Wisconsin (1964).

———, *Interpolation by generalized spline functions*, MRC Technical Summary Report #476, Madison, Wisconsin (1964).

I. J. Schoenberg, *On interpolation by spline functions and its minimal properties*, Proceedings of the conference on approximation, Oberwolfach, Germany, August, 1963.

———, *Spline interpolation and the higher derivatives*, Proc. Nat. Acad. Sci. U.S.A. **51** (1964), 24–28.

———, *Spline interpolation and best quadrature formulae*, Bull. Amer. Math. Soc. **70** (1964), 143–148.

———, *On best approximation of linear operators*, Nederl. Akad. Wetensch. Proc. Ser. A **67** (1964), 155–163.

———, *On trigonometric spline interpolation*, to appear.

Daniel G. Schweikert, *An interpolation curve using a spline in tension*, to appear.

G. Birkhoff and C. de Boor, *Error bounds for spline interpolation*, J. Math. Mech. **13** (1964), 827–836.

———, *Piecewise polynomial interpolation and approximation*, These Proceedings, p. 164.

C. de Boor and R. E. Lynch, *Generalized splines and their minimum properties*, to appear.

J. H. Ahlberg, E. N. Nilson and J. L. Walsh, *Fundamental properties of generalized splines*, to appear.

TSCHEBYSCHEFF SERIES

T. J. Rivlin, *Cebysev expansions and best uniform approximation*, IBM Res. Report RZ-93 (1962).

E. J. Remez and V. T. Gavriljuk, *Some remarks on polynomial Chebyshev approximations of functions compared to the intervals of expansions in Chebyshev polynomials.* Ukrain. Mat. Z. **15** (1963), 46–57.

David Elliott, *Evaluation and estimation of the coefficients in the Chebyshev series expansion of a function*, Math. Comp. **18** (1964), 274–284.

———, *Truncation errors in two Chebyshev series approximations*, to appear.

H. C. Thacher, Jr., *Conversion of a power to a series of Chebyshev polynomials*, Comm. Assoc. Comput. Mach. **7** (1964), 181–182.

D. Elliott and G. Szekeres, *Some estimates of the coefficients in the Chebyshev series expansion of a function*, Math. Comp. **19** (1965), 25–32.

PIECEWISE POLYNOMIAL INTERPOLATION AND APPROXIMATION[1]

GARRETT BIRKHOFF
Harvard University, Cambridge, Massachusetts

and

CARL R. DE BOOR
General Motors Research Laboratories, Warren, Michigan

A. Introduction

1. **Motivation.** Practical interest in schemes of interpolation and approximation has been greatly stimulated by the development of high-speed digital computing machines having a large storage ("memory"). Moreover, the availability of such machines has also heightened interest in the question of representing more or less arbitrary curves and surfaces by relatively simple formulas. In particular, the automobile industry would like to represent car body surfaces by formulas which could be handled by such machines.

We have been working on this problem for several years, in collaboration with the mathematics staff at the General Motors Research Laboratories, with the primary aim of developing simple, economical, accurate and flexible procedures. From the beginning, it has been our conviction that *piecewise polynomial* functions were the most suitable, and our experience indicates that they are basically satisfactory. We wish here to explain *why* we believe that they are well suited for treating *general* problems of interpolation and approximation on high-speed computing machines.

The theoretical literature on piecewise polynomial functions constitutes a small fraction of the existing mathematical literature on interpolation and approximation theory. The bulk of this literature has been concerned with the fitting of functions of *one* real or complex variable by *analytic* functions. Interpolation and approximation by *polynomial* and *rational* functions offer a wealth of alternative possibilities [**10**, Chapter VIII; **7**, **8**, **16**], and many theorems have been proved about the *convergence* of such schemes as the degree tends to infinity. However, as is well known, simple polynomial interpolation fails to converge as the mesh-length tends to zero, even for some very smooth analytic functions (e.g., $1/(1 + x^2)$ on $[-5, 5]$),[2] and uniform meshes.

For *periodic* functions tabulated on a *uniform mesh* (i.e., one with constant

---

[1] Work partly supported by the Office of Naval Research.

[2] J. F. Steffensen, *Interpolation*, 2nd ed., Chelsea, New York, 1950, p. 35. The counterexample is due to C. Runge, Z. Math. Phys. **46** (1901), 224–243.

mesh-spacing h), a reliable scheme of accurate analytic interpolation is provided by truncated Fourier series (trigonometric polynomials). This scheme was extended from truncated Fourier series to truncated Fourier integrals, by E. T. Whittaker, in his classic study of "cardinal functions" [**18**; **8**, p. 330]. These define an interpolation scheme for functions tabulated on a uniform mesh with mesh-points $x_n = nh$ $(n = 0, \pm 1, \pm 2, \cdots)$, which is ideal for many theoretical purposes. For any continuous, square-integrable function f in the Hilbert space $L_2(-\infty, +\infty)$ it reproduces exactly the component f_h from wave-numbers $q \in [-\pi/h, \pi/h]$, but replaces each Fourier component with wave-number $q \notin [-\pi/h, \pi/h]$ by a "cotabular" function with the same coefficient but different wave number q' satisfying $q' \equiv q \pmod{2\pi/h}$ and $|q'| \leqq \pi/h$. Hence it rotates the orthogonal component $f - f_h$ through 90° in the Hilbert space. It is *convergent* in the mean-square, and the error is $O(h^r)$ if the rth derivative $f^r(x) \in L_2(-\infty, +\infty)$.

However these schemes are inflexible (the mesh-spacing must be constant); they are incompatible with most boundary conditions; and we shall see (§11) that they are sensitive to roundoff errors.

Much less is known about the more difficult problems of interpolation and approximation to functions of two or more variables. The Weierstrass Approximation Theorem assures us that *any* continuous function can be *approximated* arbitrarily closely on *any* compact set by polynomials of sufficiently high degree [**4**, §6.6]. Approximations can be computed systematically, as convolutions with Bernstein polynomials; moreover one can also match finite sets of derivatives arbitrarily closely [**4**, §6.3]. From the standpoint of *existence* theory, this leaves little to be desired. Moreover, because high-speed computing machines have arithmetic units especially designed to perform rational operations, polynomials and rational functions are well adapted to them.

However, even for functions of one variable, the use of Bernstein polynomials to *compute* accurate polynomial approximations is *uneconomical* [**4**, p. 116]. In practice, Newton's and Lagrange's interpolation formulas are far more widely used, even though they may diverge if pushed too far.

2. **Piecewise polynomial functions.** To represent smooth curves and surfaces economically, with the help of high-speed digital computers, we recommend the use of *piecewise polynomial* functions.

Indeed, we will be much more specific. Although piecewise quintic polynomials have proved useful on occasion and, for some applications, approximation by piecewise quadratic or even linear functions is most suitable, in general we recommend *piecewise cubic* polynomials for fitting smooth curves, and *piecewise bicubic* polynomials for fitting smooth surfaces, as good bets to be tried first, in the absence of special reasons for trying something else.

Piecewise cubic polynomial functions of one variable, with continuous slope and curvature, have long been used by draftsmen and engineers. For practical design work, they have used *mechanical splines*: thin beams carrying loads w_i

concentrated at points x_i, according to the classical Euler-Bernoulli theory.[3] Such mechanical splines (of small "stiffness") have been used as analog computers to fair curves through given sets of points.

It was probably known to Euler that the "strain energy" minimized by such splines is proportional to $\int y''^2\,dx$ in the small-deflection (linearized) approximation. Moreover, the shape of "non-linear splines" (or elastica) minimizing $\int \kappa^2\,ds$, the integral of the squared curvature with respect to arc-length, has also been worked out [**9**, §262].

The use of mechanical splines to interpolate smooth nearly horizontal curves through a given set of points is similar to that of computing the deflection of a *thin beam* of given stiffness k. In both cases, the third derivative undergoes a jump of $w_i/k = \Delta y_i'''$ at the ith joint x_i, and the deflection $y(x)$ is given (approximately) by a cubic polynomial between successive "joints" x_i. The difference is, that in the problem of spline *interpolation* one is *given* the $y_i = y(x_i)$, whereas in the problem of the loaded beam one is given the w_i (or $\Delta y_i'''$). Moreover by *clamping* the spline at any joint, one can control the slope there.

By using clamped splines, one can represent very accurately horizontal plane sections of ship hulls.[4] Typically, ship hulls have long straight midsections, onto which a smooth, pointed bow and stern are appended. The advantages of using splines or other piecewise polynomial functions to represent such profiles seems indeed fairly obvious, if one considers the principle of analytic continuation.

It can hardly be said that this idea is either very deep or very novel. The use of generalized splines, and other piecewise polynomial functions of higher degree, to approximate smooth functions of one variable, was considered earlier very carefully by I. J. Schoenberg in an important paper [**13**] where deep results were obtained for the case of a uniform mesh on the infinite line. A thorough study of the literature would probably reveal many other relevant papers.

What is important is that spline interpolation *converges* rapidly on a wide variety of meshes, that it is insensitive to roundoff, and that it is easy to perform on high-speed computers. The demonstration of these facts seems to be new. What we consider most original about our work is the development of practical schemes of *surface-fitting*, applicable to wide classes of smooth surfaces.

B. Piecewise Polynomial Interpolation

3. **Spline functions.** To introduce the subject technically, we will adopt the approach of Schoenberg [**13**]. We define a *spline function of degree k*, with *joints* at points $x_0 < x_1 < \cdots < x_n$, as a function $f(x)$ of one real variable x, which is

---

[3] See for example J. L. Synge and B. A. Griffith, *Principles of mechanics*, McGraw-Hill, New York, 1959, §3.3.

[4] See F. Theilheimer and W. Starkweather, MTAC **15** (1961), 338–355. It was in connection with this application that the senior author first became attracted to spline functions, around 1955.

of class C^{k-1}, and is equal on each interval $[x_{i-1}, x_i]$ to a polynomial of degree k.

Spline functions of *odd* degree $k = 2m - 1$ have the basic variational property of minimizing the integral $\int [f^{(m)}(x)]^2\,dx$ for given $y_i = f(x_i)$; this is immediate if one integrates by parts. Thus, cubic spline functions ($m = 2$) appear as the logical next step after piecewise linear ("polygon") functions of x (the case $m = 1$), as a scheme of piecewise polynomial interpolation. For given y_i and endslopes y'_0, y'_n, they are easily calculated as follows.

The condition that $f(x) \in C^2$, for $f(x)$ cubic in the intervals $[x_{i-1}, x_i]$ and $[x_i, x_{i+1}]$, is equivalent to the following linear equation:

$$(3.1)\quad \Delta x_i y'_{i-1} + 2(\Delta x_{i-1} + \Delta x_i)y'_i + \Delta x_{i-1}y'_{i+1} = 3[(\Delta x_i \Delta y_{i-1}/\Delta x_{i-1}) + (\Delta x_{i-1}\Delta y_i/\Delta x_i)],$$

where $\Delta x_i = x_{i+1} - x_i$ and $\Delta y_i = f(x_{i+1}) - f(x_i)$. The resulting system of $n - 1$ equations is not only linearly independent; it is tridiagonal and *diagonally dominant*; hence it can be very stably solved for interior y'_i if y'_0, y'_n are given. Having solved for y_i and y'_i $[i = 0, 1, \cdots, n]$, one easily computes $f(x)$ in each interval $[x_{i-1}, x_i]$ by Hermite interpolation.

The preceding method can be adapted to cover also the "free endpoint" conditions $y''_0 = y''_n = 0$. In this case, one must supplement (3.1) by

$$(3.1')\qquad 2y'_0 + y'_1 = 3\Delta y_0/\Delta x_0, \qquad y'_{n-1} + 2y'_n = 3\Delta y_{n-1}/\Delta x_{n-1}.$$

Unfortunately, a valuable property is lost when one passes from $m = 1$ to $m = 2$. Whereas broken line interpolation is *local*, in the sense that the value of the interpolating function at a given point depends only on the f_i at a *fixed finite set* of neighboring points, this is not true of cubic spline interpolation. The values of $f(x)$ in any interval $[x_{i-1}, x_i]$ depend on *all* $f(x_j)$, without exception.

Local piecewise polynomial interpolation. In this respect, Bessel's method of *local cubic* interpolation has an advantage over spline interpolation. In local cubic interpolation, the numbers $y'_1, y'_2, \cdots, y'_{n-1}$ are calculated from

$$(3.2)\qquad (\Delta x_{i-1} + \Delta x_i)y'_i = \left[\Delta x_i \frac{\Delta y_{i-1}}{\Delta x_{i-1}} + \Delta x_{i-1}\frac{\Delta y_i}{\Delta x_i}\right];$$

Hermite interpolation is then again used to compute $f(x)$ in each interval. This gives a piecewise cubic polynomial of class C^1 only whose value at any point $x \in [x_{i-1}, x_i]$ depends just on the eight numbers x_j, y_j $(j = i - 2, i - 1, i, i + 1)$.

One can achieve continuity of the second derivative by increasing the degree of the polynomial pieces (and the number of points used). Jenkin's interpolation formula **[13]**, for instance, uses quartic polynomials, to obtain an interpolating function of class C^2 whose value in most intervals $[x_{i-1}, x_i]$ depends on the six numbers $y_{i-3}, \cdots, y_{i+1}$. For intervals near the endpoints x_0, x_n, it must be altered.

More generally, (local) interpolation formulas can be easily constructed **[13, 11]** for any positive integer m, which yield functions $f \in C^m$ which are piecewise polynomial of degree $k < m - 1$, with "joints" at the x_i. However, it is our impression that such formulas are more cumbersome to use than spline formulas of equal accuracy.

4. **Convergence to curves.** Let $\pi: 0 = x_0 < x_1 < \cdots < x_n = 1$ be a partition of the unit interval, and, for a given function $f(x)$, let $s(x) = s(x, \pi, f)$ denote the cubic spline which satisfies $s(x_i) = f(x_i)$, $i = 0, 1, \cdots, n$, and $s'(0) = f'(0)$, $s'(1) = f'(1)$. What happens to the error $s(x) - f(x)$ as $|\pi| = \max \Delta x_i$ shrinks to zero?

A first answer to this question was given by Ahlberg and Nilson **[1]**, where it was stated that if $f(x) \in C^2[0, 1]$, and if the mesh becomes eventually uniform as $|\pi| \to 0$, then $s(x)$ and its first two derivatives converge uniformly to $f(x)$ and its first two derivatives. We have extended this result in **[2]**, by showing that if $f(x) \in C^4[0, 1]$, and if the mesh-ratio $M_\pi = \max (\Delta x_i / \Delta x_j)$, the maximum ratio of mesh-lengths, is bounded, then $s^{(j)}(x)$ converges uniformly to $f^{(j)}(x)$, $j = 0, \cdots, 3$, as $|\pi| \to 0$. In fact,

$$|s^{(j)}(x) - f^{(j)}(x)| \leqq K \cdot |\pi|^{4-j}. \tag{4.1}$$

The uniform convergence of $s^{(3)}(x)$ to $f^{(3)}(x)$ was also proved, assuming only that $f^{(3)}(x)$ was absolutely continuous.

The technique used in **[2]** was based on a study of the *cardinal functions* $C_i(x)$ associated with spline interpolation at the joints x_i of a given partition π. These are the spline functions with joints x_i defined by

$$C_i(x_j) = \delta_{ij}, \qquad C_i'(x_0) = C_i'(x_n) = 0, \qquad i = 1, \cdots, n - 1, \quad j = 0, \cdots, n. \tag{4.2}$$

For bounded M_π, these are uniformly bounded and integrable—in fact they die away exponentially by a factor appreciably less than one in *each successive interval.*

When $f \in C^4[0, 1]$, formula (4.1) implies that the approximation to $f'(x)$ by $s'(x)$ is $O(|\pi|^3)$. A stronger statement can be made in case $x = x_i$ for some i, and π is uniform. In this case equation (3.1) reduces to

$$\frac{h}{3}(s'(x_{i-1}) + 4s'(x_i) + s'(x_{i+1})) = s(x_{i+1}) - s(x_{i-1}), \tag{4.3}$$

where $h = |\pi|$. One recognizes (4.3) as Simpson's Rule, and concludes from this (or computes directly) that

$$s'(x_{i-1}) + 4s'(x_i) + s'(x_{i+1}) = f'(x_{i-1}) + 4f'(x_i) + f'(x_{i+1}) + O(|\pi|^4), \tag{4.4}$$

in case $f \in C^5[0, 1]$ (since $s(x_j) = f(x_j)$). Hence, since $s'(0) = f'(0)$, $s'(1) = f'(1)$, and the eigenvalues of the tridiagonal matrix with general row $\{1, 4, 1\}$ are all greater than 1, it follows that

$$s'(x_i) = f'(x_i) + O(|\pi|^4).$$

It is clear that this conclusion remains true if the condition that π is uniform is replaced by the condition that π becomes asymptotically uniform as $|\pi| \to 0$. Unfortunately, the analogous result does not hold for s'': even at the joints, $s''(x) = f''(x) + O(|\pi|^2)$.

5. **Convergence and continuity.** We will now introduce some general concepts, which characterize valuable features of the (cubic) spline interpolation scheme defined in §3. An interpolation scheme J will be called *algebraically well-defined* for a real closed domain D and class Π of meshes π on D when, for any function[5] $f \in C^\infty(D)$, any $\pi \in \Pi$, $J_\pi[f]$ exists and is uniquely determined. Here, it is understood that *derivatives* of f may be admitted as values, as limiting cases (Hermite interpolation). Clearly, Lagrange, trigonometric, and (cubic) spline interpolation are all algebraically well-defined, linear interpolation schemes.

For an interpolation scheme to be a good scheme of approximation, a small maximum mesh-length $|\pi|$ must result in a small interpolation error $(J_\pi f)(x) - f(x)$. This leads to the question of whether or not a given interpolation scheme J is *convergent* on a set $S \subset C(D)$ of continuous functions on D, in the sense that

$$\max_{x \in D} |(J_\pi f)(x) - f(x)| \to 0 \qquad \text{for} \quad \pi \in \Pi, \qquad \text{as} \quad |\pi| \to 0. \tag{5.1}$$

Usually, one takes for S the set $C^k(D)$, for some $k \geqq 1$, and can often derive statements about the order ν of convergence as well, where ν is defined as the largest integer for which

$$\max_{x \in D} |(J_\pi f)(x) - f(x)| = O(|\pi|^\nu), \qquad \pi \in \Pi, \qquad f \in C^k(D). \tag{5.2}$$

Thus equal-spaced trigonometric interpolation is convergent on $C^k[a, b]$ for $k \geqq 1$, the interpolation error being $O(|\pi|^k \ln |\pi|)$ [7]. We have just seen that spline interpolation on $[a, b]$ for given $s'(a) = f'(a)$, $s'(b) = f'(b)$ *is* convergent on $C^4[a, b]$, with order of convergence equal to 4, provided Π consists of partitions with uniformly bounded mesh-ratios M_π. By contrast, as remarked earlier, polynomial or Lagrange interpolation (on uniform meshes) is not convergent even on $C^\infty(D)$ for all analytic functions! Also, not all schemes of spline interpolation are convergent. For example, if the condition $s'(b) = f'(b)$ is replaced by $s''(a) = f''(a)$, or by $s'((a + b)/2) = f'((a + b)/2)$, one would get algebraically well-defined schemes which are not convergent even on $C^\infty[a, b]$.

---

[5] Note that any set of values and derivatives can be assumed by some function $f \in C^\infty(D)$.

Theoretical results on the orders of convergence of interpolation schemes applied to a sufficiently smooth function f lose some of their practical interest because of roundoff. Although a smooth function f is to be interpolated, random roundoff errors will result in a non-smooth interpolating function g, the maximum difference between f and g being of the order of magnitude of the roundoff. Hence, it is essential for practical purposes that a small $|\pi|$ *and* a small roundoff error ε imply a small interpolation error. This demands *continuity* of the interpolation scheme in the sense that

$$\text{(5.3)}\qquad \begin{aligned} &\max_{x\in D}|f_\varepsilon(x)-f(x)|\to 0, \quad\text{and}\quad |\pi_n|\to 0, \qquad \pi_n\in\textstyle\prod, \\ &\text{imply}\quad \max_{x\in D}|(J_{\pi_n}f_\varepsilon)(x)-f(x)|\to 0, \qquad \text{as}\quad \varepsilon\to 0. \end{aligned}$$

If J is a scheme of linear interpolation by continuous functions defined on a dense subset of $C(D)$, then J_π is a linear operator from the Banach space $C(D)$ (with respect to the uniform norm $\|f\| = \max_{x\in D}|f(x)|$) into itself. In this case, J is continuous if and only if J is convergent on $C(D)$. This is a corollary of Banach's "uniform boundedness principle": J is convergent on $C(D)$ if and only if J is convergent on a dense subset of $C(D)$ and the norms of J_{π_n} are uniformly bounded as $|\pi_n| \xrightarrow[n\to\infty]{} 0$. It is analogous to the Lax-Richtmyer theorem for difference approximations to differential operators.

The main result of this section is the fact that the (cubic) spline interpolation scheme of §3 is indeed continuous. For, $(J_\pi f)(x) = \sum_i f(x_i)C_i(x)$, where $C_i(x)$ is the cardinal function of spline interpolation corresponding to the partition π (cf. §3). But, as was shown in **[2]**, $\sum_i |C_i(x)| \leqq K$ for some fixed K depending only on the maximum mesh ratio M_π. Hence, if π is a set of partitions with uniformly bounded mesh-ratio, then, for all $\pi\in\Pi$,

$$|(J_\pi f)(x)| \leqq \sum_i |f(x_i)|\,|C_i(x)| \leqq \|f\|\cdot\sum_i |C_i(x)| \leqq K\cdot\|f\|,$$

so that the operators J_π are indeed uniformly bounded, while $J_{\pi_n}f$ converges to f for all f in the dense subset $C^4[a, b]$ of $C[a, b]$.

This situation is in notable contrast with approximation by cardinal and trigonometric interpolation. That the latter is not continuous is well known.[6] As to cardinal interpolation, consider the cardinal function for cardinal interpolation with mesh-length h, $C_i(x - ih) = [\sin(\pi x/h)]/(\pi x/h)$. Since this is square-summable over i, we see that the cumulative effect of *independent* random roundoff errors of bounded size remains bounded as $h\downarrow 0$. Since it is not absolutely summable, the *cumulative* error due to *systematic* roundoff errors with alternating sign and fixed order of magnitude would be unbounded, if one lets h tend to zero.

In general, we surmise that all schemes of interpolation by *analytic* functions

[6] Cf. A. Zygmund, *Trigonometric series*, 2nd ed., Cambridge Univ. Press, London, 1959, Vol. 2.

will tend to be sensitive to roundoff errors, and any other local irregularities. This is because of the principle of analytic continuation, which makes the behavior of an analytic interpolating function in any neighborhood, however small, determine exactly its behavior everywhere.

6. **Non-linear spline interpolation.** Linearized interpolation schemes have a basic shortcoming: they are *not intrinsic* geometrically because they are not invariant under rigid rotation. Physically it seems more natural to replace linearized spline curves by *non-linear* splines (or "elastica"), well known among elasticians [**9**, §262], and this idea has been carefully considered by various people, including ourselves. Indeed, at least two computational schemes of non-linear spline interpolation have been proposed in the literature.

One scheme, proposed by A. H. Fowler and C. W. Wilson at Oak Ridge [**27**], goes in principle as follows. Choose coordinates for each segment $\widehat{P_{i-1}P_i}$ so that the x-axis is parallel to the straight line $\overline{P_{i-1}P_i}$, and approximate $\widehat{P_{i-1}P_i}$ by a cubic polynomial (linearized spline segment) in these coordinates. Then require continuity of slope *and* curvature at all interior mesh-points. This requires the iterative solution of a non-linear system of equations. A simplified discussion of this scheme, written by the General Motors Research Laboratory staff, is available as a research report [**21**].

The second scheme, proposed by D. H. MacLaren [**28**] at Boeing in 1959, sacrifices continuity of curvature, but has the advantage of being linear. In each interval, he approximates the curvature κ by $\bar{\kappa} = y''/[1 + (\Delta y/\Delta x)]^{3/2}$, and minimizes $\int \bar{\kappa}^2\, ds$.

Mechanical splines. The preceding schemes are intended to approximate true mechanical splines, or "elastica" constrained to pass through a fixed sequence of points by pure *shear forces*. (Only one of the family of curves graphed by Love [**9**, p. 404] represents such a mechanical spline.) These curves extremalize the integral $\int \kappa^2\, ds$, which is proportional to the elastic strain energy[7]; they satisfy $\delta \int \kappa^2\, ds = 0$. This equilibrium is *stable* if and only if the extremum is a local minimum of $\int \kappa^2\, ds$.

Curiously, an absolute minimum to $\delta \int \kappa^2\, ds$ does not exist except in the trivial case of a straight line; this is because one can construct large loops joining given endpoints with given endslopes, of length $2\pi r$ and curvature $\kappa = O(1/r)$, for arbitrarily large r—hence with $\int \kappa^2\, ds$ less than any preassigned positive number. Related to this, is the absence of an existence and uniqueness theory for non-linear spline curves having given endpoints, endslopes, and passing through a given sequence of internal joints.

After looking carefully into the relevant equations, one realizes that the schemes of [**27**] and [**28**] do not approximate mechanical splines more closely than

[7] In general, an elastica extremalizes $\int (\kappa^3 - \lambda_i)\, ds$, where λ is a parameter, constant in each segment, and depending on tension and bending moment at the joints; see [**21**].

other curves—nor does it seem particularly desirable to have them do so. For example, they approximate equally well to Hermite interpolation by segments of *Euler's spirals*,[8] joined together with continuous curvature. And Euler's spirals seem as natural a class of curves as the curves defined by "elastica" under pure shear forces. (The latter satisfy $2d^2\kappa/ds^2 + \kappa^3 = 0$.)

C. Interpolation: Functions of Two Variables

7. **Smooth surface interpolation.** The preceding discussion still fails to touch the basic problem of convergent interpolation for functions of two variables. However, it suggests an important first step towards solving the problem of fitting smooth surfaces.[9]

Namely, let offsets $u_{ij} = u(x_i, y_j)$ be given on a rectangular grid of points, the vertices of a *rectangular network* of lines including all the sides (boundary lines) of a *rectangular polygon* R. On the boundary vertices, let also the normal derivative (slopes) $\partial u/\partial n$ be given.[10] Then it is clear that exactly one network of linearized (cubic) *spline curves* can be passed through the given points, subject to the given boundary conditions.

The preceding construction raises the question: how can one interpolate *surface elements* in the rectangular pieces R_{ij}: $[x_{i-1}, x_i] \times [y_{i-1}, y_j]$, so as to obtain a *smooth surface*. In principle, one very simple answer to this question is the following.

At each vertex (x_i, y_j), the incident spline curves

$$u = u(x_i, y) = f_i(y) \quad \text{and} \quad u = u(x, y_j) = g_j(x) \tag{7.1}$$

have well-defined slopes $f_i'(y)$ and $g_j'(x)$. Why not *interpolate linearly* in $\partial u/\partial n$ along each edge of R_{ij}, thus achieving a joint of class C^1? To solve the problem of smooth surface interpolation in R for the given data, therefore, it suffices to find a 12-*parameter family* of functions determined by the values of u, $\partial u/\partial x$ and $\partial u/\partial y$ on the corners of each R_{ij}, interpolating to u by Hermite interpolation and to $\partial u/\partial n$ by linear interpolation along the edge.

This defines a classic boundary value problem in the theory of elasticity, associated with the *biharmonic* equation $\nabla^4 u = 0$; its solution minimizes

$$\iint (\nabla^2 u)^2 \, dx \, dy.$$

---

[8] These are curves defined by the relation $d^2\kappa/ds^2 = 0$ (whence $\kappa = a_i s + b_i$ on $\widehat{P_{i-1}P_i}$); see Am. Math. Monthly **25** (1918), 276–282.

[9] We ignore the scheme of bilinear interpolation, since it gives surfaces with edges except in trivial cases.

[10] At projecting corners, both normal derivatives; at reentrant corners, neither derivative. As an alternative, one can use the "free endpoint" condition $\partial^2 u/\partial n^2 = 0$.

Since this is an exact two-dimensional analog of the spline problem, its solution constitutes a natural method of surface fitting, proposed in [3]. There, it was noted that eight linearly independent *polynomial* solutions are available: 1, x, y, x^2, xy, y^2, x^3, y^3.

However, correspondence with Prof. E. Sternberg of Brown University made it apparent that the other four would be very hard to compute. Therefore Dr. Garabedian and one of us concocted somewhat arbitrarily four additional *piecewise polynomial* functions (F_6 F_9, F_{11}, F_{12} in the notation of [**3**]) which seemed adequate for the purpose in hand. These functions gave a surface of class C^1 which satisfied the stated boundary conditions. Though it was not of class C^2, it seemed clear that *no* solution of the problem which had piecewise linear $\partial u/\partial n$ along the interfaces $x = x_i$ and $y = y_j$ could have a continuous cross-derivative $u_{xy} = \partial^2 u/\partial x\, \partial y$. Hence, the method of surface interpolation proposed in [**3**] seems in some sense nearly "best possible" within the framework of a 12-parameter family of surface elements.

8. **Bicubic spline interpolation.** To get a solution in C^2, one must abandon the use of (piecewise) linear interpolation for getting $\partial u/\partial n$ along the edges of R_{ij} from the values of u_x, u_y at the vertices obtained from the network of splines with joints at these vertices. Instead, one must use *spline* interpolation in u_x, u_y (that is, in $\partial u/\partial n$) as well. This requires using in each R_{ij} the family of all *bicubic polynomials*

$$u(x, y) = a_{00} + a_{10}x + a_{01}y + \cdots + a_{33}x^3y^3 = \sum_{i=1}^{3} \sum_{j=1}^{3} a_{ij}x^iy^j. \tag{8.1}$$

Algebraically, the bicubic polynomials (8.1) are much simpler and more convenient to use than the elaborate functions F_6, F_9, F_{11}, F_{12} mentioned in §7. In each R_{ij}, there is one and only one bicubic polynomial (8.1) which takes on specified values of u, u_x, u_y, and u_{xy} at the four corners. Moreover, if values of these quantities are specified at all mesh-points of a rectangular grid in a rectangular polygon, and Hermite interpolation is used to fill in each rectangular element, then the function $u(x, y)$ obtained by splicing these elements together is automatically of class C^1.

If the u_{ij} are given, together with the values of $\partial u/\partial n$ at all boundary mesh-points, then u_x and u_y can be computed as in §4 to give the rectangular network of spline curves mentioned in §5. For these values of u_x, u_y, the resulting piecewise bicubic polynomial function will be not only of class C^1, but will have continuous u_{xx}, u_{yy} along mesh-lines. By specifying u_{xy} at mesh-points from approximate formulas, such as

$$u_{xy} \doteqdot \frac{u_{i+1,j+1} - u_{i+1,j-1} + u_{i-1,j-1} - u_{i-1,j+1}}{(x_{i+1} - x_{i-1})(y_{j+1} - y_{j-1})},$$

one can hope to get quite smooth interpolating functions.

However, to get interpolating (piecewise bicubic) functions of class C^2, more ingenuity is required: one must use spline interpolation in u_x and u_y (that is, in $\partial u/\partial n$), as well as in u.

The fact that simultaneous spline interpolation in the $(u_x)_{ij}$ and $(u_y)_{ij}$ gives *consistent* values of the $(u_{xy})_{ij}$, and is compatible with (8.1), can be most easily proved by using the notion of *tensor products* of functions, as follows. (See **[5]** for the original proof that bicubic spline interpolation is algebraically well-defined and more details.)

Given the joints $x_0 < x_1 < \cdots < x_m$, let $C_i(x)$ $(i = 0, \cdots, m + 2)$ be cubic spline functions with joints at the x_i such that

$$f(x) = \sum_{i=0}^{m} z_i C_i(x) + z_0' C_{m+1}(x) + z_m' C_{m+2}(x) \tag{8.2}$$

satisfies $f(x_i) = z_i, f'(x_0) = z_0', f'(x_m) = z_m'$. Let $D_j(y)$ be a corresponding basis for the cubic spline interpolation problem of §3, for given $g(y_j)$, $(j = 0, \cdots, n)$, $g'(y_0)$, $g'(y_n)$. Consider the functions

$$u(x, y) = \sum_{i=0}^{m+2} \sum_{j=0}^{n+2} a_{ij} C_i(x) D_j(y). \tag{8.3}$$

Each $u(x, y)$ is of class C^2 on $x_0 \leqq x \leqq x_m$; $y_0 \leqq y \leqq y_n$. Moreover

$$\begin{aligned}
a_{ij} &= u_{ij}, & i &= 0, \cdots, m; & j &= 0, \cdots, n; \\
a_{ik} &= \frac{\partial}{\partial y} u(x_i, y_k), & i &= 0, \cdots, m; & k &= 0, n; \\
a_{kj} &= \frac{\partial}{\partial x} u(x_k, y_j), & k &= 0, m; & j &= 0, \cdots, n; \\
a_{ij} &= \frac{\partial^2}{\partial x\, \partial y} u(x_i, y_j), & i &= 0, m; & j &= 0, n.
\end{aligned} \tag{8.4}$$

Hence, given the values at all mesh-points and the normal derivatives at the boundary mesh-points as in §7, and in addition the cross-derivative at the four corners, this interpolating function of class C^2 is determined *uniquely*.

Along each mesh-line, the surface reduces to a cubic spline, as in §7. But along each mesh-line, $\partial u/\partial n$ is a cubic spline also, as desired. In each rectangle, u is a bicubic polynomial (8.1). Its sixteen coefficients can be computed, once u, u_x, u_y, *and* u_{xy} are known at the four corners of R_{ij}. We can compute the u_x, u_y as in §3, from (3.1)–(3.1′). As $u(x, y)$ is of class C^2, we can then compute u_{xy} by spline interpolation of the u_x values along mesh-lines with constant x, or of the u_y values along mesh-lines with constant y. For example, we can solve

$$\begin{aligned}
&\Delta y_{j-1} s_{i,j+1} + 2(\Delta y_{j-1} + \Delta y_j) s_{ij} + \Delta y_j s_{i,j-1} \\
&\qquad = 3[\Delta y_{j-1} \Delta_j p_{ij}/\Delta y_j + \Delta y_j \Delta_j p_{i,j-1}/\Delta y_{j-1}],
\end{aligned} \tag{8.5}$$

as in [**5**, Equation (14)] for $s = u_{xy}$ from the values of $p = u_x$ at mesh-points.

It is of interest to generalize the preceding construction to *rectangular polygons*; see Appendix A.

Variational property. Bicubic spline functions can also be characterized by a variational property. Namely, the bicubic spline function satisfying (8.4) minimizes

$$\iint_R \left(\frac{\partial^4 u}{\partial x^2\, \partial y^2}\right)^2 dx\, dy + \int_E \left(\frac{\partial^2 u}{\partial s^2}\right)^2 ds, \tag{8.6}$$

subject to the constraints (8.4). Here E is the edge of R, and $\partial/\partial s$ signifies the tangential derivative.

If only the u_{ij} are prescribed, the minimum of (8.6) defines that spline function with the joints specified, having "free edges" with $\partial^2 u/\partial n^2 = 0$ on E. (In the case $I = J = 1$ of one rectangle, the resulting function is then bilinear!)

9. **Convergence to surfaces.** The results of §4 apply to the errors in smooth surface interpolation and bicubic spline interpolation as well.

Let $f(x, y) \in C^5$ on $0 \leqq x, y \leqq 1$ and let

$$\pi: 0 = x_0 < x_1 < \cdots < x_m = 1, \qquad \pi': 0 = y_0 < y_1 < \cdots < y_n = 1,$$

define a rectangular partition of this square, let $S(x, y)$ denote the bicubic spline function (8.1) interpolating $f(x, y)$ on this partition.

Since, for $i = 0, \cdots, m$, $S(x_i, y)$ is the cubic spline that interpolates $f(x_i, y)$ on π', one has from §4 that

$$\left|\frac{\partial^r}{\partial y^r}(S(x_i, y) - f(x_i, y))\right| = O(|\pi'|^{4-r}), \qquad i = 0, \cdots, m. \tag{9.1}$$

Similarly, since, for $i = 0, m$, $S_x(x_i, y)$ is the cubic spline that interpolates $f_x(x_i, y)$ on π', one has

$$\left|\frac{\partial^{r+1}}{\partial y^r\, \partial x}(S(x_i, y) - f(x_i, y))\right| = O(|\pi'|^{4-r}). \tag{9.2}$$

Now let $y \in [0, 1]$, and let $t(x)$ be the spline function that interpolates $f(x, y)$ on π. Then

$$\left|\frac{\partial^r}{\partial x^r} f(x, y) - t^{(r)}(x)\right| = O(|\pi|^{4-r}). \tag{9.3}$$

The difference between $t(x)$ and $S(x, y)$ is a spline function, hence can be written as $t(x) - S(s, y) = \sum_{i=1}^{n-1} a_i C_i(x) + p(x)$, where the $C_i(x)$ are the cardinal functions of §4, and $p(x)$ is a cubic polynomial. By (9.1) and (9.2),

$$|p(x)| = O(|\pi'|^4),$$

hence, by (9.1),

$$\begin{aligned} a_i = t(x_i) - S(x_i, y) - p(x_i) &= (f(x_i, y) - S(x_i, y)) - p(x_i) \\ &= O(|\pi'|^4). \end{aligned}$$

Since the $C_i(x)$ are uniformly bounded if M_π, $M_{\pi'}$ are suitably bounded (cf. §4), it follows that

$$|f(x, y) - S(x, y)| = O(|\pi|^4 + |\pi'|^4). \tag{9.4}$$

10. **General spline interpolation.** The preceding schemes have natural generalizations in two directions: to splines of higher degree and to functions of n variables.

To interpolate given values $f(x_i)$, $i = 0, \cdots, n$ by a spline function of odd degree $2m - 1$, $m > 2$, one proceeds much as in §3. One takes the quantities $f^{(j)}(x_i)$, $j = 1, \cdots, m - 1$, as unknowns to be determined from the conditions that $f^{(j)}$ be continuous across the joints for $j = m, \cdots, 2m - 2$. This results in a system of equations whose matrix is block-tridiagonal, each block being an $(m - 1) \times (m - 1)$ matrix. Given $f^{(j)}(x_0), f^{(j)}(x_n)$, $j = 1, \cdots, m - 1$, at the two endpoints, this system has a unique solution. With the $f^{(j)}(x_i)$ determined, $j = 0, \cdots, m - 1$, the $2m$ coefficients of the $(2m - 1)$st degree polynomial in each interval are then quickly computed.

An alternative approach makes use of the existence of a basis $M_i(x)$, $i = -(m - 1), \cdots, n + (m - 1)$, for the set of $(2m - 1)$st degree spline functions with joints at x_j, $j = 1, \cdots, n$, such that $M_i(x) \equiv 0$ for $x \notin [x_{i-m}, x_{i+m}]$ (this condition being properly modified for $i < m$ and $i > n - m$). The linear system which results is smaller than the system discussed earlier; its matrix is $(2m - 1)$-diagonal. This approach is equally well-suited to interpolation by spline functions of even degree. In this case, one follows Schoenberg **[13]** and puts the joints of the interpolating spline *between* the given data points. In the case of parabolic splines, the choice of the midpoint between given data points leads to a linear system with diagonally dominant tridiagonal matrix.

The generalization to functions of n variables follows the pattern of bicubic spline interpolation outlined earlier. The interpolating function becomes a tensor product of n one-dimensional interpolating functions, the interpolation conditions become correspondingly tensor products of n one-dimensional interpolation conditions.

One can also use, in any "hyper-rectangle", tensor products of spline functions of different degrees in different coordinate directions.

D. Approximation by Spline Functions

11. **Interpolation and approximation.** In applications, interpolation is commonly only a means to the end of obtaining good *approximations* to given functions or discrete data—and the latter themselves are often only approximate. Hence one naturally asks: are piecewise polynomial functions more suitable than (say) polynomial or rational functions, when it comes to approximation? As a background for this question, we recall some well-known facts.

First, as recalled already in §1, polynomials can be found which give arbitrarily good uniform approximations to any smooth function; but the degree may be extremely large. For fixed degree n, and functions of one variable, the Chebyshev Equioscillation Theorem [**4**, p. 149] shows that the best uniform approximation can also be obtained by Lagrange *interpolation* on a suitable mesh. Moreover one can today compute the points of this mesh systematically by the Remez algorithm [**8**, pp. 217–232]. The paper by Prof. Stiefel at this Symposium (p. 68) says more about their location.

From this standpoint, the most conspicuous advantage of spline interpolation over Lagrange interpolation, as a means of approximation, is that the error is less sensitive to mesh changes (see §4). A more subtle advantage is the smaller tendency to give *ripples*, whose occurrence with best uniform (Chebyshev) approximation seems indicated by the same Equioscillation Theorem. To avoid these, it seems likely that other criteria (such as best uniform approximation of derivatives) are needed, which would lead to additional computational problems.

However, it must be admitted that the preceding statements are conjectural, and not based on careful study. In practice, we have simply avoided polynomial approximation.

12. **Best approximation properties.** Actually, spline interpolation already has various "best approximation" properties, associated with its variational property of minimizing the positive quadratic functional $\int [y^{(h)}(x)]^2\,dx$. These have been derived by Walsh, Ahlberg, and Nilson [**17**], by one of us [**6**], and by Schoenberg ([**14**] and Indag. Math. **26** (1964), 155–163). For example let $s(x)$ be the spline function of odd degree $2k - 1$ which interpolates (is "cotabular" with) a given function $f(x) \in C^k[a, b]$ on the joints x_i of a given partition π of $[a, b]$. Then $s(x)$ is also the *best* approximation to $f(x)$ in the class of spline functions $S(a, b, \pi)$ with joints at the x_i, with respect to the pseudo-norm

$$\|e(x)\|^2 = \int_a^b [e^{(k)}(x)]^2\,dx. \tag{12.1}$$

It also leads to "best approximations" of linear functionals $L[f]$ such as $\int_0^1 f(x)\,dx$ or $f''(t)$ $(0 < t < 1)$ by linear combinations of the values of f at the joints x_i of a partition π: $0 \leqq x_1 < x_2 < \cdots < x_n \leqq 1$ (say). Following Sard [**12**], suppose that for fixed $m < n$, $L[p] = \sum_{i=1}^n a_i p(x_i)$ is exact for all polynomials $p(x)$ of degree m or less. Then, for $f(x) \in C^m[0, 1]$, defining $K(t)$ by

$$L[f] - \sum_{i=0}^{n} a_i f(x_i) = \int_0^1 K(t) f^{(m)}(t)\,dt, \tag{12.2}$$

the approximation $A[f] = \Sigma\, a_i f(x_i)$ to $L[f]$ is called "best" if it minimizes $\int_0^1 [K(t)]^2\,dt$. Schoenberg [**14**] has shown that if $S_m(x)$ denotes the interpolating (generalized) spline function of degree $2m - 1$, then the functional $A[f] = L[s_m[f]]$ is the "best" approximation (in this sense) to a wide class of linear functionals L.

As an application, consider the error of approximation to $\int_0^1 f(x)\,dx$ by

$\int_0^1 S(x)\,dx$, where $f(x) \in C^4$. This quadrature formula was first proposed by Holladay,[11] and later shown by Schoenberg **[13]** to be identical with Sard's best quadrature formula **[12]**. For simplicity, assume that π is uniform, $|\pi| = h$. Then it follows at once that

$$\int_0^1 f(x)\,dx = \int_0^1 S(x)\,dx + O(h^4), \tag{12.3}$$

the same order of accuracy as one gets by using the simplest Hermite-type quadrature formula in each of the n intervals of the partition. Note that in both cases (for uniform π), the value of the integral can be computed from $f(x_i)$, $i = 0, \cdots, n$, and $f'(0), f'(1)$.

Such results are valuable from a computational standpoint, since they permit the approximation of various functionals from the coefficients of interpolating splines computed by the schemes of §3.

But it should be pointed out that they are not restricted to spline functions, but apply to orthogonal projections generally.[12] Thus, for $m \geqq 1$, let $H^{(m)}$ be the Hilbert space defined on the functions $f \in C^{(m)}[0, 1]$ with absolutely continuous $(m - 1)$st and square integrable mth derivative by the inner product

$$(f, g) = \int_0^1 f^{(m)}(x)g^{(m)}(x)\,dx + \sum_1^n L_i(f)L_i(g), \tag{12.4}$$

where the L_i are any n linearly independent linear functionals, linearly independent over the set of $(m - 1)$st degree polynomials; let $\phi_j \in H^{(m)}$ be such that $L_j[f] = (f, \phi_j)$ for all $f \in H^{(m)}$, $j = 1, \cdots, n$. Let Φ be the subspace of $H^{(m)}$ spanned by the ϕ_i, and let $P = P_\phi$ be the orthogonal projection of $H^{(m)}$ onto Φ.

Then if $L[f] = (f, \psi)$ is any bounded linear functional on $H^{(m)}$, and $\bar{\psi}$ is the "best approximation" to ψ as an element of $H^{(m)}$, then the best approximation to $L[f]$ in the usual operator norm is $(f, \bar{\psi}) = \bar{L}[f]$. Moreover, for all $f \in H^{(m)}$, $\bar{L}[f] = (fP, \psi) = L[fP]$. Finally fP is the unique element of Φ which satisfies $L_i[fP] = L_i[f]$, $i = 1, \cdots, n$.

In the special case that the L_i are evaluations of $f(x)$ or some derivative $f^{(k)}(x)$ at points x_j, the space Φ consists of *piecewise polynomial* functions of degree $2m - 1$.

Finally, these facts remain true if D^m in (12.4) is replaced by other linear differential operators. Cf. also Golomb and Weinberger **[8**, pp. 117–190**]**.

13. **Data smoothing.** The preceding results, however sharp, are far from answering all the basic questions which arise in fitting *approximate data* intended to represent (say) real car body surfaces or plane sections thereof. Such discrete data always involve random errors; hence they must be *smoothed* (or "graduated") without essential loss of accuracy.

---

[11] J. C. Holladay, Math. Tables Aids Comp. **11** (1957), 233–243. We have assumed here as given also $f'(0)$ and $f'(1)$.

[12] This observation is due to C. de Boor and R. E. Lynch **[26]**.

This is a very deep problem. As is made clear in [**19**, §151], "the problem of graduation belongs essentially to the mathematical theory of probability". One must balance the *a priori* expectation of "smoothness" against the expectation that the error in the data (or their statistical deviation from the "true" mean) will be small.

In practice, this can often be achieved by considering an n-parameter family of smooth *approximating functions* $f(x, a_1, \cdots, a_n)$, where n is a small fraction of the number of data points $u(x_i) = u_i$, and minimizing the (suitably weighted) mean square deviation

$$(13.1) \qquad \sum_{i=1}^{I} w_i \, |u_i - f(x_i, a_1, \cdots, a_n)|^2, \qquad w_i > 0.$$

In some cases, some form of Chebyshev approximation might be more accurate, but the computational simplicity and generality of *least squares* approximation for *linear* families of functions

$$(13.2) \qquad f(x, a_1, \cdots, a_n) = \sum_{j=1}^{n} a_j \phi_j(x)$$

seems to make it the best bet for most applications.

For plane curves representing smooth sections of car bodies, we have found the use of formulas (13.1)–(13.2) with spline functions of degrees two, three, and four generally satisfactory. The problem of balancing smoothness against closeness of fit involves the problem of choosing the right number of joints. Since the closeness of fit depends on the location of the joints as well as on their number, one also has the *non-linear* problem of deciding on the *optimal location* of joints, for a given degree of spline (say).

We regard the determination of objective criteria for deciding this, and of mathematical methods for computing the location of optimal joints given such a criterion, as one of the most important problems concerning smoothing. We have used several criteria, including the following:

(i) For $w_i \equiv 1$, find the set of joints which minimizes (13.1),
(ii) For $w_i \equiv 1$, find the set of joints which minimizes

$$\min_{a_1, \cdots, a_n} \max_i |u_i - f(x_i, a_1, \cdots, a_n)|.$$

The error tends to oscillate in sign for both criteria, but we have not developed a rigorous theory for either of them.

A few remarks about the preceding problem may be of interest. To solve it objectively, one must clearly specify a measure N of error and a measure S of smoothness. For some "smoothing parameter" $\varepsilon > 0$, one can then try to minimize $\varepsilon N(u - f) + S(f)$ within the class of functions f, by proper choice of $a = (a_1, \cdots, a_n)$. One measure of smoothness for *discrete* data, proposed in [**19**], is provided by a sum of squares of the third divided differences; the continuous analog would consist in setting $S(f) = \int f'''^2 \, dx$, as proposed by Schoenberg [**13**]. Other criteria have been proposed by Quade and Collatz, Lanczos, and Bizley.[13] For example (Lanczos), in trigonometric interpolation, one may know from differentiability considerations that the Fourier coefficients should die off like n^{-k}. One can then truncate Fourier series beginning at some points where this fails to hold.

Unfortunately, it seems impossible to combine the geometric desideratum of invariance of the approximating scheme under rotation (and translation) with the algebraic desideratum of linearity.

The problem of interpolating between smoothed "scans" along plane sections, so as to achieve a satisfactory smooth surface, is evidently related in nature but even more complicated. We shall not discuss it here.

E. Applications to Integral and Differential Equations

14. **Integral equations.**[14] Spline functions seem ideally suited to the approximate solution of Fredholm integral equations with *smooth kernels* $K(x, y)$, such as

$$f(x) = \phi(x) + \lambda \int_0^1 K(x, y) f(y)\, dy. \tag{14.1}$$

Relative to any partition π of the interval $[0, 1]$ into n segments, one can construct by cubic spline interpolation and bicubic spline interpolation excellent approximations to $\phi(x)$ and $K(x, y)$, respectively—it being understood that π is applied to *both* independent variables ($I = J = n$).

When this is done, the right side of (14.1) is then replaced by an inhomogeneous linear operator $L[f]$ whose range is contained in the $(n + 3)$-dimensional subspace of (cubic) spline functions on $[0, 1]$ with mesh π. Moreover, writing $L[f] = S[\phi] + \lambda K_s[f] = g$, the values of $g(x_i)$, $x_i \in \pi$, and of $g'(0)$, $g'(1)$ are easily computed from those of $S[\phi]$ and $K_s[f]$, integrating in closed form polynomials (of degree 6 or less) in each segment.

This reduces (14.1) to an equation

$$f = S[\phi] + \lambda K_s[f] \tag{14.2}$$

which is equivalent to a system of linear *algebraic* equations in $n + 3$ variables, whose eigenvalues and solutions can be computed by standard methods. The results of §9 suggest that the error will be $O(n^{-3})$.

15. **Sturm-Liouville systems.** Another promising area of application for piecewise polynomial functions of degree k and class C^r is to the approximate numerical solution of boundary value problems. For functions of one variable, we will

---

[13] See W. Quade and L. Collatz, S.-B. Preuss. Akad. Wiss. (Math-Phys. Kl.) **30** (1938), pp. 29–38; C. Lanczos, *Applied Analysis*, Prentice-Hall, Englewood Cliffs, N.J., 1956, 321–344; M. T. L. Bizley, J. Inst. Actuaries Sept. (1958), 125–165.

[14] The considerations of §14 occurred independently to Prof. I. Schoenberg, with whom we have had several stimulating conversations.

consider primarily the case $k = 3$, $r = 2$ of cubic *spline* functions, emphasizing applications of the concept of "best approximation" (§12) where possible.

The simpler case $k = 1$, $r = 0$ of "polygon" (piecewise linear) functions is classic.[15] Since polygon functions are defined by a *local* interpolation formula, their use is equivalent to *finite difference methods*, and is generally subsumed under the latter. Although there are many papers relevant to this case, they are not very relevant to the use of splines.

The use of spline functions for this purpose seems to have been first suggested in [**3**]. Here it was noted that one can compute approximate eigenfunctions and eigenvalues of Sturm-Liouville systems by applying the Rayleigh-Ritz-Galerkin method to the subspace $S = S(\pi)$ of (cubic) spline functions with a given mesh

$$\pi\colon\ 0 = x_0 < x_1 < \cdots < x_{N+1} = 1.$$

EXAMPLE 1. Consider the Rayleigh quotient

$$R[f] = -J_1[f]/J_0[f], \tag{15.1}$$

where

$$\begin{aligned} J_0[f] &= \int_0^1 [f(x)]^2\,dx, \\ J_1[f] &= \int_0^1 [f'(x)]^2\,dx = -\int_0^1 f(x)\ D^2[f(x)]\,dx. \end{aligned} \tag{15.2}$$

The eigenfunctions of the Sturm-Liouville system $u'' + \lambda u = 0$, $u(0) = u(1) = 0$, are those functions satisfying the endpoint conditions, for which $\delta R = 0$.

Since the eigenfunctions $\sin m\pi x$ satisfy

$$|S_m(x) - \sin m\pi x| = O(h^4), \tag{15.3}$$

$$|S'_m(x) - m\pi \cos m\pi x| = O(h^3), \tag{15.3'}$$

the error in (15.3′) being $O(h^4)$ at mesh-points, it follows that the Rayleigh-Ritz-Galerkin method applied to the subspace $S(N)$ of (cubic) spline functions on a uniform mesh and satisfying $S(0) = S''(0) = S(1) = S''(1) = 0$ should give approximate eigenvalues μ_m (and eigenfunctions $w_m(x)$) in error by $O(h^3)$ or less, for any fixed m as $h\downarrow 0$.

However, we prefer to view the problem somewhat differently, so as to bring out the connection with the ideas of §12. For any given inner product $(f, g)_l$ defined on a function space which contains the subspace $S = S(N)$ just defined, let P_l be the *orthogonal projection* onto S. We observe (as did Galerkin) that for $f \in S$

$$R[f] = \int_0^1 f(x)P[D^2[f]](x)\,dx \Big/ \int_0^1 f^2(x)\,dx, \tag{15.4}$$

provided that P is symmetric with respect to the inner product $(f, g)_0 = \int f(x)g(x)\,dx$; hence the approximate eigenvalues and eigenfunctions are those of the linear operator PD^2, considered as an operator on S.

[15] See for example R. Courant, Bull. Am. Math. Soc. **49** (1948), 1–23.

More generally, for any projection P onto S, we define the *relativization* of D^2 to S defined by P as the operator

$$E[f] = P[D^2[f]]. \tag{15.5}$$

We then ask: how well do the eigenfunctions and eigenvalues of E approximate those of D^2? We now answer this question exactly for three projections P_0, P_1, P_2. The first two are the *orthogonal* projections associated with the inner products J_0 and J_1 respectively:

$$(f, g)_0 = \int_0^1 f(x)g(x)\,dx \quad \text{and} \quad (f, g)_1 = \int_0^1 f'(x)g'(x)\,dx. \tag{15.6}$$

The projection P_2 is that associated with the inner product $\int_0^1 f''(x)g''(x)\,dx$ and defined by spline interpolation itself; cf. §12.

It is shown in Appendix B that, for these three projections, the orders of accuracy obtained in computations of the eigenvalues are $O(h^{6-2l})$ for $l = 0, 1, 2$. In all three cases, the approximate eigenfunctions are $P_2(\sin m\pi x)$, hence their order of accuracy is $O(h^4)$.

16. **Self-adjoint elliptic equations.** A fascinating field for future research concerns the usefulness of piecewise polynomial functions in describing approximate solutions of partial differential equations. We consider now the case of self-adjoint elliptic equations, with special reference to the Poisson equation

$$-\nabla^2 u = S(x, y). \tag{16.1}$$

Since solutions of such equations minimize suitable quadratic functionals, the Rayleigh-Ritz-Galerkin method can presumably be applied in much the same way as in §15. See example 2 below.

This idea has already been applied by Synge [**23**, pp. 168 ff.] to piecewise linear ("pyramidal") functions.[16] His results are analogous to those of Pólya and Szegö,[17] but the latter made much more extensive use of analytic functions and analytic methods (especially Steiner symmetrization).

In this connection, one should also mention an ingenious method of finding *analytic approximations* to solutions of the Dirichlet problem for $\nabla^2 u = 0$ proposed by S. Bergman,[18] and applied by him to many other boundary value problems of elliptic type. It is classic [**16**, pp. 36, 45] that any harmonic function can be approximated uniformly in any compact connected domain by harmonic polynomials. Bergman's method consists in computing which harmonic polynomial of given degree most closely fits the boundary conditions (i.e., best approximates them in some sense, mean square or Chebyshev).

---

[16] It would be interesting to compare results obtained using his "square pyramid F-vectors", with results using piecewise *bilinear* functions instead.

[17] G. Pólya and G. Szegö, *Isoperimetric inequalities in mathematical physics*, Annals of Math. Study No. 27, Princeton Univ. Press, Princeton, N.J., 1951.

[18] S. Bergman, Quar. Appl. Math. **5** (1947), 69–81; Proc. VI Symposium Applied Math., Amer. Math. Soc., Providence, R.I., 1956, pp. 11–29, and refs. given there.

However, this method seems less well adapted to computing machines than *difference methods*. These define what are sometimes called *discrete harmonic functions*, satisfying some (typically, 5-point) analog of $\nabla^2 u = 0$ or (16.1), and appropriate boundary conditions. There is a large literature on such functions[19], which we will not discuss here.

Instead, we will simply point out that the approximate solutions obtained in this way *cannot* be smoothly interpolated by harmonic polynomials, and so it seems reasonable to expect that interpolation can most effectively be made using piecewise polynomial functions, fitted by local bicubic or bicubic spline interpolation, for example.

It would be interesting to know whether any approximate solutions obtained from difference approximations in this way coincided with approximate solutions obtained from the same class of piecewise polynomial trial functions by the Rayleigh-Ritz-Galerkin method. For example, does the use of piecewise bilinear functions and a square or rectangular mesh lead to the standard[20] 5-point or 9-point formula for $\nabla^2 u = 0$?

To conclude this section, we shall give a discussion of the eigenvalues of the Helmholtz equation in a square.

EXAMPLE 2. Consider the Helmholtz equation $\nabla^2 u + \lambda u = 0$ in the unit square $0 \leqq x, y \leqq 1$, with boundary condition $u = 0$. We apply the Rayleigh-Ritz-Galerkin method to the subspace of bicubic spline functions having joints on a square grid (mesh-length $h = 1/N$ in both coordinates), and satisfying the "free edge" condition $\partial^2 u/\partial n^2 = 0$ (and hence $u_{xxyy} = 0$ at the four corners). The variables are "separable", and so the approximate eigenfunctions are $w_i(x)w_j(y)$, with approximate eigenvalues $\mu_i^l + \mu_j^l$, where μ_i^l is the corresponding eigenvalue of $w_i(x)$ under P_l (cf. Example 1 in §15).

17. **Cauchy problems.** We now consider possible applications of the preceding ideas to initial value problems for partial differential equations or *Cauchy problems*. In this, we follow the general approach of **[25]**, restricting attention for simplicity to Cauchy problems whose exact solutions define C_0-semigroups G of bounded linear transformations $T_t = \exp(tL)$ of some Hilbert space $\mathfrak{H}$, with infinitesimal generator L.

For any finite-dimensional or other closed subspace S of $\mathfrak{H}$ in the domain of L, define the *orthogonal projection* G_S of G onto S as follows. Let P be the orthogonal projection of $\mathfrak{H}$ onto S, with null-space $S^{\perp}$; then $P[L[u]]$ is a bounded linear transformation L_S of S. We let G_S be the C_0-semigroup acting on S generated by PL. Equivalently, we can define the projection of T_t onto S as $\lim_{n\to\infty} (PT_{t/n})^n$.

For example, let G be the C_0-semigroup on the Hilbert space $L_2(0, 1)$ associated

[19] **[22]** and refs. given there; Duffin, etc.

[20] **[24,** Chapter 6]; R. Esch, Annals of the Harvard Computation Laboratory, Vol. 31, pp. 84–102, Harvard Univ. Press, Cambridge, Mass., 1962.

with the heat equation $u_t = u_{xx}$ and the boundary conditions $u(0) = u(1) = 0$. Let $S = S_N$ be the set of functions expressible as *truncated sine series* of the form

$$u(x) = a_1 \sin x + a_2 \sin 2x + \cdots + a_N \sin Nx. \tag{17.1}$$

In this example, since the subspace S_N is invariant under L, the orbits of G_S also define exact solutions of the given (mixed) boundary value problem.

The preceding property holds in many other examples. Thus, let L be any linear differential operator with constant coefficients on any periodic or infinite domain. Then the subspaces defined by truncated Fourier series, and by truncated Fourier integrals $\int_{-\pi N}^{\pi N} e^{iq\cdot x}\phi(q)\,dq$, are invariant under L. On the other hand, these subspaces are also the ranges of the *projection operators* defined by the schemes of trigonometric interpolation [7] and cardinal interpolation [18], already described in §1. As is explained in [25], each interpolation scheme J defines a projection operator on continuous functions $f(x)$, which maps any f into $J[\tau[f]]$, where τ is the *tabulation* operator. It follows that, knowing the initial error $\|u_0 - J[\tau[u_0]]\|$ (which expresses the loss of information caused by identifying "cotabular" functions), the error $\|u(t) - u_J(t)\|$ at any later time t is at most $\|T_t\| \cdot \|u_0 - J[\tau[u_0]]\|$.

The statements of the preceding paragraph apply specifically to trigonometric and cardinal interpolation, for which it should be remembered that the projection $P[u] = J[\tau[u]]$ is not orthogonal in the usual L_2-norm. We now make a preliminary study of the analogous situation as regards cubic spline interpolation.

Let S be the N-dimensional subspace of cubic splines defined in Example 1 (§15), and let $\mathfrak{H}$ be defined by one of the inner products $(f, g)_l$, $l = 0, 1$, of (15.6). Then, for the heat equation $u_t = u_{xx}$ and the general initial condition $u(x, 0) = \Sigma\, a_i w_i(x)$, where the $w_i(x)$ are the approximate eigenfunctions of Example 1, we have $u(x, t) = \Sigma\, a_i e^{-\mu_i^l t} w_i(x)$, where μ_i^l is the eigenvalue of $w_i(x)$. Hence G_S is a semigroup of diagonal matrices $\bar{E} = \delta_{ij} e^{-\mu_i^l t}$ relative to this basis. Numerical values of μ_i^l can be computed from the formulas of Appendix B.

Likewise, let T be the N^2-dimensional subspace of bicubic spline functions in the square, defined in Example 2 (§16), and consider the analogous inner products

$$(f, g)_0 = \int_0^1 \int_0^1 f(x, y) g(x, y)\, dx\, dy \tag{17.2}$$

and

$$(f, g)_1 = \int_0^1 \int_0^1 [f_x g_x + f_y g_y]\, dx\, dy. \tag{17.3}$$

Then, relative to the eigenfunctions $w_i(x) w_j(y)$ of this example, the semigroup defined by the heat equation is defined by the "tensor product" formula

$$u(x, y, t) = \sum a_{ij} e^{-(\mu_i^l + \mu_j^l)t} w_i(x) w_j(y). \tag{17.4}$$

APPENDIX A. PIECEWISE BICUBIC INTERPOLATION IN RECTANGULAR POLYGONS

1. **Interpolation of class C^1.** Let R be any connected rectangular polygon, whose sides all lie on mesh-lines $x = x_i$, $y = y_j$, of a fixed rectangular mesh. As in §3 and [**3**, §§1–2], we have the following result.

LEMMA 1. *Let $u_{ij} = u(x_i, y_j)$ be given at all (interior and boundary) mesh-points of R, let $p_{ij} = u_x(x_i, y_j)$ be given on the sides $x = x_i$ of R which are parallel to the y-axis (except at reentrant corners), and let $q_{ij} = u_y(x_i, y_j)$ be given on the perpendicular sides $y = y_j$. These data are compatible with one and only one network of cubic spline functions $u(x, y_j) = f_j(x)$ and $u(x_i, y) = g_i(y)$ on the mesh-lines of R.*

We next recall [**5**, Theorem 2], which states

LEMMA 2. *There exists one and only one bicubic polynomial*

$$u(x, y) = \sum_{m=0}^{3} \sum_{n=0}^{3} \alpha_{mn} x^m y^n \tag{A.1}$$

which assumes given values of u, u_x, u_y, and u_{xy} at the four corners of a given rectangle.

Lemmas 1 and 2 have the following consequence.

LEMMA 3. *Let u, u_x, u_y, and u_{xy} be given at the vertices of two adjacent rectangles R_1, R_2 having a common side $y = y_j$. Then there is one and only one function $u(x, y)$ of class C^1 on $R = R_1 \cup R_2$, which assumes the given values and is bicubic in each R_j, $j = 1, 2$. For this function, u_{xy} and u_{xxy} are also continuous.*

PROOF. By Lemma 2, there is only one such function. But for this function, $u(x, y_j)$ and $u_y(x, y_j)$ have the same values in R_1 as in R_2 at the endpoints of $y = y_j$; from these their other values are obtained by spline interpolation; hence they are the same identically. The continuity of u_x, u_{xx}, $\cdots$ and u_{xy}, u_{xxy}, $\cdots$ across the common edge $y = y_j$ follows.

THEOREM 1. *In Lemma 1, given $s_{ij} = u_{xy}(x_i, y_j)$ at all mesh-points, there exists a unique piecewise bicubic function $u(x, y)$ of class C^1 in R, for which the mesh-lines are spline curves, and which satisfies the data of Lemma 1. For this $u \in C^1(R)$, $s(x, y) = u_{xy}$ is also continuous.*

To obtain a reasonably accurate and very simple scheme of piecewise bicubic interpolation of class C^1, it suffices therefore to use some fairly good local approximation to u_{xy} at mesh-points. For example, one might use

$$\sigma_{ij} = w\left[\frac{p_{i,j+1} - p_{i,j-1}}{y_{j+1} - y_{j-1}}\right] + (1 - w)\left[\frac{q_{i+1,j} - q_{i-1,j}}{x_{i+1} - x_{j-1}}\right], \tag{A.2}$$

where $p_{ij} = u_x(x_i, y_i)$, $q_{ij} = u_y(x_i, y_i)$, and $0 \leqq w \leqq 1$ (or, $0 \leqq w_{ij} \leqq 1$). Or, one might use at interior mesh-points

$$\tau_{ij} = \frac{u_{i+1,j+1} - u_{i+1,j-1} + u_{i-1,j-1} - u_{i-1,j+1}}{(x_{i+1} - x_{i-1})(y_{j+1} - y_{j-1})}, \tag{A.2'}$$

as approximations to the "best" $s_{ij} = u_{xy}(x_i, y_j)$.

2. **Interpolation of class C^2.** The problem of devising a "well-set" piecewise bicubic interpolation scheme of class C^2 in a general (connected) rectangular polygon R is much more difficult. We will suppose below that u and its normal derivative are given and differentiable along the edges of R, and that the given values of the normal derivative are compatible in the sense that $(u_x)_y = (u_y)_x$ at external (i.e., non-reentrant) corners. Figures 1 and 2 illustrate two instructive cases.

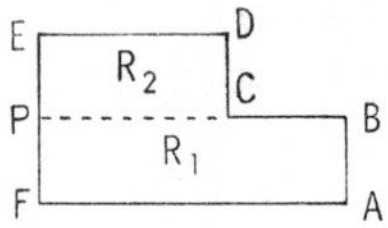

Rectangular hexagon
FIGURE 1

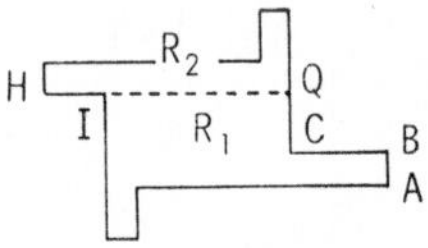

Rectangular dodecagon
FIGURE 2

Let R be subdivided into two subregions R_1 and R_2 by a mesh-line $y = y_J$, $x_0 \leqq x \leqq x_M$, and suppose that common values of u and u_y are assumed along $y = y_J$ by functions $u_k(x, y)$ defined and of class C^1 in each R_k $[k = 1, 2]$ separately. Suppose also that $u_1(x, y)$ and $u_2(x, y)$ are both *piecewise bicubic*, i.e., satisfy (A.1) in each rectangle R_{ij} bounded by pairs of adjacent mesh-lines. Finally, suppose that the values of the $u_k(x, y)$ are defined by cubic spline functions along each mesh-line, so that u_{xx} is continuous on the mesh-lines $x = x_i$ and u_{yy} on the mesh-lines $y = y_j$.

Then, by Lemma 3, u_{xy} will be continuous across $y = y_J$, together with $u, u_x, u_{xx}, \cdots$ and $u_y, u_{xxy}, \cdots$. But u_{yy}, the second normal derivative, need not be continuous. Though we know of no method for making u_{yy} continuous, the jump in u_{yy} can usually be made negligible in practice by proceeding as follows.

Where possible, use *spline interpolation* to determine u_{xy} at reentrant corners. For example, in Figure 1, use spline interpolation in u_x on $\overline{EPF}$ to compute u_{xy} at P, then use spline interpolation in u_y on $\overline{PCB}$ to compute u_{xy} at C. One can then use *bicubic* spline interpolation in R_1 and R_2, to determine functions $u_k(x, y)$ of class C^2 in R_k $[k = 1, 2]$. By splicing these functions together, one obtains a piecewise bicubic spline function of class C^1 in $R_1 \cup R_2 = R$. We now examine more closely the behavior of the higher derivatives of $u(x, y)$ along the "seam" $\overline{PC}$. By construction (cf. §5), u_{yy} is continuous across $\overline{PC}$ (i.e., it assumes the same value on both sides) at *all mesh-points*, including P and C; moreover u_{xy} and u_{xx} assume the same values at *all points*. Furthermore (§6), u_{yy} is obtained on *both* sides of $\overline{PC}$ by *spline interpolation* from the same u_{yy}, though generally different "endslopes" u_{yyx} at P and C. Due to the *stability* (§8) of spline interpolation, the difference between the values of u_{yy} along $\overline{PC}$ on the two sides will therefore be an *oscillating, exponentially damped* function as one goes away from the endpoints (for uniformly bounded mesh-length ratios $|\Delta x_i|/|\Delta x_{i'}| \leqq M_\pi$). Hence, if M_π is held fixed while the maximum mesh-length tends to zero, the values of u_{yy} will approach the same limit at all points other than reentrant corners.

In the rectangular polygon of Figure 2, no such simple procedure is possible. For expeditious computation, it seems best to assign (by local extrapolation) an approximate value to u_{xy} at C, and then to decompose R into rectangles by induction, using HIQ as one boundary; at worst, one has more than the minimum number of "seams" to consider.

Though we doubt the existence of a "stable" (i.e., uniformly bounded) procedure for finding a piecewise cubic function of class C^2 in a general rectangular polygon (e.g., in the L-shaped region of Figure 1), the following result may be of interest.

THEOREM 2. *Let the mesh-line $y = y_j$, $x_0 \leqq x \leqq x_M$ divide the rectangular polygon R into subregions R_1 and R_2. Let $u(x, y)$ be a piecewise bicubic function which is of class C^2 in R_1 and R_2 separately and on mesh-lines, and of class C^1 in R. Then $u(x, y)$ is of class C^2 in R if and only if $s_{ij} = u_{xy}(x_i, y_j)$ satisfies*

$$\text{(A.4)}\quad bs_{i,j+1} + 2(b + c)s_{i,j} + cs_{i,j-1} = 3\left[\frac{b}{c}(p_{i,j+1} - p_{i,j}) + \frac{c}{b}(p_{i,j} - p_{i,j-1})\right], \qquad i = 0, M,$$

where $b = y_j - y_{j-1}$ and $c = y_{j+1} - y_j$.

We omit the proof.

APPENDIX B. STURM-LIOUVILLE COMPUTATIONS

In order to compute the eigenfunctions and eigenvalues of $E_l = P_l D^2$, it is convenient to pick a basis $\{t_i\}_1^N$ of $S = S(N)$ and to consider the matrix representation $\bar{E}_l$ of E_l with respect to that basis. Its eigenvectors are the coefficients of the eigenfunctions of E_l with respect to $\{t_i\}_1^N$, and its eigenvalues μ_1^l are those of E_l.

For $l = 0, 1$, $P_l f$ satisfies

$$\text{(B.1)}\qquad (f, t_i)_l = (Pf, t_i)_l, \qquad i = 1, \cdots, N.$$

Hence, for $s = \sum_{i=1}^N \alpha_i t_i \in S$, with $E_l s = \sum_{i=1}^N \beta_i t_i$, $t_i'' = (D^2 t)_i$ satisfies

$$\sum_{i=1}^{N} \alpha_i (t_i'', t_j)_l = \sum_{i=1}^{N} \beta_i (t_i, t_j)_l;$$

therefore

(B.2) $\bar{E}_l = A_l^{-1}B_l, \quad A_l = \{(t_i, t_j)_l\}, \quad B_l = \{(t_i'', t_j)_l\}, \quad l = 0, 1.$

We now choose a basis $\{t_i\}_1^N$ of S convenient for the computation of $\bar{E}_k$. Define

(B.3)
$$t_i(x) = (x - x_{i-1})_+^3 - 2(x - x_i)_+^3 + (x - x_{i+1})_+^3 + a_i x$$
$$= \begin{cases} a_i x, & x \leqq x_{i-1}, \\ a_i x + (x - x_{i-1})^3, & x_{i-1} \leqq x \leqq x_i, \\ b_i(x-1) - (x - x_{i+1})^3, & x_i \leqq x \leqq x_{i+1}, \\ b_i(x-1), & x_{i+1} \leqq x, \end{cases}$$

where $a_i = 6h^2(x_i - 1)$, $b_i = 6h^2 x_i$, $i = 1, \cdots, N$. This choice makes B_1 tridiagonal, since $t_i''(x) \equiv 0$ for $x \notin (x_{i-1}, x_{i+1})$.

CASE $l = 1$. In fact, one computes that

$$B_1 = -6h^3(C + 6),$$

where C is the $N \times N$ tridiagonal matrix with general row $\{1, -2, 1\}$. With somewhat more effort, one computes that

$$A_1 = -\tfrac{3}{10}h^5(C + 30 + 120C^{-1}).$$

Consequently

(B.4)
$$\bar{E}_1 = \frac{20}{h^2}\frac{C(C+6)}{C^2 + 30C + 120}.$$

But this implies that the eigenvectors of $\bar{E}_1$ are those of C, viz., $\{\sin ijh\pi\}_{j=1}^N$. Hence if $\{\lambda_i\}_1^N$ denotes the corresponding set of eigenvalues of $C\,(\lambda_i) = 2\,(\cos ih\pi - 1)$, then the eigenvalues μ_i^1 of $\bar{E}_1$ and E_1 are

(B.5)
$$\mu_i^1 = \frac{20}{h^2}\frac{\lambda_i(\lambda_i + 6)}{\lambda_i^2 + 30\lambda_i + 120},$$

while the eigenfunctions w_i^1 of E_1 are

(B.6)
$$w_i^1(x) = \sum_{j=1}^N t_j(x) \sin ijh\pi.$$

CASE $l = 0$. One proceeds just as in the case $l = 1$. The matrix B_0 is $-A_1$. The matrix A_0 turns out to be

$$A_0 = \frac{36}{7!}h^7(C + 126) + 12h^7C^{-1} + 36h^7C^{-2}.$$

Hence the eigenvalues μ_i^0 of $\bar{E}_0$ and E_0 are

(B.7)
$$\mu_i^0 = \frac{42}{h^2}\frac{\lambda_i(\lambda_i^2 + 30\lambda_i + 120)}{\lambda_i^3 + 126\lambda_i^2 + 1680\lambda_i + 5040},$$

while the eigenfunctions w_i^0 of E_0 are again those of E_1.

In fact, one verifies that

(B.8) $$w_i^0 = w_i^1 = h^3(1 + 6\lambda_i^{-1})P_2(\sin i\pi x), \qquad i = 1, \cdots, N,$$

where P_2 is the projection associated with spline interpolation, as defined in §15.

CASE $l = 2$. In this case, one makes use of the identity valid for $f \in S$:

$$\frac{h^2}{6}(f''(x_{i-1}) + 4f''(x_i) + f''(x_{i+1})) = f(x_{i-1}) - 2f(x_i) + f(x_{i+1}).$$

This gives

$$E_2 = \frac{6}{h^2}\frac{C}{C+6},$$

so

(B.9) $$\mu_i^2 = \frac{6}{h^2}\frac{\lambda_i}{\lambda_i + 6}, \qquad i = 1, \cdots, N,$$

while the eigenfunctions of E_2 are again those of E_1 (and E_0).

In all three cases, the approximation to the eigenfunctions is, therefore, $O(h^4)$. The approximations to the eigenvalues, on the other hand, vary in order of accuracy. Let ν_i denote the eigenvalues of D^2, i.e.,

$$\nu_i = -(i\pi)^2, \qquad i = 1, 2, \cdots;$$

then one computes

$$\mu_i^2 = \nu_i\left(1 - \frac{2}{4!}h^2\nu_i + \frac{2}{6!}h^4\nu_i^2 - \cdots\right),$$

$$\mu_i^1 = \nu_i\left(1 + \frac{1}{6!}h^4\nu_i^2 - \frac{12}{8!}h^6\nu_i^3 + \cdots\right),$$

$$\mu_i^0 = \nu_i\left(1 - \frac{4}{3}\frac{1}{8!}h^6\nu_i^3 + \cdots\right).$$

Hence the application of the Rayleigh-Ritz-Galerkin method to the space of cubic splines with uniformly spaced joints gives an approximation to the eigenvalues of D^2 of order $O(h^6)$. The following table gives $-\mu_i^l$ for $l = 0, 1, 2$, $N = 1, 2, 3$, and $i = 1, 2$.

	$l = 2$	$l = 1$	$l = 0$	Exact	
$N = 1$	12.0	10.0	9.8824		
$N = 2$	10.8	9.8901	9.870300	9.86960438	$i = 1$
$N = 3$	10.39	9.8755	9.869706		
$N = 2$	54.0	41.54	39.9512	39.478416	$i = 2$
$N = 3$	48.0	40.00	39.5304		

References

1. J. H. Ahlberg and E. N. Nilson, *Convergence properties of the spline fit*, J. Soc. Indust. Appl. Math. **11** (1963), 95–104.

2. G. Birkhoff and C. de Boor, *Error bounds for cubic spline interpolation*, J. Math. Mech. **13** (1964), 827–835.

3. G. Birkhoff and H. L. Garabedian, *Smooth surface interpolation*, J. Math. and Phys. **39** (1960), 258–268.

4. P. J. Davis, *Interpolation and approximation*, Blaisdell, New York, 1963.

5. C. de Boor, *Bicubic spline interpolation*, J. Math. and Phys. **41** (1962), 212–218.

6. C. de Boor, *Best approximation properties of spline functions of odd degree*, J. Math. Mech. **12** (1963), 747–750.

7. D. Jackson, *The theory of approximation*, Amer. Math. Soc., Providence, R.I., 1930.

8. R. Langer, editor, *On numerical approximation*, Univ. of Wisconsin Press, Madison, Wisc., 1959.

9. A. E. H. Love, *The mathematical theory of elasticity*, 4th ed., Cambridge Univ. Press, London, 1934.

10. C. Runge, *Über empirische Funktionen und die Interpolation zwischen äquidistanten Ordinaten*, Zeits. Math. Phys. **46** (1901), 224–243.

11. H. Rutishauser, *Bemerkungen zur glatten Interpolation*, ZAMP **11** (1960), 508–513.

12. A. Sard, *Best approximate integration formulas; best approximation formulas*, Amer. J. Math. **71** (1949), 352–357; see also, *Linear approximation*, Math. Surveys No. 9, Amer. Math. Soc., Providence, R.I., 1963.

13. I. J. Schoenberg, *Contribution to the problem of approximation of equidistant data by analytic functions*. Parts A and B, Quar. Appl. Math. **4** (1946), 45–99, 112–141.

14. I. J. Schoenberg, *Spline interpolation and best quadrature formulae*, Bull. Amer. Math. Soc. **70** (1964), 143–148.

15. H. Thacher, editor, *Numerical properties of functions of more than one independent variable*, Annals New York Acad. Sci. **86** (1960), 677–874.

16. J. L. Walsh, *Interpolation and approximation by rational functions in the complex domain*, Amer. Math. Soc., Providence, R.I., 1956.

17. J. L. Walsh, J. H. Ahlberg, and E. N. Nilson, *Best approximation properties of the spline fit*, J. Math. Mech. **11** (1962), 225–234.

18. E. T. Whittaker, *On the functions which are represented by the expansions of the interpolation-theory*, Proc. Roy. Soc. Edinburgh (1915), 181–194.

19. E. T. Whittaker and G. Robinson, *The calculus of observations*, 4th ed., Blackie, London, 1944.

20. I. J. Schoenberg, *On trigonometric spline interpolation*, J. Math. Mech. **13** (1964), 795–826.

21. G. Birkhoff, H. Burchard, and D. Thomas, *Nonlinear interpolation by splines, pseudosplines, and elastica*, Res. Publ. General Motors Research—468 (1965).

22. B. van der Pol, Appendix IV of M. Kac, *Probability and related topics in the physical sciences*, Interscience Press, New York, 1959.

23. J. L. Synge, *The hypercircle in mathematical physics*, Cambridge Univ. Press, London, 1957.

24. R. S. Varga, *Matrix iterative analysis*, Prentice-Hall, Englewood Cliffs, N.J., 1962.

25. G. Birkhoff, *Boundary value problems, function spaces, and computing*, Trans. 10th Conference of Army Mathematicians, U.S.A.

26. C. de Boor and R. E. Lynch, *Generalized splines and their minimum properties*, unpublished MS.

27. A. H. Fowler and C. W. Wilson, *Cubic spline, a curve fitting routine*, Report Y-1400, Oak Ridge, 1963.

28. D. H. MacLaren, *Formulas for fitting a spline curve through a set of points*, Boeing Appl. Math. Report 2, 1958.

RUSSIAN LITERATURE ON APPROXIMATION IN 1958-1964

G. G. LORENTZ[1]
Syracuse University, New York

This paper does not pretend to give a complete coverage of the subject. We have tried to review and to include in our bibliography only the more important and original papers. Thus we have covered only 45–50% of the total output. Notes in Doklady were not considered if they were followed up by a detailed publication elsewhere. We have selected as the starting date of our review the year 1958. Excellent reviews of earlier papers can be found in [7]. For late papers of 1964 and additions see the Appendix at the end of this report.

1. **General principles.** Mergeljan [**108**] gives interesting applications of a general set-theoretic principle for closed sets in the plane. He obtains characterizations of sets of convergence of sequences of polynomials, due to Lavrentiev and Hartogs and Rosenthal. Further results concern the existence of a weight-function h on a given set E, with respect to which polynomials or rational functions are complete on E with weight h.

Duality theorems have been used for approximation by many authors. Garkavi [**65**] gives several results of this type. Distance from an element y of a Banach space X to a convex subset M is determined by the study of some extremal problems for linear functionals in X with respect to M. See also Havinson [**83, 84**]. (Compare the article of R. C. Buck in these Proceedings (p. 27) for more detailed information about duality theorems.)

Let X be a locally convex linear topological space, p a semi-norm on X, $p_1(\lambda_1, \cdots, \lambda_n, \cdots)$ a function of countably many arguments, for which $p_1(\lambda_1, \cdots, \lambda_n) = p_1(\lambda_1, \cdots, \lambda_n, 0, \cdots)$ is a semi-norm on R_n. Let ϕ_n, $n = 1, 2, \cdots$ and f be elements of X. Havinson [**83**] proves: A necessary and sufficient condition that for each $\varepsilon > 0$ there is an N and $\lambda_1, \cdots, \lambda_N$ for which $p(f - \sum_1^N \lambda_j\phi_j) < \varepsilon$, $p_1(\lambda_1, \cdots, \lambda_N) < \varepsilon$ is that for each functional $L \in X^*$, conditions $|L(x)| \leqq p(x)$, $x \in X$ and $|\sum_1^n \lambda_j L(\phi_j)| < p_1(\lambda_1, \cdots, \lambda_n)$ for all λ_j, n, should imply $L(f) = 0$. For related, more special results, see P. J. Davis and Ky Fan (Duke Math. J. **24** (1957), 183–192) and Havinson [**84, 85**]. In [**84**], two dual problems are discussed (here n is fixed). Problem I: Minimize $p(f - \sum_{j=1}^n \lambda_j\phi_j) + p_1(\lambda_1, \cdots, \lambda_n)$ for all λ_j; Problem II: Find sup $|L(f)|$ for all $L \in X^*$ for which $|L(x)| \leqq p(x)$, $x \in X$, $|\sum_1^n \lambda_j L(\phi_j)| \leqq p_1(\lambda_1, \cdots, \lambda_n)$. The paper [**85**] deals with the approximation of analytic functions by means of rational functions on sets of analytic capacity zero.

We note also an interesting article of Gurariĭ [**79**] on bases in spaces of continuous functions.

[1] This work has been supported, in part, by the Office of Scientific Research of the US Air Force, through contract AF 49(638)-1401.

2. **Čebyšev sets in Banach spaces.** N. V. Efimov and Stečkin [58] and Vlasov [144] study the geometry of Čebyšev subsets of a Banach space X. For a set $M \subset X$, $y \in M$ is a projection of $x \in X$ onto M if $\|x - y\| = \rho(x, M)$. M is a *Čebyšev set* if each $x \in X$ has exactly one projection. If each $x \in X$ has a projection y, and if each ray yx (starting at a projection y of x and passing through x) projects into y, then M is a *sun*. The set M is *approximative compact*, if each sequence $y_n \in M$, for which $\|x - y_n\| \to \rho(x, M)$ for some $x \in X$, contains a convergent subsequence. In a smooth n-dimensional space, each bounded Čebyšev set is convex (H. Buseman).

It is not known whether this holds for arbitrary Banach spaces. However: (1) Each bounded compact Čebyšev subset of a smooth Banach space is convex [144]; (2) In a uniformly convex smooth Banach space, a Čebyšev set M is convex if and only if it is approximative compact [58]; (3) In a uniformly convex space X, an approximative compact set M is a Čebyšev set if and only if it is a sun [58].

Garkavi [68] and [71] calls a subset $M \subset X$ an almost-Čebyšev set if the $x \in X$ which have no unique projection onto M form a set of first category in X. There exist Banach spaces X which have no almost-Čebyšev subspaces. However, each separable Banach space X has ("many") almost-Čebyšev subspaces isomorphic to a given subspace X_0 of X, if X_0 is reflexive. Garkavi gives a necessary and sufficient condition (similar to Haar's condition) in order that continuous functions $f_1, \cdots, f_n$ on a compact A span an almost-Čebyšev subspace of $C[A]$.

In [67] Garkavi continues the investigations of Phelps [Trans. Amer. Math. Soc. **95** (1960)]. He considers subspaces M of a Banach space X which are factor-reflexive (so that X/M is reflexive), in particular have a finite co-dimension m (i.e., X/M has dimension m). He is able to characterize Čebyšev subspaces of this type by the behavior of continuous linear functionals on X^*. For example: a factor-reflexive subspace M is Čebyšev if and only if each linear functional on the annihilator of M has a unique regular extension onto X^*, which preserves its norm. There are several theorems which connect the Čebyšev property of M with the properties of the set E of the extremal points of the unit sphere of X. For Čebyšev subspaces in X of finite co-dimension m one has: $\sup m \leqq r$, where r is the dimension of E. Necessary and sufficient conditions for a subspace of finite dimension to be Čebyšev are given in Garkavi [70].

In [67] and [69] Garkavi characterizes the subsets L_n of $C[A]$, of finite co-dimension n, which are sets of existence (of an element of best approximation), sets of uniqueness, or Čebyšev sets. This is done in terms of the annihilator of L_n, which consists of measures $\mu = a_1\mu_1 + \cdots + a_n\mu_n$, where $\mu_1, \cdots, \mu_n$ are some fixed measures on A. From this, some topological properties of the compact A can be derived, if it is known that $C[A]$ contains Čebyšev subspaces L_n for some given n.

3. **Polynomials of best approximation.** Zuhovickiĭ and Èskin [147] continue former work of Zuhovickiĭ, concerning approximation in Hilbert spaces. They

investigate the possibility of best approximation of a continuous function $f(t)$ on a compact A, with values in a Banach space Y, by $U(t)x_0$, where $U(t)$ for each $t \in A$ is a given linear operator from a Banach space X into Y, and the element x_0 is to be determined. For instance, $U(t)$ may be a differential operator, x_0—an n-tuple of functions.

If the polynomial of best approximation $P(x) = \sum_{k=1}^{n} a_k\phi_k(x)$ to a function f is not unique, then the polynomials of best approximation of f form a convex set. If W is a subset of $C[a, b]$, we say that the system $\phi_1, \cdots, \phi_n$ has rank r with respect to W, if the sets of polynomials of best approximation of functions $f \in W$ have the maximal dimension r. Haar's theorem characterizes systems of rank 0 with respect to $W = C$. Its generalization by G. Š. Rubinšteĭn (see Zuhovickiĭ **[18]**) corresponds to the case $W = C$ and an arbitrary rank r. Garkavi **[63]** finds a similar criterion for the subspace $W = C_s$, $s \geqq 1$, which consists of all functions with s continuous derivatives on $[a, b]$. The paper of Havinson **[82]** deals with similar problems of unicity for the L^1 metric.

Brudnyĭ and Gopengauz **[34, 78]** discuss the measure of the set $E_n \subset [a, b]$ of points x, where $|f(x) - P_n(x)| = \|f - P_n\|$, P_n being the algebraic polynomial of best approximation. Then $mE_n \to 0$ as $n \to \infty$, but there exist infinitely differentiable functions f, not polynomials, for which $mE_n > 0$ for infinitely many n. Similar results hold for the approximation by Fourier sums, and interpolation polynomials.

Kadec **[91]** has a theorem of a new kind. If T_n is a trigonometric polynomial of best approximation of a continuous function f on $[0, \pi]$, and $0 \leqq t_0^{(n)} < \cdots < t_{n+1}^{(n)} \leqq \pi$ are points where the maximum of $|f(t) - T_n(t)|$ is attained, then for many n, the $t_k^{(n)}$ are fairly uniformly distributed in $[0, \pi]$. More exactly, $\underline{\lim}\, \Delta_n n^{1/2-\varepsilon} = 0$ for each $\varepsilon > 0$, where

$$\Delta_n = \max_k |t_k^{(n)} - \pi k/(n+1)|, \qquad n = 0, 1, \cdots.$$

Boltjanskiĭ, Ryškov and Šaškin **[31]** give a geometric interpretation of Čebyšev systems of functions. An analogue of Čebyšev's theorem is given by Gol'šteĭn **[72]** for the following problem: Let functions $f(x)$, $\phi_j(x)$, $x \in K$ and $a_j(t)$, $b(t)$, $t \in E$, $j = 1, \cdots, n$, on compact sets K, E be given, as well as constants a_{ij}, b_j, $i = 1, \cdots, r$, $j = 1, \cdots, n$. Characterize the polynomial $\sum_1^n d_j\phi_j$, which satisfies the conditions $\sum_{j=1}^n d_j a_j(t) \geqq b(t)$, $t \in E$ and $\sum_{j=1}^n a_{ji} d_j = b_i$, $i = 1, \cdots, r$ and approximates best f in the uniform norm on K.

4. **Extremal problems for polynomials.** S. Bernšteĭn has solved several extremal problems for polynomials. There are many papers generalizing his results in different directions. They deal often with special classes of polynomials (for example, multiply monotone polynomials) and sometimes give an explicit expression for the extremal polynomial. Representative for papers of this type are the articles of Rymarenko, Grigor'eva and Faĭnšmidt in **[4]**.

5. **Approximation by Fourier sums and de la Vallée-Poussin sums.** Let C^* be the space of 2π-periodic continuous functions, $U_n(f, x)$, operators defined on C^* (for example, the partial sums $S_n(f, x)$ of the Fourier series of f), $K \subset C^*$ a class of functions. We are then faced with the two following problems:

I. Find an asymptotic formula

$$f(x) - U_n(f, x) = A_{U_n}(f, x) + O(B_n(K)), \tag{1}$$

where A_{U_n} is the main term, and $B_n(K)$ does not depend upon the individual function $f \in K$;

II. Find the asymptotic behavior for $n \to \infty$ of the degree of approximation of the class K by the operator U_n:

$$E_{U_n}(K) = \sup_{f \in K} \|f - U_n(f)\|. \tag{2}$$

Solution of Problem I leads often to useful information about $E_{U_n}(K)$.

Notations for classes of functions: H_1^ω is the class of functions $f \in C^*$ with $\omega(f, h) \leqq \omega(h)$, where ω is a modulus of continuity. H_k^ω is the class of $f \in C^*$ with $\omega_k(f, h) \leqq \omega(h)$, ω_k being the kth modulus of smoothness, if $\omega_k(\lambda h) \leqq (\lambda + 1)\omega_k(h)$. We write H_k^α instead of H_k^ω if $\omega(t) = t^\alpha$, $0 \leqq \alpha \leqq 1$. $W_\beta^r K$, where $K \subset C^*$, is the class of all f of the form

$$f(x) = \frac{1}{\pi} \int_{-\pi}^{\pi} \phi(x + t) \sum_{k=1}^{\infty} k^{-r} \cos (kt + \beta\pi/2)\, dt, \qquad \phi \in K \tag{3}$$

(if $\beta = r$, then $\phi = f^{(r)}$). W^r (or W_β^r) is the class of functions f $|f^{(r)}(x)| \leqq 1$ a.e., (or of the form (3) with $|\phi(x)| \leqq 1$ a.e.). The first results in the proposed direction are due to Kolmogorov (Ann. of Math. **36** (1935), 521–527), who gave an asymptotic formula for $E_{S_n}(W^r)$. Nikol'skiĭ [Trudy **15** (1945)] generalized this to

$$E_{S_n}(W^r H_1^\alpha) = C_1(\alpha) n^{-r-\alpha} \log n + O(n^{-r-\alpha}), \qquad C_1(\alpha) = \frac{2^{1+\alpha}}{\pi^2} \int_0^{\pi/2} t^\alpha \sin t\, dt. \tag{4}$$

De la Vallée-Poussin sums of $f \in C^*$ are $V_{np}(f, x) = (p + 1)^{-1} \sum_{k=n-p}^{n} S_k(f, x)$. A. V. Efimov, in a series of papers [50–54] generalizes (4). He gives asymptotic formulas for $E_{S_n}(K)$, $K = W_\beta^r H_1^\omega$ and $K = W_\beta^r H_2^\omega$, and for $E_{V_{np}}(K)$, $K = H_1^\omega$ and $K = H_2^\alpha$. He also discusses conjugate classes $\tilde{K}$, and finds asymptotic formulas for $f(x) - \sigma_n(f, x)$ of type (1), for example if $K = H_2^\omega$.

6. **Summability methods with a triangular matrix.** If Λ is the triangular matrix λ_{nk}, $k = 0, \cdots, n$, $n = 1, 2, \cdots$, we consider the approximation of $f \in C^*$ by the averages

$$U_n(f, x) = \lambda_{n0} \frac{a}{2} + \sum_{k=1}^{n} \lambda_{nk}(a_k \cos kx + b_k \sin kx). \tag{5}$$

Much work has been devoted to the determination or estimation of the degree of approximation of different classes $K \subset C^*$ by operators (5); see for example Timan [9]. Teljakovskiĭ [124, 125] gives an exact formula for the classes W^r_β. He obtains

$$(6) \quad E_{U_n}(W^r_\beta) = \frac{4}{\pi^2}\sum_{k=1}^{n} k^{-1}\xi\left(\sin\frac{\beta\pi}{2}\mu_{nk}, \lambda_{n,n-k}n^{-r}\right) + O\left(|\mu_{n0}| + \sum_{k=1}^{n}\frac{k(n-k)}{n}|\Delta^2\mu_{n,k-1}| + n^{-r}\right),$$

where $\mu_{nk} = (1-\lambda_{nk})k^{-r}$, $k = 1, 2, \cdots$, and the function $\xi(u, v)$ is defined by $\xi(u, v) = \pi\,|u|\,/2$ if $|v| \leqq |u|$, $= |u| \arcsin |u/v| + \sqrt{v^2 - u^2}$ if $|u| < |v|$. (See also Efimov [55].)

The proof depends on some deep estimates of L^1-norms of trigonometric polynomials; in fact, $E_{U_n}(W^0_\beta)$ is exactly equal to the L^1-norm of the polynomial $\lambda_{n0}/2 + \sum_{k=1}^{n} \lambda_{nk} \cos kt$. Fomin [61] gives sufficient conditions for Fourier effectivity of the matrix Λ. Some of his conditions, for example, $\sum_{k=0}^{n} |\Delta\lambda_{nk}|^2 = O(n^{-1})$, bear on the squares of the differences of the λ_{nk}.

As a special case, (6) leads to the estimation of the approximation of classes W^r, $\tilde{W}^r$ by de la Vallée-Poussin sums V_{np} with $p = p(n)$, $p/n \to \theta$ as $n \to \infty$, $0 \leqq \theta \leqq 1$ (obtained by Teljakovskiĭ earlier [123]).

In [56, 57] Efimov gives upper and lower estimates of $E_{U_n}(W^r_\beta H^\omega_1)$ and of $E_{U_n}(W^r_\beta \tilde{H}^\omega_2)$, with U_n given by (5). This allows him to find regularity conditions for the matrix Λ (such as convexity of the λ_{nk} as functions of k) and for the modulus of continuity, for which $E_{U_n}(W^r_\beta H^\omega_1)$ is of the order of the best approximation of the class $W^r_\beta H^\omega_1$.

Ganzburg [62] finds an asymptotic relation, which compares the degree of approximation of the class H^ω_1 by the sums $U_n(f, x)$ and by the Λ-means $\bar{U}_n(f, x)$ of the interpolation polynomials of f (with equidistant nodes). He proves (under some conditions on Λ):

$$\sup_{f \in H^\omega_1} |f(x) - \bar{U}_n(f, x)| = A(\omega)\,|\sin (n + \tfrac{1}{2})x|\, E_{U_n}(H^\omega_1) + O(\omega(n^{-1})).$$

The matrix Λ is Taylor effective, if for each function $f(z) = \sum_0^\infty c_k z^k$, analytic in $|z| < 1$ and continuous in $|z| \leqq 1$, $U_n(f, z) = \sum_0^n \lambda_{nk} c_k z^k \to f(z)$ uniformly, $|z| \leqq 1$. Taĭkov [122] finds necessary and sufficient conditions for the Taylor effectivity; they are weaker than the conditions of Fourier effectivity (found by Lozinskiĭ).

7. **Generalizations of inequalities of Markov and Bernšteĭn.** Some interesting inequalities have been derived by Videnskiĭ. If P_n, M_n, N_{n-1} are algebraic polynomials of the indicated degrees, $L_n(x) = \sqrt{1-x^2}N_{n-1}(x)$, and if $\phi(x) > 0$ on $[-1, +1]$ is continuously differentiable, then the inequality

$$|P_n(x)| \leqq |M_n(x) + i\sqrt{1-x^2}\, N_{n-1}(x)|, \qquad -1 \leqq x \leqq 1,$$

implies [139]

$$|\{\phi(x)P_n^{(k)}(x)\}'| \leqq |\{\phi(x)[M_n^{(k)}(x) + iL_n^{(k)}(x)]\}'|, \qquad -1 \leqq x \leqq 1.$$

If T_n is a trigonometric polynomial of degree n and $|T_n(x)| \leqq 1$ for $|x| \leqq \omega$, $0 < \omega < \pi$, then [138] $|T_n'(x)| \leqq 2n^2 \cot(\omega/2)$, and

$$|T_n'(x)| \leqq n \cos(x/2)[\sin^2(\omega/2) - \sin^2(x/2)]^{-1/2}$$

for $|x| \leqq \omega$. The inequalities are exact. See also [137]. If $P(z)$ is a polynomial with roots $x + iy$ in the region $y^2 \leqq x^2/(2n - 1) + n/2$, and $T_n(x)$ a trigonometric polynomial of degree n, then $|P(d/dx)T_n(x)| \leqq |P(in)| \cdot \|T_n\|$ (Dočev, [39]).

8. **Sharper inequalities for special polynomials.** Inequalities for polynomials $P_n(z)$ and their derivatives, which have no roots in the disc $|z| < 1$, have been studied by P. Lax, de Brujin (Nederl. Akad. Wetensch., Proc. **50** (1947), 1265–1272), Ankeny and Rivlin (Pacific J. Math. **5** (1955), 849–852) and others. Boas and Rahman [30] prove that

$$\|P_n(Re^{ix})\|_p \leqq \frac{\|1 + R^n e^{inx}\|_p}{\|1 + e^{inx}\|_p} \|P_n(e^{ix})\|_p, \tag{7}$$

where $\|f(x)\|_p$ stands for the L^p-norm of f, $1 \leqq p \leqq +\infty$. For a similar inequality see also [90]. Mamedov [105] and Mamedhanov [101] have inequalities for $M(P_n, \alpha) = \max_{-\alpha \leqq x \leqq \alpha} |P_n(x)|$ and $\bar{M}(P_n, \alpha) = \max_{|z| \leqq \alpha} |P_n(z)|$. For example, if $\alpha \geqq 1$ and P_n has no zeros in $|z| < \sqrt{\alpha} + \delta$, $\delta \geqq 0$, then $M(P_n, \alpha) = \alpha^{n/2} q^n M(P_n, 1)$, where $q = (1 + \alpha^{1/2} + \delta\alpha^{-1/2})/(1 + \alpha^{1/2} + \delta)$. It should be noted that a real polynomial $P_n(z)$ with no zeros in $|z| < 1$ is $\pm Q_n$, where $Q_n(z)$ is a polynomial with positive coefficients in z and $1 - z$. For these polynomials, the methods of author's paper (Lorentz, Math. Ann. **151** (1963), 239–251) give inequalities for $\|P_n^{(k)}\|_p$ which, except for the unknown constants, are as sharp as the inequalities for the narrower class.

9. **Other inequalities.** Ibragimov [89] proves for an algebraic polynomial P_n the inequalities $|P_n(x)| \leqq C(p)n^{p/2} \|P_n\|_p$, $-1 \leqq x \leqq 1$, $|P_n'(x)| \leqq C_1(p)n^{2+2/p} \|P_n\|_p$, $|P_n'(x)| \leqq C_2(p)(1 - x^2)^{-1/2} n^{1+2/p} \|P_n\|_p$. These inequalities are not new, but he gives numerical values for the constants $C(p)$. For similar inequalities for entire functions of finite degree see [87, 88, 151].

Properties of moduli of continuity and of smoothness of different orders, and relations between them, have been studied in many papers, for themselves, or as tools for other investigations. We mention here the papers of Motornyĭ [110], Brudnyĭ and Gopengauz [35], Trigub [133], Efimov [56], A. F. Timan [131].

10. **Degree of approximation by algebraic polynomials.** While the fundamental theorems of trigonometric approximation, due to Jackson and S. Bernšteĭn, are 50 years old, the corresponding theorems for approximation by algebraic polynomials have been found only recently. A. F. Timan and Dzjadyk proved the

following. If $f \in C[-1, +1]$ has a continuous derivative $f^{(r)}$ and if $\omega(f^{(r)}; h) \leqq \omega(h)$, where ω is a modulus of continuity (in other words, if $f \in W^r H_1^\omega$), then there is a sequence of polynomials $P_n(x)$ for which

$$(8) \qquad |f(x) - P_n(x)| \leqq C_r \Delta_n(x)^r \omega(\Delta_n(x)), \qquad -1 \leqq x \leqq 1, \quad \text{where}$$

$$\Delta_n(x) = \max\left(\frac{1}{n^2}, \frac{\sqrt{1-x^2}}{n}\right).$$

This formula shows that towards the endpoints ± 1 of the interval, one can achieve better approximation. The important fact is that the corresponding inverse theorem is also true: if f satisfies (8), then $f \in W^r H_1^\omega$, at least if $\omega(h)$ is smooth, for example if $\omega(h) = h^\alpha$, $0 < \alpha \leqq 1$. The extension of (8) to the moduli of smoothness is not trivial. Dzjadyk **[43]** and independently G. Freud (Math. Ann. **137** (1959), 17–25) showed that $\omega(\Delta_n(x))$ in (8) can be replaced by $\omega_2(f; \Delta_n(x))$. Brudnyĭ **[33]** announces $|f(x) - P_n(x)| \leqq A_s \omega_s(f;\ \Delta_n(x))$, $n = s - 1, s, \cdots$. Because of the inequality $\omega_s(f; h) \leqq h^r \omega_{s-r}(f^{(r)}; h)$, this contains all previous theorems.

Estimates of this type have been obtained also **[32, 133]** for functions defined on the exterior of an interval or on a semi-axis, in the case of approximation by integral functions of finite degree.

Let the length of the interval $[a, b]$ be less than the critical number 4, and let $f(x)$ satisfy on $[a, b]$ the necessary algebraic conditions. Then a formula corresponding to (8) (with $\Delta_n(x) = \max(n^{-2}, n^{-1}\sqrt{(x-a)(b-x)})$ holds for some polynomials P_n with integral coefficients (Trigub **[134]**). Trigub improves also the estimates of Kantorovic and Kuzmin of $E_n^e(f)$, the degree of approximation of f by polynomials with integral coefficients, in terms of $E_n(f)$, if the interval is $[0, 1]$ or $[\delta, 1-\delta]$, $\delta > 0$.

11. **Degree of trigonometric approximation.** If $f \in W^r$, i.e., if $f(x)$ has a bounded rth derivative on the circle $-\pi \leqq x \leqq \pi$, one can ask about the simultaneous approximation of the functions $f, \cdots, f^{(r)}$ by $T_n, \cdots, T_n^{(r)}$, where T_n is a trigonometric polynomial of degree n. Let $E_n(g)$ denote the degree of approximation of a function g by the polynomials T_n. Then we would like to find a T_n for which

$$\max_{s=0,\cdots,r} \frac{\|f^{(s)} - T_n^{(s)}\|}{E_n(f^{(s)})}$$

attains its minimum, which we denote by $C_{n,r}(f)$. The extremal polynomial exists, but is not in general unique. Garkavi **[64]** (see also A. F. Timan **[128]** and Berdihina **[25]**) proves that

$$C_{nr} = \sup_{f \in W^r} C_{nr}(f) = (4/\pi^2) \log(p+1) + O(\log\log\log p),$$

where $p = \min(r, n)$. He also proves the following inequality, which holds for each $f \in W^r$ and each T_n:

$$\|f^{(r)} - T_n^{(r)}\| \leqq n^r \|f - T_n^{(r)}\| + C_{nr}\{n^r E_n(f) + E_n(f^{(r)})\}.$$

We note the papers of Stečkin **[118]**, Vlasov **[145]**, Dincen **[38]**, where the degree of approximation of a function $f \in C^*$ by special operators is connected with its other intrinsic properties (order of magnitude of $E_n(f)$, properties of $\tilde{f}$).

12. **Approximation by rational functions.** Rational functions can be used with success for the approximation of analytic, and of meromorphic functions. That they can be useful for functions with singularities other than poles, has been shown strikingly by the approximation of $|x|$ by Newman (Mich. Math. J. **11** (1964), 11–14). A rational function of degree n is the quotient of two polynomials of degree n: $R_n(x) = (a_0x^n + \cdots + a_0)/(b_0x^n + \cdots + b_n)$, with not all $b_i = 0$. By $R_n(f)$ we denote the degree of approximation of a function f by the functions $R_n(x)$. There exist functions f on $[-1, +1]$, for which $R_n(f)$ tends to zero arbitrarily rapidly, and the modulus of continuity $\omega(f, h)$ tends to zero arbitrarily slowly (hence $E_n(f) \to 0$ arbitrarily slowly). It follows that for the approximation by rational functions, there do not exist analogues of Bernšteĭn's theorems about polynomial approximation. Correctly formulated inverse theorems have sets of exceptional points, of measure zero, or of arbitrary small positive measure. First results of this type are due to Gončar (Dokl. **100** (1955), 205–208). Dolženko **[40]** proves that if $\sum_{n=0}^{\infty} R_n(f) < +\infty$ for a function f defined on a subset E of the real axis, then f is absolutely continuous on E. The existence of f' a.e. on E follows, but no assumption about the order of convergence of $R_n(f)$ to zero ensures the existence of f'' at a single point of E. The situation changes, if one considers generalized derivatives. If, for a set E, $\sum_{n=1}^{\infty} \{n^{-1}R_n(f)\}^{1/(r+1)} < +\infty$ for some integer r, in particular if $R_n(f) \leqq \text{Const. } n^{-r-\varepsilon}$ for some $\varepsilon > 0$, then f has almost everywhere on E the rth generalized de la Vallée-Poussin differential (Dolženko **[41]**). If for a rational function, $|R_n(x)| \leqq M$ on a set $E \subset [-\infty, +\infty]$, then for each $\delta > 0$, there is a subset $e \subset E$, $me \leqq \delta$, such that $|R_n'(x)| \leqq (2/\delta)Mn$ on $E \setminus e$.[1] The proof is extremely simple: an equation $R_n(x) = a$ has at most n roots on E, hence the total variation of R_n on E does not exceed $2Mn$. Hence $\int_E |R_n'(x)|\, dx \leqq 2Mn$ (Dolženko **[42]**). One also has $|R_n^{(r)}(x)| \leqq C_r\delta^{-r}Mn^r$ on $E \setminus e_r$, $me_r \leqq \delta$.

Remark. A slight refinement of the above results shows the existence of a set $e \subset E$, $me \leqq \delta$, such that $|R_n(x_1) - R_n(x_2)| \leqq (2/\delta)Mn\,|x_1 - x_2|$ if $x_1, x_2 \in E \setminus e$. From this one can derive the following result, which improves a theorem of Gončar **[73]**. If $R_n(f) \leqq Cn^{-r-\alpha}$, $r = 0, 1, \cdots$, $0 < \alpha \leqq 1$ on a set E, then for each $\delta > 0$ there is a subset $e \subset E$, $me < \delta$ such that f is r times differentiable on $E \setminus e$, and $f^{(r)} \in \text{Lip } \alpha$ on this set.

Approximation of classes of analytic functions was studied by Erohin **[60]**. By A_{pR}, $1 \leqq p \leqq +\infty$, $R > 1$ we denote the class of functions $f(z)$, analytic in the disc $|z| < R$, with $\|f\|_p \leqq 1$, where the L^p-norm of f is the supremum for $0 \leqq r \leqq 1$ of the L^p-averages of $|f(z)|$ either over the circles $|z| = r$, or over the discs $|z| \leqq r$.

[1] The symbol $\setminus$ is used here to denote set subtraction.

Then we define $E_n(A_{pR}) = \sup_{f\in A_{pR}} E_n(f)$, and $R_n(A_{pR}) = \sup_{f\in A_{pR}} R_n(f)$. Erohin proves that $\lim_{n\to\infty} \sqrt[n]{E_n(A_{pR})} = \lim_{n\to\infty} \sqrt[n]{R_n(A_{pR})} = R^{-1}$. Therefore, rational functions R_n fail to give better approximation for the class A_{pR} than the polynomials P_n, although a function R_n contains $2n + 1$ parameters as against $n + 1$ parameters for P_n. (For a simple proof of this fact see also Pan **[112]**.) Erohin uses interesting representations for the functions R_n of best approximation in the L^2-norm.

Gončar studies *overconvergence* of sequences of rational functions R_n. If a series $\sum_{n=1}^{\infty} R_n$ converges with abnormal rapidity in a domain D, then it converges also outside of D **[74, 75]**.

13. Other types of approximation

1. *Nonlinear approximation.* Here we have only the deep investigation of Vituškin **[10]**.

2. *Weighted uniform approximation by polynomials.* After the expository articles by Ahiezer **[11]** and Mergeljan **[14]**, not much has been published in this field. Mergeljan **[107]** studies the degree of approximation with weight of the function $(x - a)^{-1}$, Im $a \neq 0$, by polynomials on $[-\infty, +\infty]$. See also Tonjan **[132]**. Hačatrjan **[80]** gives necessary and sufficient conditions for the weight function $\phi(x)$ under which the polynomials are dense, in the norm

$$\|f\| = \sup_{-\infty<x<+\infty} \{f(x)/\phi(x)\},$$

in the class of all entire functions f of degree zero, for which $\|f\| < +\infty$.

3. *Approximation by piecewise polynomial functions.* Brudnyĭ and Gopengauz **[35]** approximate a function $f \in C[0, 1]$ in the following way. Let $r = 1, 2, \cdots$, and the points $-1 \leqq t_1 <, \cdots < t_r \leqq 1$ be given. For $\nu = 0, 1, \cdots, n-1$, the points $x_\mu^{(n,\nu)} = (2\nu + 1 + t_\mu)/(2n)$, $\mu = 1, \cdots, r$, are obtained from the t_μ by a linear map of $[-1, +1]$ onto $I_\nu = [\nu/n, (\nu + 1)/n]$. Let $P_{r,n}(f, x)$ be the function which at $[\nu/n, (\nu + 1)/n]$ is identical with the polynomial which interpolates f at the points x_μ. Thus, in contrast with spline interpolation, we do not care about bad fit (discontinuities) at the joints ν/n. Let

$$\tau_{r,n}(f) = \sup_{k\leqq n} \|f - P_{r,k}(f)\|.$$

The $\tau_{r,n}(f)$ describe the differential—or difference properties of f better, than the ordinary degrees of approximation $E_n(f)$. The simplest examples are: $\omega_r(f, 1/n) \approx \tau_{r,n}(f)$ as $n \to \infty$ for all r without exception; a function $f \in C[0, 1]$ has a derivative $f^{(r)} \in \mathrm{Lip}_M\, 1$ if and only if $\tau_{r+1,n}(f) \leqq M[(r + 1)!2^{2r+1}n^{r+1}]^{-1}$, $n = 1, 2, \cdots$ (for some special selection of the t_μ).

4. Ofman **[111]** considers approximation of functions $f(x, y)$ in a rectangle (with sides parallel to the axes) by sums $\phi(x) + \psi(y)$ of arbitrary functions ϕ, ψ of one variable. He notices the importance of the special closed polygons, formed by horizontal and vertical segments, for the computation of the degree of approximation; he proves that the moduli of continuity of the functions of some extremal

pair ϕ, ψ do not exceed the modulus of continuity of the original function f.

5. The paper of A. F. Timan **[131]** deals with the approximation of functions $f(x)$, $0 \leqq x < +\infty$ by functions $g \in H^\omega$, which satisfy $|g(x)_1 - g(x_1)| \leqq \omega(|x_1 - x_2|)$.

14. **Approximation of functions of a complex variable.** Al′per **[19]** computes explicitly, by a direct application of Kolmogorov's theorem, the degree of approximation of some elementary functions. The expository paper of Suetin **[17]** deals with many aspects of the theory of Faber polynomials. Dzjadyk, in a series of important papers **[44, 47, 48, 49]** studies the degree of approximation of functions f, which are continuous on a compact set K, bounded by a curve C, and analytic in the interior points of K, by polynomials of degree n. Let $w = \Phi(z)$ be the conformal map of the exterior of K onto the exterior of the circle $|z| = \rho$, with $\Phi(z)/z \to 1$ as $z \to \infty$, and let $z = \Psi(w)$ be the inverse map. The difference $f(z) - P_n(z)$ is estimated in terms of $\rho_n(z)$, the distance from $z \in K$ to the level curve $|\Phi(z)| = 1 + n^{-1}$. If $K = [-1, +1]$, then $\rho_n(z)$, $z \in K$ has the order of $\Delta_n(z) = \max\,(n^{-2}, n^{-1}\sqrt{1 - z^2})$. Dzjadyk obtains theorems, which in this degenerate case reduce to results such as (8), discussed in §10. In **[44]**, Dzjadyk studies the properties of level curves $|\Phi(z)| = \text{Const.}$, and develops inequalities for the derivatives of polynomials on such curves. They are then used to derive the inverse theorems of approximation. The other papers deal with direct theorems. One of the results is as follows. Let C consist of finitely many sufficiently smooth arcs, which at the points of join form with each other angles α, $0 < \alpha < \pi$. Then a function f on K has a derivative $f^{(r)}$ on K for which $f^{(r)} \in \text{Lip}\,\alpha$, $r = 0, 1, \cdots$, $0 < \alpha \leqq 1$, if and only if

$$|f(z) - P_n(z)| \leqq \text{Const}\ \rho_n(z)^{r+\alpha} \tag{9}$$

for some sequence of polynomials P_n. Other theorems involve the degree of smoothness of the boundary. Results similar to (9) have been given by Sewell (*Degree of approximation by polynomials in the complex domain*, Princeton Univ. Press, 1942), but Dzjadyk's results go much farther. One of the tools of the theory is the "analytic transformation" $f_g(z) = D(z)$ of two functions f, g, of which f is analytic, and g periodic:

$$D(z) = \frac{1}{4\pi^2 i}\int_{-\pi}^{\pi} g(t)\,dt \int_C \frac{f\{\Psi[\Phi(\zeta)e^{it}]}{\zeta - z}\,d\zeta. \tag{10}$$

If g is the Jackson kernel, and $K = [-1, +1]$, then D is the algebraic polynomial of degree n, which has been used by A. F. Timan to prove (8).

Let A be a bounded set in the plane. Vituškin (**[140, 141]**; see also **[8]**) gives, in terms of the analytic capacity γ (= Ahlfors measure) of some sets, necessary and sufficient conditions in order that each function, uniformly continuous on A, be uniformly approximable by analytic functions, harmonic functions, or by rational functions. His results should be compared with the well-known theorems of

Mergeljan. For example: let A be closed, then each continuous function on A is uniformly approximable by rational functions if and only if for each closed domain D, $\gamma(C(A) \cap D) = \gamma(D)$. Gončar **[76, 77]** discusses approximation by harmonic functions. Some papers of Havinson, for example **[85]** deal with approximation by rational functions of the form $\sum_{k=1}^{n} \lambda_k(z - a_k)^{-1}$.

15. **Approximation of classes of functions.** If K is a class of functions $K \subset C[A]$, then the degree of approximation of K is defined by

$$E_n(K) = \sup_{f \in K} E_n(f). \tag{11}$$

The famous theorem of Favard gives the degree of approximation of the class W^p of p-times differentiable 2π-periodic functions (see §5 for the definition of this and other classes). Babenko **[21]** found $E_n(A_r^p) = R^{p-n}/[n(n-1)\cdots(n-p+1)]$, $R > 1, p = 0, 1, \cdots, n \geqq p$. The class A_R^p consists of the functions $f(z)$, analytic in $|z| < R$, which have a derivative with the property $|f^{(p)}(z)| \leqq 1$, $|z| < R$, and the approximation is by algebraic polynomials in the uniform norm on $|z| \leqq 1$.

Using Favard's theorem for $p = 1$ (the classes $\text{Lip}_1\ 1$ and W^1 are identical) and the approximation by polygonal lines, Korneĭčuk **[96]** determines the degree of the trigonometric approximation of the class H_1^ω, where $\omega(h)$ is a *concave* modulus of continuity: $E_{n-1}(H_1^\omega) = \omega(\pi/n)/2$. Thus $E_{n-1}(\text{Lip}_1\ \alpha) = (\pi/n)^\alpha/2$. A. F. Timan **[129]** gives an especially transparent proof of this. In a similar way, Korneĭčuk finds **[93, 97]** $E_n(W^pH_1^\omega)$, for $p = 1, 2, 3$, but not for larger values of p. He also proves **[95]** that in Jackson's estimate $E_{n-1}(f) \leqq A\omega(f, \pi/n)$, $n = 1, 2, \cdots$, of the degree of trigonometric approximation of an arbitrary function $f \in C^*$, the smallest possible constant A is $A = 1$. In this connection, we mention a similar result for special operators by P. C. Sikkema (Numer. Math. **3** (1961), 107–116). For Bernšteĭn polynomials $B_n(f)$, the smallest C in the relation $\|f - B_n(f)\| \leqq C\omega(f, n^{-1})$ is $C = (4306 + 837\sqrt{6})/5832$; this value is attained only for $n = 6$.

The importance of the classes W_α^r (see §6) lies in the fact that for $\alpha = r$, $W_\alpha^r = W^r$ is the class of functions $f \in C^*$ with $|f^{(r)}(x)| \leqq 1$ a.e., while for $\alpha = r + 1$ we obtain the conjugate class $\tilde{W}^r$, which consists of functions $\tilde{f}$, for which $f \in W^r$. We consider here also fractional derivatives, so that $r > 0$ is not necessarily an integer. After preliminary work by Dzjadyk ($r = \alpha$, $0 < r < 1$) and Stečkin, Dzjadyk **[45]** found the degrees of approximation $E_n(W^r)$, $E_n(\tilde{W}^r)$ for all $r > 0$, in the uniform and the L^1-norm. Sun' (**[120' 121]**, also Chinese Math. **3** (1963), 196–217, MR **20**, 3996b) found the degree of approximation of W_α^r for all $r \geqq 1$, and also for $0 < \alpha < r \leqq 1$, and for $0 < r < 1$ and $2 - r < \alpha$. See also Sun' **[119]**.

Functions of the class W^r are convolutions of bounded functions with a fixed kernel $K_n(t)$, which has an absolutely monotone derivative on a semi-axis. One obtains $E_n(W^r)$ in the C-norm by approximating the kernel K_n in the L^1-norm. The main content of Dzjadyk's papers **[45, 46]** is not the approximation of the special kernels K_n. His results are more general. He is able to find the exact value of the degree of the trigonometric approximation, in the L^1-norm, of wide classes of functions which are indefinite integrals of absolutely monotone functions, defined on a semi-axis or on an interval.

16. **Entropy.** In the paper (Lorentz, *Metric entropy, widths, and superpositions of functions*, Amer. Math. Monthly **69** (1962), 269–285 = [A]) I have reviewed results achieved in these fields until about 1960. I will assume that this paper is known to the reader and sketch the development since that time.

The entropy is a characteristic of a compact metric set A. It is a function of the argument $\varepsilon > 0$, $H_\varepsilon(A)$, $= \log N_\varepsilon(A)$, where $N_\varepsilon(A)$ is the smallest number of sets in an ε-covering of A. The asymptotic behavior of $H_\varepsilon(A)$ for $\varepsilon \to 0$ describes the set A. An exposition of this theory is given in the review by Kolmogorov and Tihomirov [**13**] and in Vituškin's book [**10**]. See also the biographical sketch of Tihomirov [**127**]. In the papers of Erohin [**59**] and Al′per [**20**], entropies of sets of analytic functions are computed, Kotljar [**100**] and Brudnyĭ and Kotljar [**36**] deal with sets of smooth functions, in Smoljak [**117**], the functions of the set are characterized by the asymptotic behavior of their Fourier coefficients. In the papers of Tihomirov [**126**] and A. F. Timan [**130**] known estimates are made more precise.

Quantities similar to $N_\varepsilon(A)$ can be defined for a subset A of a linear topological space X. Let U be a neighborhood of the origin in X, and let $N_\varepsilon(A, U)$ be the smallest number of translations $x + U$ of the set U which cover A. Kolmogorov [**92**] introduced a topological invariant of X—*the approximative dimension* of X—which is defined in terms of the asymptotic behavior of $N_\varepsilon(A, U)$ as $\varepsilon \to 0$ for all compact subsets A of X. By means of this invariant, Kolmogorov proves that the spaces of analytic functions of s variables, on a given domain D and with the topology of uniform convergence on compact subsets of D, are topologically different for different s. This work has been continued by Pelczynski and other Polish mathematicians (compare the article of S. Rolewicz, *On spaces of holomorphic functions*, Studia Math. **21** (1962), 135–160).

Another outgrowth of these ideas has been the characterization, in terms of the functions $N_\varepsilon(A, U)$, of the nuclear spaces among all linear topological spaces of type (F). This has been done by Gel′fand and Vilenkin [**2**] for some special spaces and by Mitjagin [**15**] in full generality. Further papers related to entropy are Brudnyĭ and A. F. Timan [**37**] and Garkavi [**66**].

17. **Widths.** If $\Phi = \{\phi_1, \cdots, \phi_n\}$ are given functions in $C[A]$,

$$E_n^\Phi = \inf_{a_i} \|f - \textstyle\sum_1^n a_i\phi_i\|,$$

$K \subset C[A]$ a class of continuous functions, $E_n^\Phi(K) = \sup_{f\in K} E_n(f)$, then

$$d_n(K) = \inf_{\Phi} E_n^\Phi(K) \tag{12}$$

is the nth width of K (Kolmogorov). Tihomirov [**16**] has found a method of the determination of widths based on a theorem of Borsuk about vector fields on an n-dimensional sphere. From this theorem the following lemma can be derived. If B is the closed unit ball in an $(n + 1)$-dimensional subspace X_{n+1} of a Banach space X, then the nth width of B in X (not in X_{n+1}!) is $d_n(B) = 1$. Using this, it is easy to prove that for many classical subsets K of C^* (for which the degree of the trigonometric approximation is known), the trigonometric system is the *extremal system*, for which the infimum in (12) is attained. This determines, of course, also the widths d_n. For the polynomial approximation of non-periodic functions on an interval, for example on $[-\pi, \pi]$, the situation is quite different. Tihomirov [**16**, p. 108] states that for $W^p \subset C[-\pi, \pi]$, $p = 1, 2, \cdots$,

$$d_n(W^p) = 2^p K_p n^{-p}(1 + O(n^{-1})), \tag{13}$$

where K_p is the Favard constant. This is important, since by a theorem of Nikol′skiĭ and Bernšteĭn [**1**, vol. 2, pp. 413–415], for the approximation by algebraic polynomials, $E_n(W^p) \sim \pi^p K_p n^{-p}$. Thus, the algebraic polynomials are by far not the most effective system of approximation of functions from W^p. This fact is beyond doubt. However, Tihomirov's proof of (13) is convincing only for odd values of p. Babenko [**22**] estimates the widths of classes of type W^p for periodic functions of several variables, using the method of eigenvalues of Kolmogorov. Mitjagin [**109**] treats the problem with a fresh approach. He uses theorems on multipliers of Fourier series, in particular some delicate results of Marcinkiewicz. Classes of functions which can be treated in this way are given by the inequality $\|Df\|_p \leqq 1$, where $1 \leqq p \leqq +\infty$, and $D = P(\partial/\partial x)$ is a differential operator in several variables, $P(u)$ being a polynomial with constant coefficients.

18. **Superpositions of functions.** Kolmogorov proved in 1956 the existence of 10 increasing continuous functions ϕ_k, ψ_k, $k = 1, \cdots, 5$ of one variable, defined on $[0, 1]$ such that for each function $f(x, y)$ of two variables on the square $0 \leqq x$, $y \leqq 1$, there exist 5 continuous functions g_k defined each on the range of $\phi_k(x) + \psi_k(y)$ with the property that

$$f(x, y) = \sum_{k=1}^{5} g_k(\phi_k(x) + \psi_k(y)). \tag{14}$$

It has been observed (paper [A] of §16) that one can take one function g instead of the g_k, defined on the range of all $\phi_k + \psi_k$, and that ϕ_k, ψ_k can be assumed to belong to a class Lip α, for some $\alpha > 0$. D. Sprecher observed that one can assume $\psi_k = A\phi_k$, $k = 1, \cdots, 5$, where A is some constant.

It has been conjectured that the ϕ_k, ψ_k cannot be very smooth. Vituškin [**142, 143**] and Henkin [**86**] prove the following. For an arbitrary natural N, let $\phi_k(x, y)$, $\psi_k(x, y)$, $k = 1, \cdots, N$, be given functions which are continuous for all x, y, and the ϕ_k also continuously differentiable, let D be a region of the plane. Then there exist natural numbers m, n for which $(x + my)^n$ is not representable in D in the form

$$\sum_{k=1}^{N} \psi_k(x, y) g_k(\phi_k(x, y)), \tag{15}$$

where g_k are arbitrary bounded measurable functions. The proof is not constructive, and uses entropy methods.

19. **Linear polynomial operators.** Let $L_n(f, x)$ be a linear operator which maps C^* (or $C[a, b]$) into itself. If its values are trigonometric (or algebraic) polynomials of degree n, then L_n is a trigonometric (or algebraic) polynomial operator of degree n. The theorem of Nikolaev-Lozinskiĭ-Haršiladze states that if in addition L_n preserves each polynomial of degree n, then $L_n(f) \to f$ as $n \to \infty$ cannot hold for all continuous functions f. First theorems of this type are due to Faber (Jahresbericht Deutsch. Math. Verein. **23** (1914), 192–210). In a long series of papers, Berman [**26–29**] treats this theory. The main problems are divergence theorems, operators of a certain class with the minimal norm, and the representation formula of Faber-Marcinkiewicz-Zygmund-Berman. See also Sapogov [**114, 115**]. The partial sums of Fourier series and the de la Vallée-Poussin sums play a special role among the polynomial operators, and many results of sections 5 and 6 are important here. Korneĭčuk [**94**] shows very simply that if ω is a concave modulus of continuity which is not linear, then a linear polynomial operator of degree $n - 1$ can approximate the class H_1^ω with an error equal to $E_{n-1}(H_1^\omega)$. The reader will find a detailed review of this theory in the article of M. Golomb in these Proceedings (see p. 83).

20. **Positive linear operators.** The importance of positive linear operators in the approximation theory has been recognized by Korovkin, see his book [**5**]. For a sequence $L_n(f, x)$ of positive linear operators which map $C[a, b]$ onto itself one has for example: (a) $L_n(f) \to f$ for all $f \in C[a, b]$ if and only if this relation holds for the three functions, $f_k(x) = x^k$, $k = 0, 1, 2$; (b) the degree of approximation of functions $f \in C[a, b]$ by $L_n(f)$ cannot be better than $O(n^{-2})$. New are asymptotic formulas for the difference $f(x) - L_n(f, x)$, see Korovkin [**98**], Mamedov [**102–104**]. For example, one has

$$\lim_{n\to\infty} \frac{L_n(f, x) - f(x) - \sum_{k=1}^{2m-1} \tau_n^k f^{(k)}(x)/k!}{L_n(\psi, x) - \psi(x) - \sum_{k=1}^{2m-1} \tau_n^k \psi^{(k)}(x)/k!} = \frac{f^{(2m)}(x)}{\psi^{(2m)}(x)}, \tag{16}$$

(where f, ψ are $2m$ times differentiable at x, and $\tau_n^k = L_n(\phi_k, x)$, $\phi_k(t) = (t - x)^k$), if and only if $\tau_n^{2m+2j}/\tau_n^{2m} \to 0$ as $n \to \infty$ for at least one $j = 1, 2, \cdots$. See Mamedov [**106**] for an application to saturation classes.

Another series of papers deals with special positive linear operators of C^* into itself, given by a convolution $L_n(f, x) = (f * u_n)(x)$, where u_n is a trigonometric polynomial

$$u_n(t) = \tfrac{1}{2} + \sum_{k=1}^{n} \rho_k^{(n)} \cos kt \geqq 0, \qquad 0 \leqq t \leqq \pi. \tag{17}$$

We quote among others Korovkin [**98, 99**], Bausov [**24**], Petrov [**113**]. For operators of this type one can study their approximation on classes Z_α. A function

$f \in C^*$ belongs to Z_α if it satisfies the inequality $|f(x+t) - 2f(x) + f(x-t)| \leqq |t|^\alpha$. In [**98, 113**] the asymptotic behavior for $n \to \infty$ of $\inf_{u_n} \sup_{f \in Z_\alpha} \|f - L_n(f)\|$, $\alpha = 1, 2$ is determined, where the infimum is taken over all polynomials u_n of type (17).

Let $f_1, \cdots, f_m \in C[a, b]$. Baskakov [**23**] determines all functions f for which $L_n(f_i) \to f_i$, $n \to \infty$, $i = 1, \cdots, m$ implies $L_n(f) \to f$, for each sequence of positive linear operators L_n. A system of continuous functions $f_0, \cdots, f_m$ on a compact Hausdorff space A is a K-system of order m if for each sequence $L_n(f)$ of positive linear operators on $C[A]$, $L_n(f_i) \to f_i$, $i = 0, \cdots, m$ implies $L_n(f) \to f$ for all $f \in C[A]$. In his interesting paper [**116**], Šaškin (see also Volkov [**146**]) studies the topological properties of A, which follow from the existence on A of K-systems of a given order. He gives necessary and sufficient conditions for K-systems (in terms of properties of matrices $\|f_i(x_j)\|$); if $1, f_1(x), \cdots, f_m(x)$ is a K-system on A, then A can be homeomorphically imbedded into R_m in such a way that no three points of the image are on one straight line. There are K-systems on A if and only if A has finite dimension. For certain compact sets A, $f_0, \cdots, f_m$ is a K-system if and only if it has Čebyšev rank (see §3) $m - 2$.

21. **Saturation classes.** Saturation classes for summation methods of Fourier series have been defined by Favard. Determination of saturation classes of many methods is due to Zamansky, Favard, Butzer, Alexicz, Sunouchi and Watari, and Haršiladze [**81**]. Tureckiĭ [**135, 136**] gives a general theory of saturation classes. Let Λ be a triangular matrix (λ_{nk}), and let the sequence of operators be given by

$$L_n(f, x) = \tfrac{1}{2}a_0 + \sum_{k=1}^{n} \lambda_{nk}(a_k \cos kx + b_k \sin kx),$$

where a_k, b_k are the Fourier coefficients of the function $f \in C^*$. Assume that $\phi(n)$ is a function of n which tends to zero as $n \to \infty$, and let $K \subset C^*$. Assume that $\|f - L_n(f)\| = O(\phi(n))$ holds if and only if $f \in K$; and that $\|f - L_n(f)\| = o(\phi(n))$ holds only if f is a constant (or some other "trivial" function, for example a trigonometric polynomial of a fixed degree m). Then K is the saturation class of the operators L_n, and $\phi(n)$ is the optimal approximation order. Tureckiĭ assumes that, for some integer p, and a constant C, $(1 - \lambda_{nk})/\phi(n) \to d_0 k^p + \cdots + d_p$, as $n \to \infty$, and that

$$\|L_n(f)\| \leqq C \|f\|. \tag{18}$$

He deduces then that $\phi(n)$ is the optimal order of approximation, and that the saturation class K consists of all $f \in C^*$ for which $f^{(p-1)} \in \text{Lip } 1$ (if p is even) or $\tilde{f}^{(p-1)} \in \text{Lip } 1$ (if p is odd). However, his proof (in the part which uses (18) [**136**, pp. 420–422]) is not convincing. Mamedov [**106**] formulates saturation theorems for positive operators L_n on $C[a, b]$ or C^*.

22. **Interpolation, quadrature formulas.** Let $x_{k,n}$, $k = 1, \cdots, n$, $n = 1, 2, \cdots$ be a triangular matrix of interpolation nodes in $[-1, +1]$, and let $\omega_n(x) = \prod_1^n (x - x_{kn})$. The matrix (x_{kn}) is called normal if $\omega_n''(x_{k,n})(x - x_{k,n})/\omega_n'(x_{k,n}) \leqq 1$

for $-1 \leqq x \leqq 1$. Erdös and Turan have conjectured some 25 years ago (Ann. of Math **38** (1937), 142–155; **39** (1938), 703–724; **41** (1940), 510–553) that for a normal matrix of nodes, $|\omega_n(x)| \leqq C(\varepsilon)2^{-n}$, $-1 + \varepsilon \leqq x \leqq 1 - \varepsilon$, $(\varepsilon > 0)$. This is proved by T. Frey **[61a]**. This result has important applications to convergence problems of the Lagrange and Hermite-Fejér interpolation polynomials.

Korobov **[97a, 97b]** selects the nodes of quadrature formulas by number-theoretic methods. Let E_s^α denote the class of functions

$$f(x_1, \cdots, x_s) = \sum_{m_1, \cdots, m_s = -\infty}^{+\infty} c_{m_1 \cdots m_s} \exp 2\pi i(m_1 x_1 + \cdots + m_s x_s),$$

$0 \leqq x_j \leqq 1$, $j = 1, \cdots, s$, for which the Fourier coefficients satisfy

$$|c_{m_1, \ldots, m_s}| \leqq \text{Const.}\ \bar{m}_1^{-\alpha} \cdots \bar{m}_s^{-\alpha},\ \bar{m}_j = \max(1, |m_j|).$$

Let $\{b\}$ denote the fractional part of the real number b, let N be a prime. Korobov proves the existence of $a_1, \cdots, a_s$, for which

$$(19)\quad \int_0^1 \cdots \int_0^1 f(x_1, \cdots, x_s)\, dx_1 \cdots dx_s = N^{-1} \sum_{k=1}^{N} f(\{ka_1/N\}, \cdots, \{ka_s/N\}) + R,$$

where $|R| \leqq \text{Const.}\ N^{-\alpha+\varepsilon}$, $\varepsilon > 0$. For N uniformly distributed nodes one gets a larger error, of order of $N^{-\alpha/s}$. There are applications to interpolation (Smoljak **[117a]**), integral equations. See also Rjaben'kiĭ **[113a]**, Sobol' **[117b]**, Solodov **[117f]**.

S. L. Sobolev **[117c, 117d, 117e]** studies quadrature formulas $\int_S f(x)\, dS \cong \sum_{k=1}^n c_k f(x_k)$ for functions f defined on the surface S of the n-dimensional unit ball. He considers formulas which are invariant under certain groups of rotations of S, and determines those of them which are exact for all spherical harmonics of a given degree, and have the smallest possible n.

23. **Books and journals.** The following books entirely or partly on Approximation Theory have appeared since 1958:

1. V. I. Krylov, *Approximate calculation of integrals*, (1959) **[6]**. This excellent book considers the problem mainly from a theoretical point of view, but has many useful practical hints.

2. *Mathematics in USSR during forty years*, 1917–1957, (1959) **[7]**. There exist similar issues for 1917–1937 and for 1917–1947. The first volume contains, among others, the articles:

S. M. Lozinskiĭ and I. P. Natanson, *Metric and constructive theory of functions of a real variable*, pp. 295–380.

S. N. Mergeljan, *Approximations of functions of a complex variable*, pp. 383–397.

The articles describe the progress in these fields achieved by Russian mathematicians in 1917–1957, but mainly in 1947–1957.

Volume 2 contains a complete bibliography of Russian mathematicians in 1917–1957, and useful biographical data about the authors.

3. A. G. Vituškin, *The estimation of complexity of the tabulation problem*, (1960) [**10**]. The real subject of this book is nonlinear approximation, mainly inverse theorems. The first half of the book brings an exposition of the theory of entropy, as developed by Kolmogorov, the author, and others.

4. P. P. Korovkin, *Linear operators and approximation theory*, (1959) [**5**]. This book is an elementary text, written for the students of Teachers Institutes, rather than for University students. The role of positive operators is stressed. In the English translation (Hindustan Publ. Corp., Dehli, 1960) the book has lost much of its charm.

5. A. F. Timan, *Theory of approximation of functions of a real variable*, (1960) [**9**]. This book is an encyclopaedia of the subject until 1959, and contains a wealth of results. Calculations, rather than principles are stressed.

6. D. G. Grebenjuk, *Polynomials of best approximation, whose coefficients satisfy linear relations*, (1960) [**3**]. This is an extension of old investigations of V. A. Markov, Pšeborskiĭ, and Shohat.

7. *Investigations on modern problems of the constructive theory of functions*, (1961) [**4**]. This book contains 76 articles of different authors on approximation of functions and related subjects. The duplication with journal papers is considerable. However, some of the articles contain a useful review of the field in question.

8. V. I. Smirnov and N. A. Lebedev, *Constructive theory of functions of a complex variable*, (1964) [**8**]. This book contains: Chapter 1. Interpolation, transfinite diameters, convergence and divergence of interpolation polynomials, theorems of Mergeljan and Vituškin on approximation by polynomials and by rational functions in a domain; Chapter 2. Faber polynomials; Chapter 3. Quadratic approximation of functions in a domain, orthogonal functions in a domain; Chapter 4. Functions orthogonal on a contour; Chapter 5. Uniform approximation: polynomials least deviating from zero, inequalities of Markov, Bernšteĭn and their generalizations, approximation by generalized polynomials.

In addition to the books, very useful are also the reviews in the journal Uspehi Mat. Nauk, for example [**11–18**]. This journal also contains descriptions of doctoral dissertations, of some papers accepted for publication, etc.

BIBLIOGRAPHY

ABBREVIATIONS:

Dokl. = Doklady Akademii Nauk SSSR
Izv. = Izvestija Akad. Nauk SSSR, Serija Matem.
Mat. Sb. = Matematičeskiĭ Sbornik
Trudy = Trudy Matem. Instituta im. V. A. Steklova
Uspehi = Uspehi Matematičeskih Nauk
M. R. = Mathematical Reviews. M.R. **A**, B means M.R. vol. **A**, p. B, or vol. **A**, #B.
Zbl. = Zentralblatt für Mathematik und ihre Grenzgebiete

A. BOOKS

1. S. N. Bernšteĭn, *Collected works*, Izdat. Akad. Nauk SSSR, Moscow. Vol. 1, *The constructive theory of functions* [1905–1930], 581 pp., 1952, M.R. **14,** 2. Vol. 2, *The constructive theory of functions* [1931–1953], 627 pp., 1954, M.R. **16,** 433.

2. I. M. Gel′fand and N. Ja. Vilenkin, *Generalized functions*. No. 4, *Some applications of harmonic analysis. Equipped Hilbert spaces*, Fizmatgiz, Moscow, 1962, 472 pp., M.R. **26,** 4173.

3. D. G. Grebenjuk, *Polynomials of best approximation, whose coefficients satisfy linear relations*, Izdat. Akad. Nauk Uzbek. SSR, Taškent, 1960, 239 pp., M.R. **25,** 376.

4. *Investigations in modern problems of the constructive theory of functions*, V. I. Smirnov, editor, Fizmatgiz, Moscow, 1961, 368pp.

5. P. P. Korovkin, *Linear operators and approximation theory*, Fizmatgiz, Moscow, 1959, M.R. **27,** 561.

6. V. I. Krylov, *Approximate calculation of integrals*, Fizmatgiz, Moscow, 1959, 327pp., M.R. **22,** 2002.

7. *Mathematics in USSR during forty years*, 1917–1957, Fizmatgiz, Moscow, 1959, Vol. 1, 1002pp., Vol. 2, 819pp.

8. V. I. Smirnov and N. A. Lebedev, *Constructive theory of functions of a complex variable*, Nauka, Moscow-Leningrad, 1964, 438pp.

9. A. F. Timan, *The theory of approximation of functions of a real variable*, Fizmatgiz, Moscow, 1960, 624pp., M.R. **22,** 8257.

10. A. G. Vituškin, *The estimation of the complexity of the tabulation problem*, Fizmatgiz, Moscow, 1959, 228pp., M.R. **22,** 8265.

B. REVIEWS

11. N. I. Ahiezer, *On weighted approximations of continuous functions by polynomials on the entire axis*, Uspehi **11** (1956), No. 4 (70), 3–43, M.R. **18,** 802.

12. A. O. Gel′fond, *On uniform approximations by polynomials with integral rational coefficients*, Uspehi **10** (1955), No. 1 (63), 41–65, M.R. **17,** 30.

13. A. N. Kolmogorov and V. M. Tihomirov, *ε-entropy and ε-capacity of sets in functional spaces*, Uspehi **14** (1959), No. 2 (86), 3–86, M.R. **22,** 2890.

14. S. N. Mergeljan, *Weighted approximations by polynomials*, Uspehi **11** (1956), No. 5 (71), 107–152, M.R. **18,** 734.

15. B. S. Mitjagin, *Approximative dimension and bases in nuclear spaces*, Uspehi **16** (1961), No. 4 (100), 63–132, M.R. **27,** 2837.

16. V. M. Tihomirov, *Widths of sets in functional spaces and the theory of best approximations*, Uspehi **15** (1960), No. 3 (93) 81–120, M.R. **22,** 8268.

17. P. K. Suetin, *Fundamental properties of Faber's polynomials*, Uspehi **19** (1964), No. 4 (118), 125–154.

18. S. I. Zuhovickiĭ, *On approximation of real functions in the sense of P. L. Čebyšev*, Uspehi **11** (1956), No. 2 (68), 125–159, M.R. **19,** 30.

C. ARTICLES

19. S. Ja. Al′per, *Asymptotic values of best approximation of analytic functions in a complex domain*, Uspehi **14** (1959), No. 1 (85), 131–134, M.R. **21,** 3577.

20. S. Ja. Al′per, *On ε-entropy of certain classes of functions*, Dokl. **132** (1960), 977–979, M.R. **23,** A 3992.

21. K. I. Babenko, *On the best approximation of a class of analytic functions*, Izv. **22** (1958), 631–640, M.R. **23,** A 1048.

22. K. I. Babenko, *Approximation of periodic functions of several variables by trigonometric polynomials*, I, II, Dokl. **132** (1960), 247–250, M.R. **22,** 12341; Dokl. **132** (1960), 982–985, M.R. **22,** 12342.

23. V. A. Baskakov, *On some convergence criteria for linear, positive operators*, Uspehi **16** (1961), No. 1 (97), 131–134, M.R. **23,** A 3470.

24. L. I. Bausov, *The order of approximation of functions of class Z_α by linear positive polynomial operators*, Uspehi **17** (1962), No. 1 (103) 149–155, M.R. **27,** 1756.

25. E. A. Berdihina, *Simultaneous approximation of functions and of their derivatives*, Izv. **28** (1964), 757–772.

26. D. L. Berman, *A series of papers on linear polynomial operators in the Doklady.*

I: **120** (1958), 1175–1177, M.R. **20,** 5387;
II: **138** (1961), 747–750, M.R. **24,** A 962;
III: **140** (1961), 519–521, M.R. **24,** A 2835;
IV: **143** (1962), 759–762, M.R. **24,** A 3463;
V: **144** (1962), 467–470, M.R. **25,** 2367;
VI: **144** (1962), 951–953, M.R. **26,** 4180;
VII: **151** (1963), 755–757, M.R. **27,** 1827;
VIII: **153** (1963), 9–11, M.R. **28,** 473;
IX: **155** (1964), 17–19, M.R. **28,** 5143.

27. D. L. Berman, *Linear trigonometric polynomial operators in spaces of almost-periodic functions*, Mat. Sb. **49** (1959), 267–280, M.R. **22,** 3942.

28. D. L. Berman, *Linear polynomial operators on groups*, Izv. Vysš. Učeb. Zaved. Matematika, (1960), No. 4 (17), 17–28, M.R. **24,** A 3230.

29. D. L. Berman, *Extremal problems of the theory of polynomial operators*, Mat. Sb. **60** (1963), 354–365, M.R. **27,** 516.

30. R. P. Boas and K. I. Rahman, *Some inequalities for polynomials and entire functions*, Dokl. **147** (1962), 11–12, M.R. **26,** 2610.

31. V. G. Boltjanskiĭ, S. S. Ryškov and Ju. A. Šaškin, *On k-regular imbeddings and their application to the theory of approximation of functions*, Uspehi **15** (1960), No. 6 (96), 125–132, M.R. **23,** A 2867.

32. Ju. A. Brudnyĭ, *Approximation by entire functions on the exterior of an interval and on a semi-axis*, Izv. **23** (1959), 595–612, M.R. **22,** 1690.

33. Ju. A. Brudnyĭ, *Generalization of a theorem of A. F. Timan*, Dokl. **148** (1963), 1237–40, M.R. **26,** 4096.

34. Ju. A. Brudnyĭ and I. E. Gopengauz, *On the measure of the set of maximal deviation*, Izv. **24** (1960), 129–144, M.R. **22,** 11130.

35. Ju. A. Brudnyĭ and I. E. Gopengauz, *Approximation by piecewise polynomial functions*, Izv. **27** (1963), 723–746, M.R. **28,** 396.

36. Ju. A. Brudnyĭ and B. D. Kotljar, *The order of growth of ε-entropy for certain compact classes of functions*, Dokl. **148** (1963), 1001–1004, M.R. **26,** 4102.

37. Ju. A. Brudnyĭ and A. F. Timan, *Constructive characteristics of compact sets in Banach spaces and ε-entropy*, Dokl. **126** (1959), 927–930, M.R. **22,** 2891.

38. B. L. Dincen, *Deviation of analytic functions from the arithmetic means of Faber series*, Dokl. **157** (1964), 250–253.

39. Kiril Dočev, *On a theorem of S. Bernšteĭn*, Dokl. **146** (1962), 17–19, M.R. **26,** 532.

40. E. P. Dolženko, *The rapidity of approximation by rational fractions and properties of functions*, Mat. Sb. **56** (1962), 403–432, M.R. **26,** 1671.

41. E. P. Dolženko, *On the properties of functions of several variables, sufficiently well approximable by rational functions*, Izv. **26** (1962), 641–652, M.R. **26,** 6658.

42. E. P. Dolženko, *Estimates of derivatives of rational functions*, Izv. **27** (1963), 9–28, M.R. **26,** 6319.

43. V. K. Dzjadyk, *A further strengthening of Jackson's theorem on the approximation of continuous functions by ordinary polynomials*, Dokl. **121** (1958), 403–406, M.R. **21,** 249.

44. V. K. Dzjadyk, *On the problem of S. M. Nikol'skiĭ in the complex domain*, Izv. **23** (1959), 697–736, M.R. **22,** 865.

45. V. K. Dzjadyk, *On the best approximation on classes of periodic functions, defined by kernels which are integrals of absolutely monotone functions*, Izv. **23** (1959), 933–950, M.R. **22,** 2844.

46. V. K. Dzjadyk, *On the question of the best approximation of absolutely monotone and certain other functions in the metric L, by trigonometric polynomials*, Izv. **25** (1961), 173–238, M.R. **24,** A 386.

47. V. K. Dzjadyk, *On the problem of approximation of continuous functions in closed regions with corners and on the problem of S. M. Nikol'skiĭ*, Izv. **26** (1962), 797–824, M.R. **27,** 313.

48. V. K. Dzjadyk, *To the theory of approximation of analytic functions, continuous in closed regions, and on the problem of S. M. Nikol'skiĭ*. II, Izv. **27** (1963), 1135–1164, M.R. **27,** 4937b.

49. V. K. Dzjadyk, *Theorems on the transformation and approximation of analytic functions* Dokl. **151** (1963), 269–272, M.R. **27,** 4937a.

50. A. V. Efimov, *On the approximation of some classes of continuous functions by sums of Fourier and sums of Fejér*, Izv. **22** (1958), 81–116, M.R. **20,** 3417.

51. A. V. Efimov, *Approximation of functions with a given modulus of continuity, by Fourier sums*, Izv. **23** (1959), 115–134, M.R. **22,** 1787.

52. A. V. Efimov, *The approximation of periodic functions by the sums of de la Vallée-Poussin*, Izv. **23** (1959), 737–770, M.R. **22,** 9792a.

53. A. V. Efimov, *Approximation of continuous periodic functions by Fourier sums*, Izv. **24** (1960), 243–296, M.R. **22,** 9792b.

54. A. V. Efimov, *On the approximation of periodic functions by the sums of de la Vallée-Poussin*. II, Izv. **24** (1960), 431–468, M.R. **22,** 9792c.

55. A. V. Efimov, *On linear summability methods for Fourier series*, Izv. **24** (1960), 743–756, M.R. **23,** A 1204.

56. A. V. Efimov, *Linear methods of approximation of continuous periodic functions*, Mat. Sb. **54** (1961), 51–90, M.R. **26,** 6671.

57. A. V. Efimov, *Linear methods of approximating certain classes of continuous periodic functions*, Trudy **62** (1961), 3–47, M.R. **26,** 4103.

58. N. V. Efimov and S. B. Stečkin, *Some properties of Čebyšev sets*, 4 papers.
Dokl. **118** (1958), 17–19, M.R. **20,** 1947;
Dokl. **121** (1958), 582–585, M.R. **20,** 6026;
Dokl. **127** (1959), 254–257, M.R. **21,** 5883;
Dokl. **140** (1961), 522–524, M.R. **25,** 424.

59. V. D. Erohin, *The asymptotic behavior of ε-entropy of analytic functions*, Dokl. **120** (1958), 949–952, M.R. **21,** 1530.

60. V. Erohin, *On the best approximation of analytic functions by rational functions with free poles*, Dokl. **128** (1959), 29–32, M.R. **21,** 7312.

61. G. A. Fomin, *Linear methods of summation of Fourier series*, Mat. Sb. **65** (1964), 144–152.

61a. T. Frey, *Conditions of convergence of interpolation sequences which correspond to normal sequences of nodes. Proof of the conjecture of Erdös and Turan*, Mat. Sb. **54** (1961), 137–176, M.R. **26,** 6651.

62. I. M. Ganzburg, *Extension of an asymptotic formula of A. F. Timan to classes of functions with a given continuity modulus*, Izv. **27** (1963), 485–528, M.R. **27,** 2764.

63. A. L. Garkavi, *Dimensionality of polyhedra of best approximation for differentiable functions*, Izv. **23** (1959), 93–114, M.R. **21,** 3706.

64. A. L. Garkavi, *On the simultaneous approximation of a periodic function and of its derivatives by trigonometric polynomials*, Izv. **24** (1960), 103–128, M.R. **22,** 3921.

65. A. L. Garkavi, *Duality theorems for the approximation by elements of convex sets*, Uspehi **16** (1961), No. 4 (100), 141–145, M.R. **24,** A 2828.

66. A. L. Garkavi, *On the best net and the best section of a set in a normed space*, Izv. **26** (1962), 87–106, M.R. **25,** 429.

67. A. L. Garkavi, *On the best approximation by the elements of infinitely-dimensional subspaces of a certain class*, Mat. Sb. **62** (1963), 104–120, M.R. **27**, 6076.

68. A. L. Garkavi, *On Čebyšev and almost Čebyšev subspaces*, Dokl. **149** (1963), 1250–1255, M.R. **26**, 6737.

69. A. L. Garkavi, *Approximation properties of subspaces of finite defect in the space of continuous functions*, Dokl. **155** (1964), 513–516, M.R. **28**, 3320.

70. A. L. Garkavi, *Uniqueness of the solution of the L-problem of moments*, Izv. **28** (1964), 553–570, M.R. **28**, 1525.

71. A. L. Garkavi, *On Čebyšev and almost Čebyšev subspaces*, Izv. **28** (1964), 799–818, M.R. **28**, 2635.

72. E. G. Gol′šteĭn, *On an infinitely-dimensional analogue of the problem of linear programming*, Dokl. **140** (1961), 23–26, M.R. **25**, 371 (see also Dokl. **141** (1961), 274–276, M.R. **25**, 372 and Dokl. **144** (1962), 21–22, M.R. **25**, 2360).

73. A. A. Gončar, *Inverse theorems of best approximation by rational functions*, Izv. **25** (1961), 347–356, M.R. **23**, A 2685.

74. A. A. Gončar, *On overconvergence of sequences of rational functions*, Dokl. **141** (1961), 1019–1022, M.R. **26**, 300.

75. A. A. Gončar, *On series of rational functions*, Dokl. **143** (1962), 1246–1249, M.R. **25**, 357.

76. A. A. Gončar, *Uniform approximation of continuous functions by harmonic functions*, Izv. **27** (1963), 1239–1250, M.R. **28**, 2231.

77. A. A. Gončar, *Approximation of continuous functions by harmonic functions*, Dokl. **154** (1964), 503–506, M.R. **28**, 2390.

78. I. E. Gopengauz, *On the deviation of functions from the interpolation polynomials of Lagrange and Hermite*, Izv. **24** (1960), 297–308, M.R. **22**, 4904.

79. V. I. Gurariĭ, *On bases in spaces of continuous functions*, Dokl. **148** (1963), 493–495.

80. I. O. Hačatrjan, *On weighted approximation of entire functions of degree zero by polynomials on the real axis*, Dokl. **145** (1962), 744–747, M.R. **25**, 3311.

81. F. I. Haršiladze, *Saturation classes for some summation processes*, Dokl. **122** (1958), 352–355, Zbl. **88**, p. 50.

82. S. Ja. Havinson, *On uniqueness of functions of best approximation in the metric of the space L^1*, Izv. **22** (1958), 243–270, M.R. **21**, 254.

83. S. Ja. Havinson, *Some problems of completeness of systems*, Dokl. **137** (1961), 793–798, M.R. **23**, A 1044.

84. S. Ja. Havinson, *On two classes of extremal problems for polynomials and for moments*, Izv. **25** (1961), 557–590.

85. S. Ja. Havinson, *On approximation with account taken of the size of the coefficients of the approximants*, Trudy **60** (1961), 304–324, M.R. **25**, 183.

86. G. M. Henkin, *Linear superpositions of continuously differentiable functions*, Dokl. **157** (1964), 288–290.

87. I. I. Ibragimov, *Extremal problems in the class of entire functions of finite degree*, Izv. **23** (1959), 243–256, M.R. **22**, 871.

88. I. I. Ibragimov, *Some inequalities for entire functions of exponential type*, Izv. **24** (1960), 605–616, M.R. **22**, 5736.

89. I. I. Ibragimov, *Some inequalities for algebraic polynomials*, Mat. Sb. **52** (1960), 863–878, M.R. **23**, A 456.

90. I. I. Ibragimov and R. G. Mamedov, *Some inequalities for complex polynomials*, Dokl. **138** (1961), 526–528, M.R. **24**, A 814.

91. M. I. Kadec, *On the distribution of points of maximal deviation for the approximation of continuous functions by polynomials*, Uspehi **15** (1960), No. 1 (91), 199–202, M.R. **22**, 3920.

92. A. N. Kolmogorov, *Linear dimension of topologic vector spaces*, Dokl. **120** (1958), 239–241, M.R. **20**, 4171.

93. N. P. Korneĭčuk, *Best uniform approximation of differentiable functions*, Dokl. **141** (1961), 304–307, M.R. **24,** A 2182.

94. N. P. Korneĭčuk, *On the existence of a linear polynomial operator which gives best approximation on a class of functions*, Dokl. **143** (1962), 25–27, M.R. **25,** 2366.

95. N. P. Korneĭčuk, *The exact constant in the theorem of Jackson on best uniform approximation of continuous periodic functions*, Dokl. **145** (1962), 514–515, M.R. **27,** 521.

96. N. P. Korneĭčuk, *On best approximation of continuous functions*, Izv. **27** (1963), 29–44, M.R. **26,** 6661.

97. N. P. Korneĭčuk, *The exact value of best approximations and widths of certain classes of functions*, Dokl. **150** (1963), 1218–1220, M.R. **27,** 3984.

97a. N. M. Korobov, *Computation of multiple integrals by the method of optimal coefficients*, Vestnik Moskov. Univ., Ser. Mat. Meh. Astr. Fiz. Him. (1959), No. 4, 19–25, M.R. **22,** 4913.

97b. N. M. Korobov, *Application of number-theoretic series to integral equations and interpolation formulas*, Trudy, **60** (1961), 195–210, M.R. **24,** A 2815.

98. P. P. Korovkin, *An asymptotic property of positive methods of summation of Fourier series and the best approximation of functions of the class Z_2 by linear positive polynomial operators*, Uspehi **13** (1958), No. 6 (84), 99–103, M.R. **21,** 253.

99. P. P. Korovkin, *Best approximation of functions of class Z_2 by certain linear operators*, Dokl. **127** (1959), 513–515, M.R. **21,** 6497.

100. B. D. Kotljar, *The order of growth of ε-entropy on the class of quasi-smooth functions*, Uspehi **18** (1962), No. 2 (110), 135–138, M.R. **27,** 1548.

101. D. I. Mamedhanov, *Some extremal problems in the class of polynomials and of rational functions*, Dokl. **151** (1963), 1277–1279, M.R. **27,** 5893.

102. R. G. Mamedov, *The asymptotic value of the approximation of differentiable functions by linear positive operators*, Dokl. **128** (1959), 471–474, M.R. **22,** 899.

103. R. G. Mamedov, *The asymptotic value of the approximation of multiply differentiable functions by linear positive operators*, Dokl. **146** (1962), 1013–1016, M.R. **25,** 4293.

104. R. G. Mamedov, *The order and asymptotic value of the approximation of a non-differentiable function by linear positive operators of a certain type*, Dokl. **147** (1962), 297–300, M.R. **26,** 1673.

105. R. G. Mamedov, *Inequalities for polynomials and rational functions*, Dokl. **152** (1963), 1958–1060, M.R. **27,** 3783.

106. R. G. Mamedov, *Local saturation of a family of linear positive operators*, Dokl. **156** (1964), 499–502, M.R. **29,** 461.

107. S. N. Mergeljan, *Best approximation with weight on the straight line*, Dokl. **132** (1960), 287–290, M.R. **22,** 11250.

108. S. N. Mergeljan, *Certain classes of sets and their applications*, Dokl. **138** (1961), 285–289, M.R. **24,** A 1408.

109. B. S. Mitjagin, *Approximation of functions in L^p- and C-spaces on the torus*, Mat. Sb. **58** (1962), 397–414, M.R. **27,** 2772.

110. V. P. Motornyĭ, *An inequality for the moduli of smoothness of a periodic function with a bounded derivative*, Dokl. **154** (1964), 45–47, M.R. **28,** 2393.

111. Ju. P. Ofman, *On the best approximation of functions of two variables by functions of the form $\phi(x) + \psi(y)$*, Izv. **25** (1961), 239–252, M.R. **23,** A 2684.

112. V. Ja. Pan, *On the approximation of analytic functions by rational functions*, Uspehi **16** (1961), No. 5 (101), 195–197, M.R. **24,** A 1409.

113. I. M. Petrov, *The order of approximation of functions of the class Z_1 by linear positive polynomial operators*, Uspehi **19** (1964), No. 2 (116) 151–154, M.R. **29,** 413.

113. I. M. Petrov, *The order of approximation of functions of the class Z_1 by linear positive polynomial operators*, Uspehi **19** (1964), No. 2 (116) 151–154.

113a. V. S. Rjaben'kiĭ, *Tables and interpolation of a certain class of functions*, Dokl. **131** (1960), 1025–1027, M.R. **23,** A 461b.

114. N. A. Sapogov, *A sharpening of the theorem of Lozinskiĭ and Haršiladze on polynomial approximations*, Dokl. **143** (1962), 53–55, M.R. **25,** 381a.

115. N. A. Sapogov, *On the norms of linear polynomial operators*, Dokl. **143** (1962), 1286–1288, M.R. **25,** 381b.

116. Ju. A. Šaškin, *Systems of Korovkin in the space of continuous functions*, Izv. **26** (1962), 495–512, M.R. **26,** 5418.

117. S. A. Smoljak, *ε-entropy of the classes $E_s^{\alpha k}(B)$ and $W_s^{\alpha}(B)$ in the metric of L_2*, Dokl. **131** (1960), 30–33, M.R. **23,** A 461a.

117a. S. A. Smoljak, *Interpolation and quadrature formulas for the classes W_s^{α} and E_s^{α}*, Dokl. **131** (1960), 1028–1031, M.R. **23,** A 461c.

117b. I. M. Sobol′, *Evaluation of multiple integrals*, Dokl. **139** (1961), 821–823, M.R. **25,** 3608.

117c. S. L. Sobolev, *Various types of convergence of quadrature and cubature formulas*, Dokl. **146** (1962), 41–42, M.R. **25,** 3606.

117d. S. L. Sobolev, *The formulas of mechanical cubature on the surface of a sphere*, Sibirsk Mat. Ž. **3** (1962), 769–796, M.R. **25,** 4637.

117e. S. L. Sobolev, *On the number of nodes of cubature formulas on the sphere*, Dokl. **146** (1962), 770–773, M.R. **25,** 4636.

117f. V. M. Solodov, *On the error in the numerical integration*, Dokl. **148** (1963), 284–287, M.R. **25,** 2011.

118. S. B. Stečkin, *The approximation of periodic functions by Fejér sums*, Trudy **62** (1961), 48–60, M.R. **28,** 5287a.

119. Jun-Šen Sun′, *On the best approximation of classes of functions representable in convolution form*, Dokl. **118** (1958), 247–250, M.R. **21,** 2144.

120. Jun-Šen Sun′, *On the best approximation of periodic differentiable functions by trigonometric polynomials*, Izv. **23** (1959), 67–92, M.R. **21,** 2155.

121. Jun-Šen Sun′, *On the best approximation of periodic differentiable functions by trigonometric polynomials*. II, Izv. **25** (1961), 143–152, M.R. **23,** A 3413.

122. L. V. Taĭkov, *On summation methods of Taylor series*, Izv. **26** (1962), 625–630, M.R. **25,** 5339.

123. S. A. Teljakovskiĭ, *On the approximation of differentiable functions by linear means of their Fourier series*, Izv. **24** (1960), 213–242, M.R. **22,** 3937.

124. S. A. Teljakovskiĭ, *Norms of trigonometric polynomials and the approximation of differentiable functions by averages of their Fourier series*. I, Trudy **62** (1961), 61–97, M.R. **27,** 2777a.

125. S. A. Teljakovskiĭ, *Norms of trigonometric polynomials and the approximation of differentiable functions by linear averages of their Fourier series*. II, Izv. **27** (1963), 253–272, M.R **27,** 2777b.

126. V. M. Tihomirov, *On the ε-entropy of some classes of periodic functions*, Uspehi **17** (1962), No. 6 (108), 163–169, M.R. **26,** 1698.

127. V. M. Tihomirov, *The work of A. N. Kolmogorov on ε-entropy of classes of functions and superpositions of functions*, Uspehi **18** (1963), No. 5 (113), 55–92, M.R. **29**, 214.

128. A. F. Timan, *To the question of simultaneous approximation of functions and their derivatives on the whole real axis*, Izv. **24** (1960), 421–430, M.R. **22,** 3922.

129. A. F. Timan, *A geometric problem in the theory of approximation*, Dokl. **140** (1961) 307–310, M.R. **24,** A 2788.

130. A. F. Timan, *On the order of growth of ε-entropy of spaces of real continuous functionals, defined on a connected compactum*, Uspehi **19** (1964), No. 1 (115), 173–177, M.R. **29,** 213.

131. A. F. Timan, *A non-linear functional equation in the class of functions convex on a semi-axis*, Izv. **28** (1964), 515–526.

132. V. A. Tonjan, *On weighted polynomial approximation of analytic functions in infinite domains*, Dokl. **133** (1960), 535–536, M.R. **23,** A 2537.

133. R. M. Trigub, *Approximation of functions with a given modulus of smoothness on the exterior of an interval and on a semi-axis*, Dokl. **132** (1960), 303–306, M.R. **23,** A 60.

134. R. M. Trigub, *Approximation of functions by polynomials with integral coefficients*, Izv. **26** (1962), 261–280, M.R. **25,** 373.

135. A. H. Tureckiĭ, *Saturation classes for certain summation methods of Fourier series of continuous periodic functions*, Uspehi **15** (1960), No. 6 (96), 149–156, M.R. **23,** A 2709.

136. A. H. Tureckiĭ, *Saturation classes in the space C*, Izv. **25** (1961), 411–442, M.R. **23,** A 1988.

137. V. S. Videnskiĭ, *Generalizations of Markov's theorem on the evaluation of a polynomial derivative*, Dokl. **125** (1959), 15–18, M.R. **22,** 2667.

138. V. S. Videnskiĭ, *Extremal estimates for the derivative of a trigonometric polynomial on an interval shorter than its period*, Dokl. **130** (1960), 13–16, M.R. **22,** 8272.

139. V. S. Videnskiĭ, *Some estimates of derivatives of rational functions*, Izv. **26** (1962), 415–426, M.R. **24,** A 672b.

140. A. G. Vituškin, *Some theorems on the possibility of uniform approximation of continuous functions by analytic functions*, Dokl. **123** (1958), 959–962, M.R. **21,** 2057.

141. A. G. Vituškin, *Necessary and sufficient conditions a set should satisfy in order that any function continuous on it can be approximated uniformly by analytic or rational functions*, Dokl. **128** (1959), 17–20, M.R. **22,** 775.

142. A. G. Vituškin, *Some properties of linear superpositions of smooth functions*, Dokl. **156** (1964), 1003–1006, M.R. **29,** 211.

143. A. G. Vituškin, *Proof of the existence of analytic functions of several variables, not representable by linear superpositions of continuously differentiable functions of fewer variables*, Dokl. **156** (1964), 1258–1261, M.R. **29,** 2427.

144. L. P. Vlasov, *On Čebyšev sets in Banach spaces*, Dokl. **141** (1961), 19–20, M.R. **24,** A 1596.

145. V. F. Vlasov, *Constructive characteristics of a class of functions*, Dokl. **142** (1963), 773–775.

146. V. I. Volkov, *On the conditions of convergence of sequences of linear positive operators in the space of continuous functions, defined on closed surfaces*, Uspehi **15** (1960), No. 1 (91), 181–185, M.R. **23,** A 2037.

147. S. I. Zuhovickiĭ and G. I. Èskin, *Some theorems on best approximation by unbounded operator functions*, Izv. **24** (1960), 93–102, M.R. **22,** 3997.

Appendix

This appendix contains additions, including some late papers of 1964. The numeration refers to the sections of the main text.

2. There are many important results of I. Singer on Čebyšev sets in Banach spaces, and related topics. A review of his results (which have appeared mainly in Rumanian) will be given in the forthcoming book of P. L. Butzer on approximation. For a characterization of the element of a convex subset of a Banach space X which approximates best a given $x \in X$ see Garkavi **[151]**.

6. A. I. Rubinšteĭn **[154]** estimates from below the degree of approximation of functions $f \in H_1^\omega$ for many classical summation methods of Fourier series. Teljakovskiĭ **[156]** gives sufficient conditions for the Fourier effectiveness of methods (5). His results contain theorems of Hille and Tamarkin (for Nörlund methods), Nikolskiĭ (convexity of the λ_{nk}), and A. V. Efimov **[53]**. If $\sum_{k=0}^{n-1} |\Delta\lambda_{nk}| \leqq C$ and

$$\sum_{n=2}^{n-2} \left| \sum_{k=1}^{q} (\Delta\lambda_{n,m-k} - \Delta\lambda_{n,m+k})/k \right| \leqq C, \qquad q = \min\left\{\left[\frac{m}{2}\right], \left[\frac{n-m}{2}\right]\right\},$$

then $\lim U_n(f, x) = f(x)$ for each $f \in C^*$ and each x if and only if $\lim_{n\to\infty} \lambda_{nk} = 1$ for each k and $\sum_{k=1}^{n-1} |\lambda_{nk}|/(n-k) \leqq \text{Const.}$

7. For compact sets K with the boundary C which have been described in §14 one has for each polynomial P_n and each real s,

$$\|P_n^{(k)}(z)\rho_n(z)^{k-s}\|_p \leqq A\,\|P_n(z)\rho_n(z)^{-s}\|_p,$$

where the norm is the L^p-norm on the curve C; the function $\rho_n(z)$ has been defined in §14 (Andraško **[149]**). If the sharpest angle of C is $\alpha\pi$, it follows that $\|P_n^{(k)}\|_p \leqq An^{2-\alpha}\,\|P_n\|_p$; for $p(1-\alpha) > 1$, $k = 1$ this was shown by Szegö and Zygmund (J. Anal. Math. **3** (1953–54), 225–244). For inequalities for trigonometric polynomials of several variables see Babenko **[22]**, Teljakovskiĭ **[155]**.

9. Rubinšteĭn **[154]** constructs a function $f \in H_1^\omega$ for which $\overline{\lim}_{h\to 0}\,\{|f(x+h) - f(x)|/\omega(|h|)\} \geqq C > 0$ for each x.

14. Al′per **[148]** finds conditions for a function on an arbitrary compact subset of the plane to be approximable by polynomials, whose coefficients are integral algebraic numbers of the field generated by the equation $\zeta^2 + a\zeta + b = 0$, $a^2 - 4ab < 0$.

A closed subset A of the plane is a K-set if there is a function $r(t)$, increasing to $+\infty$ as $t \to +\infty$, with the property that each point z of the complement A' of A can be connected to ∞ by a Jordan curve which is in A' and outside of the circle $|\zeta| < r(|z|)$. The following theorem of Arakeljan **[150]** contains Mergeljan's theorem. In order that each function, continuous on A and analytic in the interior points of A, should be uniformly approximable on A by entire functions, it is necessary and sufficient that A be a K-set. Another result is as follows. One can find for each function f, continuous on A, and for each function $\varepsilon(t) > 0$, $\varepsilon(t) \to 0$ as $t \to +\infty$ an entire function g for which $|f(z) - g(z)| \leqq \varepsilon(|z|)$, $z \in A$, if and only if A is a nowhere dense K-set.

23. 9. N. M. Korobov, *Number-theoretic methods in numerical analysis*, (1963) **[153]**. This book deals with quadrature formulas and other approximations for functions of many variables, developed by the author **[97a, 97b]** (see §22). Classical quadrature formulas are not suitable for the computation of integrals of high multiplicity. In the Monte-Carlo method, the interpolation nodes are selected at random. This the author replaces by nodes selected by number-theoretic methods. Contents of the book: Chapter 1. Number-theoretic lemmas, classes of functions, admissible quadrature formulas, estimation of the remainder term from below. Chapter 2. Quadrature formulas with not uniformly distributed and with parallelepipedal nets of nodes. Chapter 3. Optimal coefficients, algorithms of their computation. Chapter 4. Interpolation of functions, integral equations. Appendix. A table of optimal coefficients.

Additional Bibliography

148. S. Ja. Al′per, *Approximation of functions on closed sets by polynomials with integral coefficients*, Izv. **28** (1964), 1173–1186.

149. M. I. Andraško, *Inequalities for the derivative of an algebraic polynomial in the metric L^p, $p \geqq 1$, in a region with corners*, Ukrain. Mat. Z., **16** (1964), 431–444.

150. N. U. Arakeljan, *Uniform approximation by entire functions on closed sets*, Izv. **28** (1964), 1187–1206.

151. A. S. Džafarov and I. I. Ibragimov, *Some inequalities with weight for entire functions of finite degree*, Uspehi **19**, (1964), No. 6 (120), 149–154.

152. A. L. Garkavi, *On a criterion for an element of best approximation*, Sibirsk. Mat. Ž., **5** (1964), 472–476, M.R. **29**, 1486.

153. N. M. Korobov, *Number-theoretic methods in numerical analysis*, Fizmatgiz, Moscow, 1963, 224 pp.

154. A. I. Rubinšteĭn, *On ω-lacunary series and on functions of classes H^ω*. Mat. Sb. **65** (1964), 239–271.

156. S. A. Teljakovskiĭ, *Conditions of integrability of trigonometric series and their application to the study of linear summability methods of Fourier series*, Izv. **28** (1964), 1209–1236.

155. S. A. Teljakovskiĭ, *Bounds for the derivatives of trigonometric polynomials of several variables*, Sibirsk. Mat. Ž. **4** (1963), 1404–1411, M.R. **28**, 2409.

INDEX

Alexander duality theorem, 128
algorithm(s) for rational approximation, 57
—, rhombus, 140
—, ε–, 145
—, η–, 141
—, vertex to vertex, 61
almost-Tschebyscheff set, 192
alternation theorem, 39, 40
annulus, 4
approximation(s), application of, 154, 157, 159
—, best, *see* best approximation
— by de la Vallée-Poussin sums, 194
— by Fourier sums, 194
— by piecewise polynomial functions, 199
— class, 94
—, constrained linear, 122
—, degree of, *see* degree
—, efficient, 21–25
—, exponential, 46, 47, 131
—, good, 30, 37
—, minimax, 19
—, nonlinear, 111, 199
— of a function, given a table of contaminated values, 24
— of functions of a complex variable, 200
— of functions of several variables, 43, 57, 154, 161
—, polygonal, 154, 160
— procedure, linear, 83
—, production, 155
—, rational, 46, 57, 154, 160, 198
—, rational-exponential, 46
—, simultaneous, of a function and its derivatives, 197
—, spline, 155
—, stabilized, 57, 123
— to special functions, 154, 162
—, trigonometric, 197
—, Tschebyscheff, *see* Tschebyscheff
— under side conditions, 154, 162
approximately compact, 129, 131
approximative dimension, 202
approximator, asymptotically optimal, 96
—, optimal, 92
asymptotic error, 90
— formulas, 194
asymptotically optimal approximator, 96
atomic measure, 24

Banach phenomenon, 19
— space(s), finite dimensional, 111, 116
— —, infinite dimensional, 128, 131
— —, smooth, 118, 131
— —, uniformly convex, 131
Bernstein, S., 71
— lemma, 3, 5
best approximation(s), 1, 30, 103, 112, 177
— — operator, 108
— —, polynomials of, 192
— —, stabilized, 57
best Tschebyscheff approximation, 11, 12
Betti number, 128
bicubic polynomial(s), 173, 185
— spline interpolation, 173
block, 50
—, negative, 50
—, positive, 51
boundedly compact, 128
— embedded, 128
Bulirsch transformation, 135

cardinal functions, 168
Carmichael, R. D., 8
Cauchy problems, 183
characterization theorem (of best approximations), 103
Chebyshev, see *Tschebyscheff*
classes of functions, 194, 201, 214
compact, approximately, 129, 131
—, boundedly, 128
complex variable, 200
computers, electronic, 152
constrained linear approximation, 122
continued fractions, 10, 139
continuous interpolation scheme, 170
convergence, 18
— acceleration, 134
—, degree of, 1, 5, 7
—, ellipse of, 70
convergence of poles, 1, 7

convergence, regions of, 1, 3
—, supergeometric, 135
convergent interpolation scheme, 169
convex, strictly — space, 118, 127
convolution operator, 88
critical points, 117
curvature, 119, 121, 122

data smoothing, 178
de la Vallée-Poussin sum(s), 87, 89, 194
deformation retracts, 126
degree of approximation, 1, 29
— — — by polynomials, 196
— — — by rational functions, 198
— — — of classes of functions, 194, 201, 214
— of convergence, 1, 5, 7
— of trigonometric approximation, 197
differentiable manifold, 117
dimension, approximative, 202
direct product of Hilbert spaces, 22
distributions, 130
duality, 27
— theorem(s), 29, 191
— —, Alexander, 128

efficiency, 23
—, strong, 23
efficient approximation, 21–25
elastica, 171
electronic computers, 152
ellipse of convergence, 70
— of regularity, 73
embedded, boundedly, 128
engineering questions, 20
entire functions, inequalities for, 196
entropy, 202
error, asymptotic, 90
estimation, nonlinear, 154, 159
Euclidean space, 118
Euler transformation, 134
existence problem, 128
—, sets of, 192
exponential approximation, 46, 47, 131
— fitting, 154, 158
— functions, 123
extension of operator, 22
extremal problems, 27, 193
— properties, 3
— systems, 203
extreme point, 34

finite dimensional Banach spaces, 111, 116
folding, 120
Fourier effective matrix, 195, 214
— series expansion, 84
— sums, approximation by, 194
functional analysis, 154, 158
functions, special, 154, 162

gamma function, 1, 15
Garabedian-Wall g-decomposition, 140
general spline interpolation, 176
generalized interpolations, 89
— interpolators, 98
— rational functions, 101
global uniqueness theorem, 119
good approximations, 30, 37
Green's function, 2

Haar subspace, 101, 102, 104
Hadamard, J., 10
Hilbert space(s), 17–25

inclusion theorem, 44
inequalities for entire functions, 196
— for polynomials, 195, 214
— for rational functions, 198
—, system of, 45
infinite dimensional Banach spaces, 128, 131
integral equations, 180
interpolation(s), generalized, 89
—, local cubic, 167
— problem for H^∞, 29
— scheme, continuous, 170
— —, convergent, 169
—, smooth surface, 172
—, spline, *see* spline
interpolators, generalized, 98
intrinsic methods, 171

joints, optimal, 179
Jordan arc, 10
— region, 10

K-system of functions, 205
Kerĭn-Milman theorem, 34

L^2-spaces, 18
least maximum deviation, 154, 158
linear approximation procedure, 83
— operators, positive, 204
— polynomial operators, 204
local cubic interpolation, 167
— uniqueness theorem, 119
locally solvent, 114
— unisolvent, 115
Lozinskiĭ-Haršiladze theorem, 84

$M^{\perp}$, 28, 29, 31, 33–36
manifold(s), 111
—, differentiable, 117
—, unisolvent, 116
mapping, polar, 27
maps, 19
measure, 17, 24, 25
—, atomic, 24
mechanical splines, 165, 171
minimal solution, 44
minimax approximation, 19
minimization, 154, 159
moduli of continuity, 196
monogenic function, 2
Montessus de Balore, *R. de*, 10
multipliers, 92

negative block, 50
nonlinear approximation, 111, 199
— estimation, 154, 159
— splines, 166, 171
norm(s), 27
—, *p* and other, 154, 160
—, *p*th powers, 1, 9, 10
—, Tschebyscheff, 1, 10, 14
nuclear spaces, 202
number-theoretic methods, 206
nup point(s), 126, 130

operator, extension of, 22
optimal approximator, 92, 96
— joints, 179
Ostrowski, *A. M.*, 6

p and other norms, 154, 160
*p*th power norm, 1, 9, 10

Padé functions, 1, 10
— table, 1
parameter space norm, 113
phase equations, 78
— function, 68, 70
piecewise polynomial functions, 165
polar mapping, 27
poles, degree of convergence of, 1, 7
polygon, rectangular, 185
polygonal approximation, 154, 160
polynomial(s), bicubic, 173, 185
—, inequalities for, 195, 214
— of best approximation, 192
— operators, linear, 204
—, special, 196
— with integral coefficients, 197
— with positive coefficients, 196
positive block, 51
— linear operators, 204
production approximation, 155
projection(s), 18, 83, 111, 125, 128
—, characterization of, 117
— on objects, 124
— on submanifolds, 116
— operator, 126, 130
—, unique, 118
Property *Z*, 113
pyramidal functions, 182

quadrature formulas, 206
—, Romberg, 135

rank, 24
rational approximation, 46, 57, 154, 160, 198
— functions, 49, 123, 129, 130
— —, generalized, 101
— —, inequalities for, 198
— —, sequences of, 1
rational-exponential approximation, 46
Rayleigh-Ritz-Galerkin method, 183, 189
rectangle, Tschebyscheff approximation on, 40
rectangular polygon, 185
reducible set, 15
regions of convergence, 1, 3
regular transformations, 134
regularity, ellipse of, 73
rhombus algorithms, 140
— rules, *g*-, 140
— —, *ε*-, 145

rhombus rules, η–, 142
Rice, J. R., 15
Romberg quadrature, 135
Russian books, 206

S-fraction, 139
saturation classes, 205
Schläpler, F., 72
sequences of rational functions, 1
sets of existence, 192
— of polynomials of best approximation, 193
— of uniqueness, 192
several variables, 43, 57, 154, 161
Shanks, D., 136
side conditions, 154, 162
simultaneous approximation of a function and its derivatives, 197
smooth Banach space, 118, 131
— surface interpolation, 172
smoothing data, 178
smoothness measure, 179
solvent, locally, 114
special functions, 154, 162
— polynomials, 196
spline(s) approximation, 155
— function, 166
— interpolation, 154, 162, 166
— —, bicubic, 173
— —, general, 176
—, mechanical, 165, 171
—, nonlinear, 166, 171
stabilized approximations, 123
— best approximation, 57
stationary stochastic process, 24
Stieltjes series-to-series transformation, 138
— summation, 138
stochastic process, 21, 24
strictly convex space, 118, 127
strong efficiency, 23
— uniqueness theorem, 105
Sturm-Liouville systems, 180, 187
submanifold(s), 115–117
summability methods, 194, 214
supergeometric convergence, 135
superpositions of functions, 203
surface fitting, 166, 172

tables of special functions, 154
tabulation operator, 184
Taylor effective matrix, 195
tensor product(s), 174, 184
Tietze phenomenon, 19
trace, 25
trigonometric approximation, degree of, 197
Tschebyscheff abscissas, 69
— alternant, 68
— approximation, 83
— —, best, 11, 12
— — on a rectangle, 40
— — with several variables, 43
— nodes, 74
— norm, 1, 10, 14
— operator, 108
— series expansion, 84, 154, 163
— set(s), 118, 131, 192
— —, almost-, 192

uniform boundedness principle, 170
uniformly convex Banach space, 131
unique projection, 118
uniqueness, 33
— problems, 111
—, sets of, 192
— theorem, 104
— —, global, 119
— —, local, 119
— —, strong, 105
unisolvent, 115
—, locally, 115
unisolvent manifolds, 116

values of a function, 19
variance, 25
varisolvent, 123–125
vertex to vertex algorithm, 61

widths, 202
Wynn, P., 145

Z property, 113
Zygmund sum, 97